RARE METAL EXTRACTION

by Chemical Engineering Techniques

by

W. D. JAMRACK, B.Sc., A.R.I.C.

Formerly Research Manager at U.K.A.E.A.
Springfields, Lancashire

660
J

A Pergamon Press Book

THE MACMILLAN COMPANY
NEW YORK

1963

THE MACMILLAN COMPANY
60 Fifth Avenue
New York 11, N.Y.

This book is distributed by
THE MACMILLAN COMPANY · NEW YORK
pursuant to a special arrangement with
PERGAMON PRESS LIMITED
Oxford, England

Set in Times No. 327, 10 on 12 pt. and printed in Great Britain at
J. W. ARROWSMITH LTD., BRISTOL

INTERNATIONAL SERIES OF MONOGRAPHS ON
CHEMICAL ENGINEERING
GENERAL EDITOR: P. V. DANCKWERTS

VOLUME 2

RARE METAL EXTRACTION BY CHEMICAL ENGINEERING TECHNIQUES

CONTENTS

v

PREFACE

THE aim of this book is to describe processes which are applicable to the extraction and purification of rare metals and to illustrate by fairly detailed examples from the metals uranium, thorium, zirconium, hafnium, titanium, niobium, tantalum, beryllium and vanadium. The techniques are not necessarily limited to this range of metals, and it is indeed the author's hope that this work may stimulate thought on their application over a wider field.

The chemical engineering approach is adopted, in that rare metal extraction and purification is divided into a number of "unit processes", each of which is discussed individually in a separate chapter. Much of the subject matter has been taken from those branches of extraction metallurgy and chemistry which can contribute, since in many places they are closely linked with chemical engineering. Further metallurgical processing, after the initial production of the metal in ingot, powder or sponge form, is not included, since this is not typically the province of the chemical engineer. In addition to the examples in each chapter, demonstrating the application of individual unit processes to particular metals, a selection of complete flowsheets has been included in the last chapter. These flowsheets are typical of modern processes, but their number is by no means comprehensive. Others can be pieced together to suit individual circumstances, from the unit process examples quoted, or from the fairly extensive lists of references. The reference titles are given in full so that they may also be used as a bibliography, to aid a wider or more detailed study of any particular topic.

Besides published research papers, review articles and works of reference, material for a volume of this type normally arises from an author's own background and experience. In this connection, I wish to acknowledge the work of those of my colleagues and associates in the U.K. Atomic Energy Authority whose work has contributed to the design of various Authority processes which have been discussed. I also wish to thank those outside the Authority, concerned with rare metal extraction, whose factories I have had the privilege of visiting.

Thanks are due to Mr. J. C. C. Stewart, the Managing Director of the Production Group, for permission to publish U.K.A.E.A. material. I am also grateful to the librarians, information officers, and photographers of the Springfields and Windscale Works; Mrs. B. Withrington, Mr. F. Cross, Mr. E. Moore, Mr. G. R. Taylor and Mr. H. Stocks, for the supply of published literature, U.K.A.E.A. reports and illustrations. Mrs. S. Strong and Mrs. H. J. D. Coulter deserve special mention for their patient typing of a none too legible manuscript.

W.D.J.

CHAPTER 1

INTRODUCTION

THIS book is concerned with the extraction of a number of rare metals. They do not fall into any well-defined chemical or metallurgical category, but are selected because they have all progressed from being almost laboratory curiosities to the stage of industrial production on a moderate scale in approximately the last two decades.

Two of the metals, uranium and thorium, have an obvious connection with the atomic energy industry which has arisen during and since the 1939–45 war, and have no major uses, in metallic form, outside that field. They are required mainly as fuels for nuclear reactors and their standards of purity are probably greater than those of any other metals which have been produced on a similar scale. This arises partly because trace impurities such as silicon or iron might confer adverse metallurgical properties, but is chiefly because of the necessity to exclude minute quantities of elements with high neutron-capture "cross-sections". Specification limits for boron, cadmium and some rare earth elements, for example, may be quite realistically fixed at a fraction of 1 ppm.

Other metals such as beryllium, hafnium, niobium, vanadium, and zirconium are known to have nuclear and other properties which make them desirable materials of construction in various designs of nuclear reactor[1], but also they have, or may have in the future, important uses outside that field. All these metals except hafnium have been used or proposed for "canning materials" to clad and protect the nuclear fuel metals from corrosion by the reactor coolants or moderators, air, carbon dioxide, water, heavy water, graphite or molten sodium, etc. In some cases the specifications for neutron-absorbing impurities are of the same order as for the fuel metals uranium and thorium. Hafnium, however, with a high neutron-capture cross-section, is a useful material for reactor control rods and exhibits favourable metallurgical properties under irradiation.

Titanium and tantalum are normally extracted for quite different purposes. Titanium metal has a high strength-to-weight ratio, a good hot strength up to 500 °C and will stand prolonged exposure to air at about this temperature. Hence its value as a material of construction in gas turbines and for certain parts of aircraft which are exposed to high temperatures.

It has also been employed for the construction of items of chemical plants where use can be made of its corrosion resistance towards hydrochloric acid, sulphuric acid and other aqueous reagents. Tantalum also finds applications based upon its corrosion resistance towards nitric acid and other acids. It is also used to some extent in surgery owing to it not being attacked by body fluids.

The various chemical extraction stages from ore to metal are discussed: some of the intermediates arising from these stages have major industrial uses or potential uses of their own. Pure thorium oxide, for example, has been employed for many years in the manufacture of incandescent gas mantles and this is at present probably still the major outlet for thorium in any form. It is anticipated that new uses will be found for most of these metals or their pure intermediates in the near future and as a result many of the process stages described will achieve a wider application.

The classical metallurgical processes of smelting the oxides with carbon in the presence of a fusible slag, such as are used for the production of many of the commoner metals, are not applicable to the range of rather rare elements about which this book is written, if the metals are required in pure condition. The latter are all fairly strongly electropositive elements whose oxides are not readily reduced. In addition, in many cases, it is important to produce the metal from a halide rather than an oxide, and otherwise exclude oxygen or air from the system, because of the deleterious effect of traces of oxygen upon the metallurgical properties. The selection of a particular pure compound of an element, together with a suitable reactant which will allow the element to be produced in metallic form, is based upon thermodynamic and chemical data.

Similarly, the production of the compounds in a pure condition is essentially by means of a series of chemical reactions. First, use is made of the differences in the chemical properties of the desired element and those of any unwanted impurities, and then the desired compound is prepared by reaction with a suitable chemical reagent or reagents. The stage of transformation of the known chemistry from the laboratory to an industrial scale process is accomplished by chemical engineering methods, and a breakdown can be made into unit operations of the same general types as are used throughout the whole chemical industry. Problems arise involving materials of plant construction, both metallic and non-metallic, the flow of materials, the relationship of one process to another and the economic optimization of the processes, which are entirely typical of the traditional chemical engineering field. This should not imply that rare metal extraction processes are solely the preserve of the chemical engineer, but on the contrary it offers the suggestion that the typical chemical engineering approach might prove useful to those metallurgists, chemists, or others who are interested in the extraction of rare metals.

The fundamental chemical engineering processes are essentially of general application and can usually be discussed without reference to particular elements, although admittedly much of the interest and progress arises from the application of these processes to novel materials processed under unorthodox conditions. Hence the division of this book into a series of individual processes which can be applied to a range of metals, rather than an arrangement in terms of specific metals. Numerous detailed examples are included in the text for those interested only in particular metals rather than in general applications however.

Mineral dressing techniques and the physical beneficiation of ore shave not been covered in this volume, although they have applications in rare metal extraction, since it is a large field with an adequate literature of its own. Also, the novelty associated with the use of mineral dressing techniques belongs generally to an earlier period than, for example, ion-exchange, solvent extraction, or Kroll type reduction processes. An up-to-date description of mineral dressing plant is given by Cremer and Davies.[2]

This book does not deal with chemical engineering principles but only with those applications of the chemical engineering technique which can be of use in a particular field. The aim is therefore to provide factual information on existing types of process exemplified by a range of rare metals. It is hoped that this might assist in guiding the design of other processes involving similar problems in the future.

REFERENCES

1. MCINTOSH, A. B. Metallurgy of nuclear power production. *The Engineer* **200**, 759 (1955).
2. CREMER, H. W. and DAVIES, T. *Chemical Engineering Practice*, vol. 3, *Solid Systems*. Butterworths (1957).

CHAPTER 2

ORE BREAKDOWN PROCESSES

THE first metallic iron to be extracted was undoubtedly obtained by smelting a high-grade ore consisting of a relatively pure iron oxide mineral. Most of the other common metals which are extracted today in vast tonnages throughout the world, e.g. copper, lead, zinc, antimony, tin and nickel, can similarly be obtained directly by the smelting of high-grade mineral ores with some form of carbon. A certain degree of physical beneficiation is however carried out in some cases, e.g. copper and tin, to remove inert gangue material or other useful by-product minerals, before smelting. With some of the more electropositive of the common metals, e.g. magnesium and aluminium, it may even be necessary to convert a high-grade ore to a more tractable compound by chemical means before production of the metal by electrolysis.

Some of the rarer metals, e.g. beryllium, thorium, vanadium and zirconium, are electropositive in character and usually occur in nature as fairly refractory minerals. Silicates and phosphates are common examples, but the compounds concerned are often much more complex than this. Consequently the ores cannot be broken by smelting processes since the minerals are not always readily converted to oxide and the oxides in any case cannot easily be reduced to the pure metals by carbon. It is in fact necessary to separate the ore breakdown stage from subsequent metal production, and in most cases a considerable degree of purification may be necessary after breakdown and before the final conversion to metallic form. Breakdown of these refractory ores is often accomplished by reaction with powerful chemical reagents such as concentrated acids, alkalis, fluorides, or gaseous chlorine at high temperature and specialized chemical engineering plant is usually required. Since these reagents are reactive towards other mineral impurities in the ore, it is important, for reasons of reagent economy, to employ a reasonably high grade of ore, or possibly an ore which has first been beneficiated by physical means. Fortunately, the metals concerned have at present only limited application in industry and it is usually still possible to mine them in relatively high grades. In some cases, however, e.g. beryllium, this situation is unlikely to continue for many years.

Other rare metals are available as low-grade ores, but in chemical forms such as oxides which can sometimes be converted to soluble compounds by leaching with dilute acids or alkalis. Uranium is the prime example of this, but certain vanadium and thorium ores can also be treated by dilute acid or alkali leaching processes. In the case of uranium particularly, the type of process and equipment employed for leaching is becoming increasingly complex and is amenable to the application of chemical engineering techniques. Consequently, with improved processes, the grade of ore which is regarded as workable on an economic basis is becoming extremely low and is, at the present time, for uranium, often between 0·01 and 0·2 per cent. The choice of "cut-off" grade of ore and selection of the reagent, whether acid or alkali, depends to a high degree upon local conditions. The relative cost and availability of the two classes of reagent, their relative leaching efficiency with the particular ore, and the waste involved in the use of reagents for the extraction of associated minerals from the ore, must all be taken into account. The presence of high concentrations of limestone in an ore, for example, inevitably leads to the use of an alkaline rather than an acid reagent.

It is convenient to discuss dilute acid leaching first. Much of the equipment and some of the chemical principles are common with dilute alkali leaching. Other breakdown techniques are only employed when these cheaper processes have been found unsuccessful.

DILUTE ACID LEACHING

Batch leaching

Many acid leaching processes are carried out as simple batch operations in which measured quantities of acid, water, and ore are added to suitably agitated vessels and contacted for an appropriate time under known conditions of temperature and acid concentration, etc. The acid concentration would normally be expected to fall throughout the process and relative quantities would be such that the final acidity would be appropriate for the subsequent treatment stages. In a process of this type, charging and discharging operations generally require more labour than if they were performed in a continuous manner and, in addition, provision has to be made for intermediate storage of at least one batch before separation of the liquid from the solid phase.

Continuous co-current leaching

It is frequently possible to design the leaching process on a continuous co-current basis, where acid, water and ore are fed into a vessel continuously, or at regular intervals, and discharged in a similar manner. In these circumstances the agitation system is usually designed to suspend the solids sufficiently in the liquid phase so as to allow them both to overflow from the vessel in the same proportions as in the feed. It will be appreciated that with single-vessel, co-current, continuous leaching of this type the chemistry of the system can be considerably different from that of a batch system even with the same proportions of acid and ore. In co-current leaching, for example, the acidity of the process is essentially controlled at the fairly low value of the outgoing product solution, whereas a high range of acidity might be present from start to finish of a batch process. This feature may be a disadvantage if the rate of solution of the desired mineral decreases markedly at low acid concentrations, since the residence time, and hence the capacity of the leaching vessel, may become prohibitively large. However, in other cases a considerable gain in acid economy might be possible if, for example, the desired component is freely soluble in acid of all concentrations above a threshold value, but if the solubility of unwanted minerals, particularly the common siliceous ones, can be decreased by the lower acidity. In this manner the whole chemical constitution of the leach liquor might be changed, with advantage to the process.

Another feature of co-current leaching in a single vessel is always deleterious: this arises from the fact that each portion of ore is not leached for a constant time, but an infinite range of leaching times exists. This range is distributed about a mean value $T = V/v$, where V is the volume capacity of the vessel and v is the volumetric flow rate through it. Clearly, "by-passing" of a small proportion of the ore will take place, i.e. some of it will pass directly from the feed to the overflow point in almost zero time without appreciable leaching. A small proportion at the other extreme will have a residence time tending to infinity. With an inefficient system of agitation, the denser or coarser particles might in fact remain in the vessel for an infinite period, or until the vessel "sanded up" to an extent which necessitated cleaning out.

Assuming steady-state conditions and efficient agitation in a single co-current leaching vessel, it is easily shown[1] that the probability of a particle remaining in the vessel after time t is equal to $\exp(-t/T)$.

The probability of any particle first remaining in the vessel for time t and then leaving during an additional interval δt is $1/T \exp(-t/T) \, \delta t$.

The function $1/T \exp(-t/T)$ is plotted as a continuous function in Fig. 2.1 ($N = 1$ for a single vessel) in units of the mean residence time T. The proportion of material with a residence time between any two values is given by the area under the curve lying between the two values. It is clear that a high proportion of the ore is leached for periods which are widely different from the mean residence time.

In order to achieve a continuous co-current system in which a higher proportion of the ore is leached for a period near to the mean residence time, several vessels may be used in cascade. The ore, acid and water are fed to the first vessel as in the single-stage system but the overflowing slurry then passes to a second similar vessel and from there possibly to other vessels. The leaching acidity in this system usually falls in steps from the first to the last vessel. With most systems the course of the chemical reaction is such that the range of acidity covered is still substantially less than in a batch system, unless the capacity, and hence the residence time, of the first vessel is much smaller than the later ones.

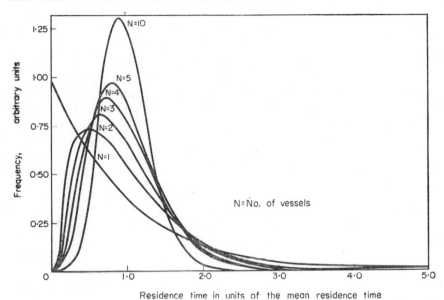

FIG. 2.1. Co-current leaching. Frequency distribution of residence times in a series of N vessels (U.K.A.E.A. copyright).

For a number of vessels of equal size, it can be shown that the frequency distribution of residence times is equal to:

$$\frac{t^{N-1}}{T^n(N-1)!} \exp(-t/T) dt$$

The mean residence time is then NV/v.

This function is plotted in Fig. 2.1 for various numbers of vessels (N) up to 10, the total mean residence time for each system being constant irrespective of the number of vessels. Again, the area under the curve lying between any two values of time is equal to the fraction of the material having residence times between these values. It is obvious from the shape of these graphs that as the number of vessels increases, the proportion of ore leached for times near to the mean residence time becomes substantially greater. Thus a closer approximation to the fixed residence time of a batch leaching system is obtained.

Continuous counter-current leaching

A third method of leaching is possible, based upon the counter-current principle. A series of vessels can be used in which acid passes from one vessel to another through the series in one direction whilst ore passes relatively in the opposite direction. Several different transfer patterns are possible, depending upon whether the solid or liquid is moved from vessel to vessel or whether both are moved simultaneously. Figure 2.2 shows such a pattern based upon the assumption of liquid-phase movement only,

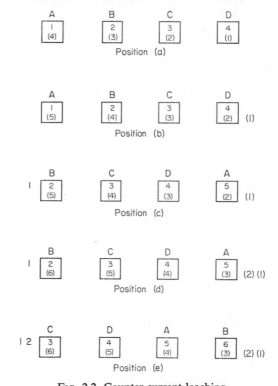

FIG. 2.2. Counter-current leaching.

which might be implemented in practice by simple decantation from the leaching vessels themselves. A four-stage system of vessels labelled A, B, C and D might contain initially portions of ore numbered 1, 2, 3, and 4 respectively, and portions of acid numbered (4), (3), (2) and (1) respectively, as in (a). After the first set of leaching operations, movement would take place to give the situation represented by (b), i.e. acid portion (1) would leave the system, (2) would pass from C to D, (3) from B to C, and (4) from A to B. A new portion of acid (5) would simultaneously be added to A. After the second set of leaching operations, acid portions would again move one place in the same direction as before but no new acid would be added to *A*. Instead, ore portion 1 would be removed from *A* and a new portion of ore 5 would replace it. The acid portion (2) leaving vessel *D* would be added to this new ore, This situation is shown in (c). The third transfer is to the positions shown in (d) where acid portion (2) leaves the system from the vessel *A*, in exchange for a new portion (6) added to vessel *B* at the other end. Similarly, the fourth transfer, shown in (e), involves movement of expended ore portion 2 from the system and its replacement by a new portion 6 at the opposite end. This type of transfer pattern can then continue indefinitely.

This method is more suited to the extraction of a high-grade ore where a large proportion of the acid is needed to dissolve the ore and the rate of solution falls markedly with decreasing acid concentration or with increasing metal ion in solution. The advantage of such a process is then that the highest concentration of acid contacts the lowest concentration of the wanted mineral in the ore. The acid used to extract the ore at its richest mineral content, a process which is relatively easy, is of comparatively low concentration and may already contain a substantial quantity of metal ion in solution. In this way, a high efficiency of extraction can be obtained simultaneously with minimum acid usage.

Counter-current leaching of ores is rarely used in practice, since the criteria which make the technique favourable are of infrequent occurrence. A very serious disadvantage of the method applied to low-grade ores is the fact that solid–liquid separation must be carried out at each transfer of acid from one vessel to another. This increases the required filtration or decantation capacity over that needed for a co-current or batch system, by a factor approximately equal to the number of stages involved. It should also be noted that the full benefit of the counter-current method of operation may not be gained, in practice, by virtue of the retention of a proportion of the liquor by the solid during each separation operation. A high ratio of acid to ore and efficient solid–liquid separation minimizes this effect, but militates against an economic process.

It is not generally regarded as feasible to run a counter-current leaching system of this type, involving a number of vessels, in a truly continuous manner with alternate leaching and separating stages. However, continuous counter-current decantation washing systems bear some resemblance to this and are discussed later.

Percolation leaching

Percolation leaching may also be regarded as a partially counter-current process. In its simple form the process involves the passing of the leaching acid down a column, or through a bed, of ore which has been ground to a suitable particle size.[2] A suitable grid or filter medium is used as a support at the base of the column or bed. This system has the characteristic that the highest concentration of acid contacts the lowest grade of ore, and vice versa. It is, however, a batch process with an end effect, i.e. the leaching of the last traces of desired component involves a disproportionate acid usage, or other special measures.

Unfortunately, a particle size distribution which may be satisfactory for good flow characteristics and a satisfactory residence time in a percolation leaching bed is not necessarily ideal for a high extraction efficiency. Also, the gradual effect of acid upon the various minerals in the ore may seriously influence the flow rate. For example, particles may break down into smaller ones, or siliceous materials might become hydrated and gelatinous. Also, the dissolution of parts of the ore may create voids which are subsequently filled, perhaps in an irregular manner by movements of the bed. Even under ideal circumstances, the behaviour of an industrial scale bed of perhaps 10 ft diameter may be less satisfactory than a laboratory model a few inches in diameter because of the different packing characteristics of the ore in the two different environments and because of the difficulties associated with the achievement of uniform distribution of the flowing liquid over the whole cross-section of the bed. These difficulties may be alleviated by the installation of special supports and redistributor plates at intermediate points up the column.

In view of the operational difficulties involved in percolation leaching systems, they are usually only employed with ores having exceptionally favourable properties. If percolation leaching is possible however, it has the distinct advantage that the necessity for an expensive solid–liquid separation stage is avoided. Also, the throughput of an individual piece of plant can be very high if the required residence time is not unduly long, since the plant is completely packed with solid ore during operation.

Percolation leaching takes place as a natural process where the rock containing a desired mineral is of suitable physical form and location. Acid may be introduced into rain-water from either decaying vegetable matter or sulphur minerals and it may be subsequently passed through deep beds of the ore to give a useful concentration of metal ion in solution. Use has occasionally been made of natural leaching of this type, e.g. by the recovery of metal ions from mine water which might require pumping to the surface for other reasons. In such cases, the natural leach liquor would not be the sole source of metal values, but would be fed into the main ore treatment plant at an appropriate point.

Leaching equipment

The basic design of a leaching vessel for a batch, co-current or counter-current system can be identical with that used in other chemical processes involving solid–liquid reactions. A stirred vessel is commonly employed, with a flat base if it is intended to overflow the slurry in a continuous process, or a conical base with a bottom outlet pipe and valve, where a vessel must be emptied completely in a batch process.

Agitation can be by means of a slow moving gate stirrer, possibly with a trailing chain, when it is necessary to suspend coarse "sands" to overflow from a flat based continuous vessel, but higher speed impeller type stirrers have also been used. In the latter case it may be advisable to fit baffles to the vessel walls for better mixing and to avoid a deep vortex, with its disadvantageous effect upon vessel capacity. Impellers can also be used in conical base vessels and must be designed to agitate in the conical portion in addition to the upper cylindrical section of the vessel. An air bleed may also be necessary at the base of the cone to prevent blockage of the bottom outlet pipe and valve. In the uranium industry "pachucas" have been widely used as shown in Fig. 2.3. These are conical base vessels in which a current of air is used as the sole means of agitation. It is important to design the throat and the angle of the cone to give uniform distribution of air across the vessel, and this may vary with the "pulp density" and other characteristics of the leach slurry. Some pachucas[3] have a central air inlet tube running from the top to near the base of the vessel. This is surrounded by a concentric tube of larger diameter, up which the slurry of ore and leaching acid is lifted by the rising air. The slurry returns to the main body of the vessel near the top, so causing circulation and agitation of the whole pachuca contents. The precise design of pachucas, and in fact of all agitation systems, is too often based upon personal preference, since some of the factors are not easily amenable to calculation. In such circumstances an optimum design is best achieved as a result of a large-scale development programme with a representative ore and characteristic chemical conditions.

Traditional materials of construction for leaching vessels in which sulphuric acid is used are timber, pitch-pine often being recommended, or bitumen-lined concrete. Rubber-lined mild steel is now more commonly employed, a fairly soft rubber being preferred under conditions where erosion is likely to be serious. Lead-lined mild steel is occasionally used, but it is expensive, easily eroded and its excessive weight introduces special support problems. In certain parts of Australia, however, these disadvantages appear to be outweighed by the ready availability of the metal and also of tradesmen skilled in its fabrication. Various plastic materials such as polythene, polyvinyl chloride, nylon and poly-tetrafluorethylene are coming into more frequent use as acid-resistant coatings for metals, and no doubt leaching plants will be constructed of these materials in future. Lead has been replaced by Epoxy resin as a coating for certain parts of the Port Pirie Uranium plant,[4] for example. Stainless-steel vessels have been used for the leaching of higher grade ores with nitric or sulphuric acids when the initial cost is justified. Corrosion by sulphuric acid is inhibited by "passivating" the surface of the metal with a little nitric acid.

Acid leaching of low-grade ores is most commonly carried out under ambient temperature conditions, which may reach say 40°C to 50°C where the chemical reaction between the minerals and the leaching acid is particularly exothermic. Steam heating by jackets, coils, or even live steam sparge pipes, is occasionally employed where the cost can be justified by increased leaching efficiency. When leaching at elevated temperatures is necessary, a heat exchanger may be employed to transfer heat from an outgoing batch to the succeeding ingoing one.

Pressures above atmospheric have been employed for the leaching of ores in recent years, and this necessitates a completely new design of equipment. The process is usually operated on a batch basis with individual pressure vessels.

The pressure leaching technique was originated in connection with the leaching of ores by sodium carbonate solution, where high temperatures and pressures were necessary for high leaching efficiency. Acid leaching processes do not generally require these conditions since the gain in efficiency is relatively small and the high additional capital cost would not therefore normally be justified. However, at a temperature of 130°C, a pressure of 35 psi and an oxygen partial pressure of 10 psi, it is possible to oxidize sulphur and sulphur-containing minerals, e.g. pyrite (FeS_2) or pyrrhotite (FeS), *in situ*, to sulphuric acid. These are common constituents of low-grade ores and enough sulphuric acid is generated to carry out the leaching process. Thus the saving of sulphuric acid may more than offset the additional capital cost.

Clearly, many of the basic design features of a pressure leaching process are similar to those which obtain when leaching at atmospheric pressure and ambient temperature, e.g. particle size, solids content of the pulp, agitation conditions. However, the design of a very large closed pressure vessel with agitation system and steam heating is quite different from that of a simple pachuca. Advantage is clearly to be gained by keeping the size of the pressure vessel as small as possible and maintaining a rapid cycle of charging, leaching and discharging so as to obtain the maximum throughput. Timber, rubber-lined or plastic-lined vessels cannot be used and are replaced by special types of stainless steel as constructional materials. The vessel must be fitted with an external steam jacket or internal steam coil, and a pressure-tight gland is necessary for the stirrer shaft.

Air has been used in place of pure oxygen, but to maintain the same partial pressure of oxygen in the system, the total pressure must be raised from 35 psi to 75 psi, i.e. 10 psi oxygen, 25 psi steam and 40 psi nitrogen.

A design of autoclave for continuous operation has been suggested by

Gray.[5] His small pilot scale model was tubular in shape, constructed of mild steel, lined with stainless steel. It was designed to operate at pressures up to 500 psi and 200°C using compressed air for agitation, the excess air being removed via a pressure release valve.

Ore treatment prior to leaching

It is usually necessary to leach an ore under carefully selected conditions of particle size distribution and solids content of the slurry. In addition, it may be advisable to change the chemical form of the desired mineral (or of unwanted minerals) to allow them to be leached more (or less) readily, and it may be necessary to reject deleterious minerals before leaching. Many of the ore treatment techniques employed before leaching belong to the field of mineral dressing and it is not appropriate to discuss them here in detail. However, some of them have a bearing upon the chemistry, the chemical engineering, or the economics of the leaching process itself and cannot escape being mentioned.

The time required for the dissolution of individual mineral grains during the leaching process is clearly dependent upon their size. In the case of a fairly high-grade ore it would be necessary to grind to an optimum degree so as to allow the leaching reaction to proceed rapidly but without undue vigour, so that heat evolution and foaming may be kept under control. More commonly, the ore is of low grade and the mineral values are so widely disseminated that the individual lumps of ore must be crushed and then ground in order to release the values and allow them to come into adequate contact with the leaching acid. In these circumstances other features play an important role in the selection of optimum grinding conditions. The cost of grinding a low-grade ore, for example, may be a signicant proportion of the total processing costs and could lead to a larger particle size than would be advisable on strictly chemical grounds. The effect of particle size on solid–liquid separation, after the leaching stage itself, can also be important, and in some cases over-riding, since neither filtration nor decantation will operate satisfactorily with a very fine "slimy" ore. In addition, it should not be forgotten that grinding will render other unwanted minerals more amenable to leaching and these will compete with the mineral values for the available acid, besides introducing complications into the chemistry of subsequent stages. Each ore must be considered on its merits to assess the relative importance of the above factors before attempting to design a grinding circuit.

A wide variety of crushing and grinding equipment is available for the preparation of ore feeds to mineral dressing processes,[3, 6] and similar stages can be used prior to leaching, if mineral dressing techniques themselves have not in fact preceded leaching. Jaw crushers are usually employed, of appropriate capacity and jaw size to reduce the mined ore to pieces of

4–6 in. in size. These can be followed by gyratory crushers or cone crushers, to give say a 0·5 in. feed to a ball mill or rod mill. Wet milling is a more economic and less dusty operation than dry milling and is usually preferred unless there are special reasons (e.g. reaction with water) against it. Rod mills are more suited than ball mills to the production of particles within a close size range from hard materials, but circuits often include rod mills followed by ball mills in series where a low particle size is ultimately required.

Vibrating screens can be used for the separation of oversize material, which is then returned to the mill. Air cyclones have been used for classification operations after dry milling and their counterparts, hydrocyclones, are now coming into more frequent use as classifiers in conjunction with wet milling operations.

A solids content as high as possible is required during the leaching operation, in order to maintain the extractable metal ion concentration at its maximum and also to minimize the size of the leaching vessels and any subsequent filtration plant. About 60 per cent[7] (weight of solids per total weight) is often ideal; this may involve feeding at an even higher solids content if the weight of added acid is not negligible. Usually, the major part of the water would not be added with the acid but would originate from the grinding circuit, and often the optimum solids content of the latter is too low for efficient leaching. It is then necessary to include a "thickener" between the milling and leaching operations. A thickener is best operated under continuous conditions by feeding the slurry of low solids density in from the top at the centre, and overflowing the clear liquor at the top around the circumference. Thickened slurry is taken continuously from the centre of the base, the latter usually being in the shape of a shallow cone.

Ore leaching efficiencies may sometimes be improved by roasting before leaching. The object may be to volatilize unwanted minerals containing, for example, arsenic and antimony, to oxidize sulphides, to decompose carbonates to oxides, to render other minerals insoluble in the leaching acid, to dehydrate a "slimy" ore and so aid filtration, or to increase the solubility of the desired mineral. An example of the latter is the "salt-roasting" technique applied to carnotite ores of the Colorado Plateau area in the U.S.A. Carnotite is a mineral containing both vanadium and uranium, and the object of roasting at 850°C with the addition of sodium chloride is to convert the vanadium to water-soluble vanadate and so allow this to be removed before leaching out the uranium with acid.

Iron minerals and tramp iron introduced from the crushing and grinding stages can often be removed conveniently before leaching by electromagnetic separation. This has been shown to result in substantial economies in the use of leaching acid when the grade of ore is of the same order as, or even less than, the iron content.

FIG. 2.3. Pachuca leaching tanks at Western Reefs Uranium Plant, South Africa (Arden, T.V. Ref. 7).

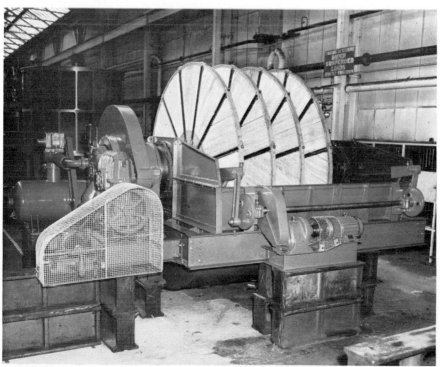

FIG. 2.4. Rotary vacuum disc filter (Automatic Coal Cleaning Co. Ltd. and Davey, Paxman and Co. Ltd.).

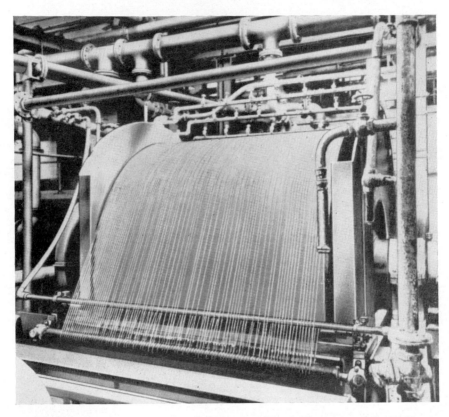

Fig. 2.5. Rotary vacuum string discharge filter (Davey, Paxman and Co. Ltd.).

Solid–liquid separation

The leaching process is not complete until the leach liquor containing the dissolved mineral values has been separated from the leached ore. Furthermore, in view of the relatively high solids content of the slurry during leaching, a simple separation is insufficient; the leach liquor retained by the wet leached ore invariably contains sufficient dissolved mineral values to make washing with water an economic proposition. Flowsheets for carrying out these separation and washing operations are usually based either upon filtration or thickening, but centrifuges and hydrocyclones may play a greater part in future. When ores of very low grade are leached, the throughput of the separation systems are necessarily very high and continuous systems are therefore preferred. The capital cost of the plant required for these stages is often greatly in excess of that of the leaching stage itself.

Continuous filtration is discussed by Coulson and Richardson.[8]. It commonly employs rotary vacuum filters. These are usually cylindrical in shape, rotating about a horizontal axis with a filter medium on the curved surface and a vacuum applied from inside. Rotating disc filters are less frequently employed (see Fig. 2.4). These have a number of discs on the same shaft with vacuum applied from inside but the flat surfaces of the discs hold the filter medium. The methods of continuous discharge of the filter cake during operation, and of replacement of the filter medium at intervals, are less elegant than those applicable to rotating cylinders.

A typical rotating cylinder filter is fabricated of stainless steel and has a drum about 10 ft long by 6 ft in diameter. The whole of the curved surface is in the form of a grid, acting as a support for a filter cloth or stainless-steel filter gauze. The cross-section of the drum is divided into segments some of which are under vacuum, others open to atmosphere and others under positive pressure, according to a predetermined filtration cycle. A rotary valve controls the state of individual segments according to their position in the cycle at any time.

The drum feed can be from above, in which case it is applied as a uniform slurry from an agitated trough, or it can be from below, when the drum is partially immersed in the trough. The latter arrangement allows a rather larger proportion of the drum surface to be used for filtration, spray washing and suction drying and in general the feed can be more uniform. However, with a relatively coarse, granular or dense ore, it may not be possible to obtain satisfactory adhesion of the cake to the ascending portion of the drum, and a top feed may then be preferred. In other cases, with an entirely different type of slurry, the cake produced may be highly gelatinous and adhere to the filter medium to such an extent that it both restricts the filtration rate to a very low figure and cannot easily be removed after suction drying. This type of slurry with its very low solids content is rarely obtained as a result of ore leaching operations since the conditions would probably have been unacceptable at the leaching stage itself. It could, however, result from the leaching of a high-grade ore where the removal of the mineral values left only a small, highly hydrated, gelatinous residue in the pulp. This type of slurry can, in general, be filtered using a bottom feed and a pre-coat of a diatomaceous earth type of filter-aid on the drum. The pre-coat may be several inches thick and can be supported on a cloth or gauze, to which it adheres very well under suction. The gelatinous solids are filtered at a reasonable rate on the very large effective surface area presented by the filter aid, and they are removed at the end of the cycle together with a thin layer of pre-coat. This allows, a new, non-blinded, pre-coat surface to be presented for the next cycle.

Several different types of discharge mechanism are used on rotary drum filters. For a loosely adhering cake it may be sufficient to merely apply a positive pressure to one of the segments at the end of the cycle and blow the partially dried cake away. Usually, however, the applied pressure would be released by the removal of only a small portion of the cake, so becoming ineffective for the major part. An oscillating pressure may be more effective, since it generally causes the filter cloth to vibrate and the resulting mechanical agitation loosens the cake. It is common practice, however, to use a blunt deflector blade to scrape the dried cake away, in conjunction with a steady positive pressure. When a pre-coat is used and it is important to remove only the top surface, a positive pressure cannot be employed. It may in fact be necessary to retain the suction for the whole filtration cycle. The top layer is then cut away by means of a sharp blade, the depth of penetration being carefully adjusted, perhaps with a precision of about one-thousandth of an inch. A mechanism is then needed to advance the blade for each revolution of the drum, and usually this is geared to the drum drive. Eventually, the pre-coat reaches a predetermined minimum thickness and a new coat has to be applied, the blade then being returned to its starting position corresponding to zero penetration of the new cake.

String discharge devices are in use as in Fig. 2.5, whereby a series of parallel endless strings are incorporated in the filter cake as it is formed. The strings rotate in the same direction and at the same speed as the drum along with the cake up to the point of discharge. Then they diverge from the drum at an angle so that partially dried cake adheres to the strings and leaves the drum surface. After collection of the cake, the strings rejoin the drum at its under surface ready for incorporation with new cake.

It is usually possible to wash the filter cake whilst it is on the surface of the drum, whether or not it is associated with a pre-coat. This is accomplished by the application of fine sprays of water along the whole length of the drum and at a point in the cycle where the major part of the filtrate has been removed. Suction is still applied to the cake during that part of the cycle devoted to washing and, if necessary, the wash liquor can be collected separately from the main filtrate. Since its content of mineral values is considerably less than that of the main filtrate, it may be appropriate not to use it for unnecessary dilution of the latter, but to recycle it to an earlier stage in place of water, e.g. to the leaching vessel.

A single filtration and drum washing operation is often insufficient for removal of all the soluble mineral values from the filter cake. Consequently, two filters may be employed in series, the suction dried cake from the first being reslurried with water for feeding to the second. A washing operating can again be used on the second drum. In order to avoid a very large increase in the volume of leach liquor, by the addition of two portions of drum wash water and one portion of reslurry wash water, a counter-current system is necessary. In such a system, the recovered wash water from the second filter might be used for making up the slurry feed to the same filter. The main filtrate from the second filter could be used as wash liquor for the first filter, and this wash liquor on subsequent recovery, as stated previously, could be used at the leaching stage.

The process of allowing the lower part of a slurry to increase in solids content by sedimentation, combined with decantation of the clear liquor from above, is referred to as "thickening". The use of this process in a single stage to increase the solids content of a slurry when passing from a ball mill to a leaching stage has already been noted. However, the process is of greater value as an alternative to filtration for the removal of leach liquor, and subsequently applied wash liquor, from a leached ore. It is necessary to dilute the leach slurry to say 15 to 20 per cent solids content so that it can settle to say 60 to 70 per cent content during thickening. Wash liquor, containing mineral values would normally be used for dilution. The thickeners, or decantation vessels, are often quite large[6], in order to allow residence times of the order of days, i.e. typically 100 ft diameter by 15 ft deep, with shallow cone bases. In connection with an acid leach process they would usually be rubber-lined, but alternative coatings are now becoming available as for the leaching vessels. The vessels are fitted with very slow stirrers, the design of which is such as to rake the thickened slurry to the middle of the base and so into the apex of the cone, without appreciable disturbance of the clear supernatant liquor.

The feed mechanism can be a simple launder made of timber or rubber-lined steel, etc., passing along a radius at the top of the thickener and slightly inclined in a downwards direction towards the middle of the vessel. The feed slurry is pumped, or allowed to flow by gravity, into the launder from a large batch holding tank, or a small stirred vessel in which the slurry dilution process is carried out continuously. The clear liquor overflow is collected from around the circumference and pumped to its destination. The thickened underflow is discharged through a gate vale or a specially designed throat at the apex of the conical base and passed to its destination by means of a slurry pump. The underflow discharge system must be designed to prevent blockages and sometimes two discharge pipes are provided, of different bores, to cope with variations of solids content or flowrate. Elaborate alarm systems are sometimes installed to draw immediate attention to underflow blockages or failure of slurry pumps, etc. This is justified on the grounds that on cessation of flow, settling can take place to such an extent in the tank that it becomes quite impossible to restart. Clearance of a blockage would be valueless once the thickened slurry has ceased to be in motion over the whole base of the thickener and it might be necessary to remove between 100,000 and one million gallons of liquor and slurry before re-use of the vessel.

Great attention has to be paid to the mechanical design of large thickeners since their contents may weigh thousands of tons. They are usually stressed externally and supported upon concrete rafts. A tunnel must then be provided underneath for maintenance of the underflow system. An alternative design, as used at the Port Pirie uranium refinery in South Australia, is to support each vessel upon several hundred concrete piles. These enter the ground to the extent of about 40 ft and allow the base of the vessel to be suspended about 6 ft above ground level. Good access is thus provided to the underflow discharge point and this would not become flooded in the event of leakage.

It will be appreciated that a single thickening stage will always be less efficient than a single filtration stage for the removal of liquor from the spent ore, since the thickened slurry must always retain sufficient moisture to allow it to flow from the vessel in a continuous system, and this moisture will contain its normal concentration of dissolved mineral values. However, a large number of reslurry washing stages, say three or four, can increase the efficiency to a value similar to that of a two-stage filtration system. The flow pattern of a four-stage counter-current decantation washing system of this type is as follows: The leach slurry is first diluted to the feed solids content and is fed to thickener number 1. The overflow from this becomes the "pregnant liquor" containing the main part of the mineral values. The underflow from thickener 1 is mixed with the overflow from thickener 3 and is fed to thickener 2. The overflow from 2 is the wash liquor used for dilution of the leach slurry, and the underflow from 2 is mixed with the overflow from 4 and fed to thickener 3. The underflow from 3 is mixed with water and fed to thickener 4. The underflow from 4 is the spent washed ore which may be reslurried with water or any available waste liquor and pumped to a "tailings dam" for disposal. A system of this type, as used at the Australian Port Pirie Uranium plant, is shown in Fig. 2.6.

Assuming no preferential sorption of mineral values from the solution on to the spent ore, the extraction efficiency of a counter-current decantation system may be calculated as follows:

Let F be the solids content of the feed (expressed as a percentage), and U be the solids content of the underflow (expressed as a percentage).

For a single stage,

$$\text{Efficiency} = 100\left(1 - \frac{100F - UF}{100U - UF}\right)$$

For n stages,

$$\text{Efficiency} = 100\left[1 - \left(\frac{100F - UF}{100U - UF}\right)^n\right]$$

Similar considerations apply to filtration where only reslurry washing is involved. Usually however, additional washing is given on the filter and the efficiency is not then amenable to calculation without detailed knowledge of the manner in which the wash water displaces the filtrate from the filter cake in each individual case.

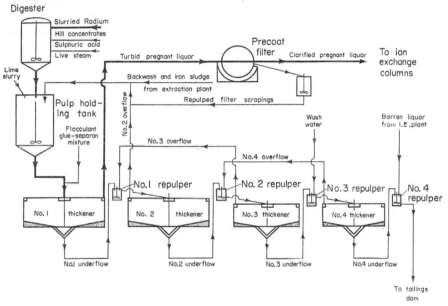

FIG. 2.6. Counter-current decantation washing at the Port Pirie Uranium Plant (Almond, J.N. Ref. 4).

Although a large number of techniques are available to chemical engineers for the separation of solids from liquids, rotary vacuum filtration and counter-current decantation are the two most commonly employed in connection with the leaching of low-grade, rare metal ores by dilute acids. It play be expected that hydrocyclones, centrifuges or centrifugal filters will play a greater role in future since they are suitable for continuous operation at high throughput.

Filter presses are not at all suitable for the filtration of the large quantity of solids involved in the processing of low-grade ores. The large labour requirement for these filters can be reduced by designing them to operate on a continuous automatic cycle, but their throughput is still relatively low.

Flocculating agents

Various natural materials have been used to improve the rate of settling or filtration. Animal glue, being cheap and readily available, has been employed in large quantities in the South African uranium industry for example.[9] An American comparison of the efficiency of glue, locust bean gum, guar gum and pear cactus extract, in connection with the leaching of uranium ores, has been given in a paper by Rosenbaum and Clemmer.[10] They included several synthetic materials in their trials, of which the Dow Chemical Company's "Separan" proved to be the most satisfactory. Under a variety of conditions of use, this material gave filtration and sedimentation rates which were superior to those with most natural accelerators. The rates were as much as 25 to 50 times those obtained without a filter aid or sedimentation aid.

Other synthetic materials of equal efficiency to Separan are now coming into frequent use and are marketed at about 10/– per lb or less. Examples are the Cyanamid Company's Aerofloc 3000, the Monsanto Chemical Company's Lytron and I.C.I.'s new reagents D.S. 3037 and 3047. These materials are polyelectrolytes, and they are generally referred to as flocculating agents since their action is to neutralize the electric charge on the surface of the ore particles and allow them to coalesce in a similar manner to the formation of a gel from a colloidal sol. Excess of the reagent can sometimes "peptize" the particles again, presumably by reversal of the sign of their original charge. The reagents consist of high molecular weight polymers, e.g. the sodium salt of polyacrylonitrile. They are made up into solutions of about 1 per cent concentration before use and applied at concentrations as low as 0.01 to 0.1 lb/ton of solids in the leach slurry. The method of addition is important, since it is necessary to obtain efficient mixing with the minimum agitation and so avoid breaking the flocs after formation. With some ores it is advantageous to add the reagent to the slurry in stages to economize on the total usage.

The effect of flocculant is to increase the solids content of the thickened slurry or filter cake besides increasing the rate of sedimentation or filtration. Full advantage cannot always be taken of the flocculant in the case of rotary vacuum filtration because the dense, heavily flocculated pulp sometimes has a slippery texture which does not adhere well to the drum. It may then be necessary to use rather small quantities of flocculant to optimize the process as a whole.

Other difficulties may arise because of the partially selective effect of the flocculant upon different minerals or particles of different sizes. This can result in a filtrate or decantate which is too cloudy for passing to the next stage of the extraction process, e.g. to ion-exchange or solvent extraction. In cases of this type it has sometimes been found advantageous to add glue in addition to the synthetic reagent, but a much smaller quantity of glue is used than if this were the sole aid. In many processes, a special clarification stage is in any case incorporated after the main filtration or decantation stage. This may be a simple sand bed, graded with coarse material at the bottom and the finest sand or diatomaceous silica at the top. Pressure sand bed clarifiers are sometimes preferred since their high filtration rate leads to a smaller area and lower capital and maintenance costs. A third alternative is a rotary vacuum pre-coat filter, but this would often be regarded as an expensive stage to be used for clarification alone.

Acid leaching of uranium ores

The uranium industry, which has developed during and since the 1939–45 war, has given a great impetus to acid leaching and in fact many of the techniques and much of the plant have been developed specially for this industry. It is of interest therefore to outline the chemistry of uranium leaching as the prime example of acid leaching, since it is anticipated that many of the problems will be paralleled by similar ones in other ore leaching processes. The chemical problems are frequently the result of side reactions in which common minerals play a predominant role, and these minerals are associated with ores of the other rare metals just as frequently as with uranium ores.

Most of the uranium ores which are worked today are found in deposits of 0·1 to 0·5 per cent grade, with the narrower range 0·1 to 0·2 per cent becoming increasingly prominent. Very large reserves of shales and phosphate rock ores exist with a grade of only 0·01 per cent, and the use of these is being contemplated in some parts of the world. A large South African uranium industry has existed for a number of years based upon an average ore grade of about 0·025 per cent, but this is made economic by being associated with gold[9], the mining and grinding costs being shared by the two extraction processes.

The primary minerals pitchblende and uraninite predominate, and their composition approximates to U_3O_8 or a mixture of oxides intermediate between U_3O_8 and UO_2. These oxides are easily leached by dilute sulphuric acid, in the presence of an oxidant to convert the uranium to the hexavalent condition. It is customary to regard the form of the resulting uranium in solution as being uranyl sulphate, UO_2SO_4. In practice, however, high proportions of the anionic complexes $UO_2(SO_4)_2^{2-}$ and $UO_2(SO_4)_3^{4-}$ are also present. Use is made of these complexes in the later stages of uranium refining for the extraction of the uranium by anion-exchange, preparatory to the production of a fairly high-grade concentrate.

Alternatively, dilute nitric acid can be employed for leaching without any other oxidant, but its higher cost, the more expensive materials of plant construction, and the unsuitability of the solution for subsequent process stages, usually make this method unattractive. Nitric acid is used in one special case, where the ore grade is high, i.e. between 30 and 80 per cent and the leaching stage can be followed directly by a final tributyl phosphate or ether extraction process to give a product of very high purity. This applies at the Springfields refinery in the United Kingdom, where a high-grade partially purified chemical concentrate is the usual feed, but an equally high-grade mineral pitchblende has also been successfully treated from time to time.

Some secondary materials, which have been produced geologically as a result of natural chemical action on the primary minerals, have their uranium already in the hexavalent state and are fairly readily leached by dilute sulphuric or hydrochloric acid without an oxidant: these include carnotite, autunite, and torbernite.[7] Other secondary minerals such as davidite and pyrochlore are more refractory and are not amenable to dilute acid leaching.

Hydrochloric acid has only been employed to a minor extent, with certain carnotite ores which are relatively low in limestone content. The process[11] involves roasting the ore at 850°C with sodium chloride followed by leaching with water to remove vanadium. Dilute hydrochloric acid, produced by scrubbing the roaster gases with water, is then used to leach out about 90 per cent of the uranium, together with a small additional proportion of vanadium. In general, unless the limestone content is sufficiently high to warrant alkali leaching, the hydrochloric acid process has been superseded by processes based upon dilute sulphuric acid with or without an oxidant.

In view of the low grade of ore generally employed, every effort is made to economize on sulphuric acid usage. Quantities of the order of 50 to 200 lb of acid per ton of ore are commonly added and, clearly, only a small proportion of this is actually needed for the dissolution of say 4 lb U/ton, according to the equation:

$$2U_3O_8 + 6H_2SO_4 + (O_2) \rightarrow 6UO_2SO_4 + 6H_2O.$$

The remaining acid is required for the dissolution of, or reaction with, other minerals present in the ore. Limestone, for example, reacts readily, and may form a saturated solution of calcium sulphate, which crystallizes and impedes settling or filtration later. Silica forms silicic acid and gelation of this causes blockages in subsequent ion-exchange stages or poor phase separation in solvent extraction stages. Metallic iron from the grinding circuit releases hydrogen, and sulphide minerals, usually containing iron or copper, release hydrogen sulphide gas.

i.e. $$Fe + H_2SO_4 \rightarrow FeSO_4 + H_2;$$

$$FeS + H_2SO_4 \rightarrow FeSO_4 + H_2S.$$

When iron has entered the solution, it plays a part in the oxidation of tetravalent uranium to the hexavalent uranyl sulphate[7] and although it has been described as a catalyst,[12] its effect is not always beneficial. The cheapest oxidants available are usually sodium chlorate or manganese dioxide. The latter may be used in the form of the mineral pyrolusite, which contains 65 to 70 per cent MnO_2. Besides usually being cheaper, manganese dioxide has the advantage that it can be recovered after extraction of the mineral values, by precipitation of the hydroxide, followed by oxidation with air.

The oxidant used in the leaching operation must be in sufficient excess to oxidize the ferrous iron in solution to the ferric condition before any is available for oxidation of the uranium. The ferrous-to-ferric oxidation consumes further acid, besides oxidant, in addition to that required for dissolution of the iron, i.e.

$$2FeSO_4 + MnO_2 + 2H_2SO_4 \rightarrow Fe_2(SO_4)_3 + MnSO_4 + 2H_2O.$$

It is sometimes advantageous to delay the addition of the oxidant until a high proportion of the metallic iron and iron sulphides have dissolved, since the nascent hydrogen and hydrogen sulphide can otherwise behave as reducing agents and require still further quantities of oxidant and acid, i.e.

$$H_2 + MnO_2 + H_2SO_4 \rightarrow MnSO_4 + 2H_2O,$$

and

$$H_2S + MnO_2 + H_2SO_4 \rightarrow MnSO_4 + 2H_2O + S.$$

In other cases the iron sulphide minerals pyrite (FeS_2) or pyrrhotite (FeS) are present in the ore in a sufficiently reactive or finely divided form to undergo oxidation by air during the operations of grinding, storage, or conveying, prior to leaching. This can apply particularly when the moist ore, or a slurry of high solids content, is allowed to stand for periods of days with good access of air. Reactions of the following type then take place:

$$4FeS + 9O_2 + 4H_2O \rightarrow 2Fe_2O_3 + 4H_2SO_4,$$

or $$4FeS_2 + 15O_2 + 14H_2O \rightarrow 4Fe(OH)_3 + 8H_2SO_4.$$

These reactions actually liberate sulphuric acid and it is clear that considerable savings can be made in acid and oxidant costs if the reactions can be encouraged.

One method of encouraging these reactions to take place rapidly in the leach liquor itself is to use pressure acid leaching of the type proposed by Forward and Halpen,[13] and later studied by Gray.[5] Optimum reaction temperatures and total pressures may vary with individual ores, but 130°C and 35 psi are satisfactory in some cases in the presence of oxygen, or 75 psi in the presence of air, the oxygen partial pressure being 10 psi in both cases. Besides the two reactions given above, others take place in these circumstances, as follows.

$$2FeS_2 + 7O_2 + 2H_2O \rightarrow 2FeSO_4 + 2H_2SO_4,$$

and
$$4FeS_2 + 15O_2 + 2H_2O \rightarrow 2Fe_2(SO_4)_3 + 2H_2SO_4.$$

It is frequently possible for these various reactions to take place in a pressure leaching system so that an excess of sulphuric acid is liberated which is sufficient to leach the uranium from the ore. Thus leaching reagent costs can be virtually eliminated.

Since the pressure leaching technique cannot always be employed owing to high capital costs, attention is still being paid to the chemistry of the more conventional acid leaching system with a view to improvement in reagent costs, and in some of these matters the iron and iron minerals still play a central role. Electromagnetic separation, for example, a well-known technique in other fields, is sometimes applied as a means of removing iron minerals and it can result in sulphuric acid savings of several tens of lb/ton. It should not be forgotten, however, that iron minerals which are capable of entering the solution in the fully oxidized ferric condition do not consume oxidant, and can themselves oxidize tetravalent uranium to the required hexavalent condition. High usage of acid can therefore sometimes be balanced by relatively low usage of oxidant, or even the complete absence of a special oxidant. Another way in which ferric iron in solution may be beneficial is in the complexing action which it exerts upon phosphate ions in solution. This prevents the phosphate from forming complexes with the uranyl ion in solution, which would render the uranium less extractable by ion-exchange resins, or solvents, after leaching.

"Constant pH leaching" is a system which has given considerable acid economy in some cases. When this technique is applied to a conventional batch leaching process, acid is added to the vessel at a controlled rate equal to the acid usage so that the pH does not fall below a value of say 1·8. Leaching takes longer than if the whole of the acid were added initially with the ore, when the pH might have started at a very low figure and slowly risen to pH 1·8. The absence of low pH (or high acidity) conditions prevents or minimizes the acid attack on some minerals such as silica or possibly iron sulphides, so avoiding wasteful acid losses. The principle depends of course on the fact that uranium, being present as a readily soluble oxide, can be leached selectively at low acidities. The acidity in the first vessel of a continuous co-current leaching system would usually be higher than that in a single batch vessel operated at a constant pH. When constant pH leaching is applied to a co-current system, therefore, it is necessary to add acid to each vessel of the cascade at a controlled rate.

In a counter-current uranium ore leaching system, it is not possible to maintain the pH at a constant value. The system is already fairly critical in this and other respects when leaching a typical uranium ore. For example in a two-stage system, incoming ore enters vessel 1 together with once used acid from vessel 2. An abnormality in the ratio of acid to ore, or the acid requirements of the incoming ore, might easily cause the pH in vessel 1 to rise to the point where certain uranium compounds would precipitate. Such a compound might be formed if, for instance, the new batch of ore had enough metallic iron or ferrous iron-containing minerals to reduce the uranium to the tetravalent state. Phosphate minerals, usually present in the ore, would cause the precipitation of uranous phosphate at a pH of 1·25. Once precipitated, the uranous phosphate would pass into vessel 2 where it would redissolve only slowly. Consequently, a high proportion of the uranium might leave vessel 2 with the spent ore. This type of problem has been met in practice during early South African development work.[14]

Acid leaching of thorite

Most commercial thorium is extracted from monazite, which is not amenable to breakdown by dilute acids. Thorite, or thorium silicate, is an alternative thorium ore which occurs in fairly large quantities in some parts of the world, for example in the tailings from the tin beneficiation processes in Nigeria. The ore contains principally zircon (zirconium silicate), but this is of much smaller value than the 5 to 10 per cent thorite content.

The thorium can be leached from thorite by a prolonged treatment with hot aqueous nitric or hydrochloric acid:[23, 24]

i.e. $$Th(SiO_3)_2 + 4HNO_3 \rightarrow Th(NO_3)_4 + 2H_2O + 2SiO_2.$$

Nitric acid is preferred on grounds of plant corrosion and particularly if the extract is to become the feed to a solvent purification stage. 6N, or better, 12N acid at the boiling-point extracts about 97 per cent of the thorium in 24 hr and the amount of zirconium in solution is only about 0·25 per cent of the thorium content. Although the acid concentration is fairly high, comparatively little is used in the reaction and one batch will serve to leach several batches of ore at a ratio of 1·5 tons/ton of thorite.

The thorium concentration thus builds up to a fairly high level in solution but a proportion of soluble thorium remains physically adhering to the large bulk of zirconium residue. This is conveniently removed by a simple washing treatment with water, preferably in a counter-current manner. In order to avoid too high a total volume of solution, the thorium is precipitated at pH 7 to 8 by means of sodium hydroxide and the resulting product dissolved in the acid leach liquor. The final thorium concentration can in this way reach 100 to 200 g/l. with an overall thorium recovery of 93 per cent.

The plant used for the leaching and precipitation stages is best made of stainless steel and consists of quite conventional stirred vessels and filters.

CONCENTRATED ACID BREAKDOWN

The breakdown of an ore with a concentrated acid, on an industrial scale, is only justified if the mineral values are fairly high in concentration and of some economic importance. A high acid wastage upon unwanted minerals, e.g. carbonates, oxides, sulphates, phosphates and silicates, can normally be expected if these are present, and in any case the quantity of acid required merely to wet the ore and form a workable pulp is of necessity high. Corrosion problems are generally more severe than with dilute leaching acids and require more expensive materials of construction.

Concentrated acids are usually only employed for refractory ores which do not respond to less severe breakdown techniques, and for the same reason might be expected to be used at fairly high temperatures. If cost, availability, and plant corrosion did not already provide sufficient grounds for a choice of sulphuric acid, its higher boiling-point than other acids would usually do so.

Breakdown equipment

Reaction vessels, for batch operation on a scale of say 10 tons, which are fairly resistant to attack by concentrated sulphuric acid, can be fabricated of cast iron, tantalum iron or high silicon iron. Such vessels are cast in one piece and are not very highly resistant to thermal shock; hence the limit on size. Steam jackets are impracticable, electric heating is usually too expensive, and oil- or gas-firing is usually employed. Agitator systems are commonly made from mild steel and allowed to corrode, being regarded as expendable. In view of the high solids content of the slurry, the viscosity is often extremely high. Consequently, agitators must be fabricated in a robust manner and a low-speed, high-torque, drive system installed. Gate type stirrers are generally used.

Unlike dilute acid leaching vessels, those handling hot concentrated sulphuric acid may have to be fitted with lids and adequately vented to remove corrosive acid fumes. More stringent safety measures than with dilute acids may similarly be necessary in view of the high reactivity of sulphuric acid towards water and organic materials and the possibility that pipelines and pumps, etc., might be manufactured in relatively brittle cast iron and be subject to mechanical fracture.

Continuous sulphuric acid breakdown processes are possible in which the acid and ore are fed together at the top of a rotating, inclined, heated kiln. The reaction products and excess sulphuric acid can then be removed continuously from the lower end. It is necessary that the reactants and products shall not be sufficiently mobile for "by-passing" to take place when flowing down the reactor, otherwise residence times will vary widely about the mean value. A kiln of this type resembles that commonly used for the manufacture of hydrofluoric acid by the reaction of sulphuric acid with fluorspar (calcium fluoride).

Sulphuric acid breakdown of monazite[23, 24]

The outstanding example of the use of concentrated sulphuric acid in the breakdown of rare metal ores is the thorium and rare earth industry, based upon monazite, which is established in many parts of the world. Monazite is usually mined as a beach-washed sand which can be readily upgraded by physical means to the virtually pure mineral. Commercial quantities of the mineral are produced in India (Travencore), Brazil, Australia, Malaya, Nigeria, Korea and South Africa. The mineral consists of the phosphates of the whole range of rare earths, in which some of the rare earths have become partially replaced by thorium. The total rare earth content may be about 50 per cent, but the thorium content is often between 5 and 10 per cent. The manufacturer's objective in the past has been to seek a market for the two materials in approximately the proportions prevailing in the mineral, and the sulphuric acid breakdown process has usually been designed to take both into solution, separation being effected at a later stage. The advent of nuclear energy and the possibility of this new industry requiring large quantities of thorium in future years may cause the sulphuric acid breakdown stage to be operated in a different manner so as to take the whole of the thorium into solution and reject a high proportion of the rare earths. In either case, however, the usage of acid at the breakdown stage is controlled by purely physical conditions, i.e., the ease with which the acid/ore mixture can be agitated. Two tons of approximately 95 per cent sulphuric acid per ton or ore is commonly used. A concentration of 93 per cent has been stated to be optimum.[25] In some plants it has been reduced to as little as 1·4 tons, with some operational difficulty and a reduction in efficiency by a few per cent. The reaction, for thorium, may be represented as:

$$TH_3(PO_4)_4 + 6H_2SO_4 \rightarrow 3Th(SO_4)_2 + 4H_3PO_4.$$

The mode of operation is generally to heat a batch of sulphuric acid to a temperature of about 180°C and feed the monazite sand slowly whilst stirring. The reaction is exothermic and the temperature is usually maintained at about 220°C to 230°C for several hours without the application of further external heat. This depends to some extent upon the particle size of the sand but it is normally left unground at a size range of about 30 to 120 mesh. A total breakdown time of at least 4 hr is necessary. The viscosity of the breakdown paste increases markedly, particularly in the early stages. This aggravates the tendency to foaming caused by evolution of gaseous helium and thoron. Thoron is the fifth member of the radioactive decay chain after thorium itself. It emits a short lived α-radiation and decays to a series of α-, β- and γ-emitters, all short-lived solid elements. Adequate ventilation is required for its removal, but the hazard is less than from the radon associated with uranium ores, which can deposit radioactive isotopes with long half-lives. The helium content of the minerals is not hazardous and arises as a direct result of the α-radioactivity of the various species, since α-radiation consists of helium nuclei. The helium is mostly trapped in the crystal lattice of the monazite mineral until released by acid attack.

The viscous breakdown paste sets to a fairly solid mass on cooling, and satisfactory means must be provided for tipping the vessel or otherwise removing the paste whilst still warm. This often places a limitation on the size and design of the breakdown vessel since it is perhaps constructed of heavy gauge cast iron, fitted with a robust stirrer mechanism and is built into a gas or oil-heated furnace. A continuous rotating sulphator has been used in the U.S.S.R.[26] for carrying out the breakdown reaction at 200 to 300°C. This avoids some of the mechanical difficulties associated with the agitation and discharge of the breakdown paste.

The next stage of the breakdown process consists of extraction of the breakdown mixture with water. This is normally carried out in lead-lined vats since the breakdown vessel itself would not be resistant to corrosion by the resulting dilute sulphuric acid. The temperature is usually maintained below 30°C because rare earth sulphates are more soluble at lower temperatures than at high temperatures.[27] If thorium only is being extracted there may be some advantage in controlling the temperature at 45°C, which corresponds to a maximum thorium solubility in the thorium sulphate–sulphuric acid phase diagram. This process stage requires prolonged agitation for times of 12 to 15 hr in order to leach the soluble thorium and rare earth sulphates away from insoluble siliceous matter, unreacted monazite and "mesothorium" residues. Large lumps of insoluble matter may be removed by screening. They are then crushed and returned for extraction. The final insoluble residues are removed by filtration, usually in plate and frame type filter presses.

The mesothorium residues consist of the various members of the thorium radioactive decay series beginning with the longest lived mesothorium I, of half-life 6–7 years. Mesothorium I is an isotope of radium which has a sulphate of very low solubility and is isomorphous with barium sulphate. Consequently, it is common practice to add about 1 lb of barium sulphate to each ton of monazite at the breakdown stage to act as a scavenger for mesothorium I. This ensures that the very small weight of the highly radioactive mesothorium I remains with the insoluble residue rather than being associated with the leach liquor as a colloidal sol.

For efficient extraction of the thorium and rare earths, usually to the extent of about 99 per cent, 10 tons of water are used for leaching the breakdown product for every ton of monazite. This can, if necessary, be reduced to as little as 7 tons without seriously impairing the extraction efficiency, but the mechanical difficulties of breaking up the cake are greater, and the rate of extraction is lower. If subsequent processing has the primary object of thorium recovery, about 50 per cent of the rare earth sulphates can be rejected at the water leaching stage by limiting the water usage to 4·5 tons/ton of monazite and extracting at 45°C. The thorium extraction efficiency may be reduced in these circumstances to about 95 per cent and the quantity of solids in the filter presses greatly increased.

A number of methods are available for the removal of phosphate from the thorium and rare earth elements in the breakdown liquor. For example, the thorium and rare earths may be precipitated from the liquor as oxalates, using oxalic acid, or the liquor may be added to concentrated sulphuric acid at about 200°C to evaporate water and precipitate the anhydrous sulphates, or the sodium double sulphates may be crystallized out after adding sodium sulphate.[28]

Thorium can be separated from rare earths in solution by methods based upon either basicity separation, i.e. the preferential precipitation of thorium phosphate with alkali at a pH below 2,[29] or precipitation of ammonium rare earth double sulphates with ammonia.

Solvent extraction is now coming into use as a method for the final purification of thorium from uranium and other impurities, to the stringent specification imposed when the element is used for nuclear purposes (Chapter 4).[30]

An interesting feature of the anhydrous sulphate precipitation method is that the precipitation reagent (concentrated sulphuric acid) can be recycled and used for a subsequent monazite breakdown. The recycled sulphuric acid is contaminated with a high proportion of phosphoric acid and within limits this can be tolerated. It has even been stated[31] that sulphuric acid containing a proportion of phosphoric acid allows more efficient breakdown than sulphuric acid alone, owing to the greater solubility of the thorium and rare earths in the mixed acids.

Sulphuric acid breakdown of beryl

The United States Brush Beryllium Corporation operate the Kaufmann and Kjellgren process for the sulphuric acid breakdown of beryl. Beryl is the principal beryllium mineral and consists of a beryllium aluminium silicate, $3BeO.Al_2O_3.6SiO_2$. It is mined in Argentina, Brazil, South Africa, Southern Rhodesia, India and parts of the U.S.A. When pure it has a beryllium oxide content of about 14 per cent. The commercial mineral is usually fairly pure, with 10 to 12 per cent BeO, equivalent to about 4 per cent beryllium.

It is necessary to fuse beryl at a temperature of about 1700°C and quench in water to make it reactive towards concentrated sulphuric acid. This operation can be carried out in an electric furnace lined with graphite, the heat being supplied by passing an electric current through the molten beryl itself. Some advantage in reactivity is gained if the glassy "frit", after quenching, is heated a second time, to 900 to 950°C, before treatment with sulphuric acid. The breakdown efficiency is thus increased from 50–60 to 90–95 per cent.[32] The function of the second heat treatment is to precipitate the unreactive beryllium oxide out of solid solution in the silica component and so make it reactive. A gas-heated rotary kiln is employed at this stage.

The sulphuric acid reaction involves a quantity of acid which is stoichiometrically equivalent to the reaction:

$$3BeO.Al_2O_3.6SiO_2 + 6H_2SO_4 \rightarrow 3BeSO_4 + Al_2(SO_4)_3 + 6SiO_2 + 6H_2O.$$

The acid concentration may be as low as 93 per cent and it is made into a slurry with the heat-treated frit, after the latter has been ground to pass a 200-mesh screen. The preferred method of carrying out the sulphation process consists of spraying the acid ore slurry as a jet on the the preheated inner surface of a mild-steel mill, at a temperature of 250–300°C.

After sulphation, several methods are available for isolating the beryllium in a high state of purity; the process operated by the Brush Beryllium Corporation[32] is described below:

The reaction cake is leached with water in a solid bowl type continuous centrifuge to extract the beryllium and aluminium sulphates and remove the silica. A typical analysis of the liquor is:

>Beryllium   13   g/l.
>Aluminium 15   ,,
>Iron   2   ,,
>Silicon   0·1   ,,
>Free sulphuric acid 1N.

The free acidity is continuously neutralized with ammonia, which allows the major part (about 75 per cent) of the aluminium to crystallize out as ammonium alum $(NH_4)_2Al_2(SO_4)_4.24H_2O$. The alum crystals are removed in a centrifuge and the beryllium is purified from the remaining aluminium by the addition of sodium hydroxide, followed by boiling. The sodium hydroxide is added continuously as a dilute solution, together with a solution of the chelating agent EDTA (ethylene diamine tetra-acetic acid). Soluble sodium aluminate and beryllate are formed and other impurities are prevented from precipitating by the chelating agent, e.g.

$$BeSO_4 + 4NaOH \rightarrow Na_2BeO_2 + Na_2SO_4 + 2H_2O.$$

Boiling of this solution allows the beryllium to precipitate as the hydroxide, in a fairly pure condition:

$$Na_2BeO_2 + 2H_2O \rightarrow Be(OH)_2 + 2NaOH$$

After centrifuging and drying, a 97 per cent yield of beryllium hydroxide is obtained which has the following approximate analysis (on a BeO basis):

	%
Aluminium	0·15
Iron	0·05
Silicon	0·05
Sodium	0·15

Variants of this breakdown process are also in use. In the Degussa process, for example,[33] the beryl is fused with limestone before sulphuric acid breakdown, and the Joy–Windecker process similarly involves fusion with sodium carbonate before breakdown. The reaction mechanism in these cases is believed to be the conversion of the beryl into a complex silicate, followed by its decomposition with sulphuric acid, i.e.

$$3BeO.Al_2O_3.6SiO_2 + 6CaCO_3 \rightarrow 3BeO.Al_2O_3.6CaSiO_3 + 6CO_2,$$

and $3BeO.Al_2O_3.6CaSiO_3 + 12H_2SO_4 \rightarrow$
$$3BeOSO_4 + Al_2(SO_4)_3 + 6CaSO_4 + 6SiO_2 + 12H_2O.$$

The full stoichiometric amount of sodium or calcium carbonate does not appear to be necessary and 75 per cent of this quantity allows subsequent leaching efficiencies of 97 to 98 per cent to be obtained. Reagent consumption is high when these carbonate fluxes are employed since in addition to the flux itself, an additional quantity of sulphuric acid must be provided which is almost sufficient to neutralize it.

The Degussa Company of Germany produced about 10 tonnes of beryllia and 4 tonnes of beryllium metal flake during the 1939–45 war by the sulphuric acid breakdown or beryl.[34] Batches of 100 kg of ground beryl were heated with 50 kg of powdered limestone at 1400–1500°C in a gas-fired rotary kiln about 1·5 m outside diameter and 3 m long. After 1·5 hr. "sintering", the product was discharged into water, dried and ground before acid breakdown. The latter operation was carried out with 300 kg of the "frit" and 480 kg of concentrated sulphuric acid in a welded steel tank 5 m by 2 m by 1·5 m high. Forty litres of water were required to start the reaction, which then proceeded to completion in about 2 hr without the application of external heat. A steam-jacketed, lead-lined tank was next used to dissolve the sulphates in 350 l. of water. Hot filtration, after addition of glue, then removed silica and calcium sulphate, and the aluminium was crystallized out as ammonium alum on addition of powdered ammonium sulphate. After removal of the alum in a rubber-lined centrifuge, ferric hydroxide and calcium sulphate were precipitated together, by the addition of hydrogen peroxide (for oxidation of ferrous to ferric sulphate) and calcium carbonate. A fairly pure beryllium hydroxide could then be precipitated from the final filtrate by addition of ammonia.

At the time that this plant was operating, the extreme toxicity of beryllium compounds was not fully appreciated. Eight deaths were caused at the Degussa Company which could be directly attributed to beryllium compounds, two of them at the sulphate extraction stage.[33]

Uranium and vanadium ore opening by concentrated acid

An "acid-cure" process has been used commercially at Shiprock, New Mexico, for the breakdown of carnotite ore to recover uranium and vanadium. The damp ore was mixed to a dough with concentrated sulphuric acid and allowed to stand for up to 24 hr before leaching with water. The vanadium extraction efficiency was greater than that obtained by dilute acid leaching, but the process has now been discontinued owing to the relatively high acid usage. A variation of this technique has been suggested[39] in which the acid-cured mixture is contacted directly with an organic solvent, to extract the uranium in a pure condition and avoid an aqueous leaching and filtration stage.

Digestion with hot sulphuric acid of moderate concentration is used at Port Pirie in South Australia. The ore, mined at Radium Hill, contains the refractory mineral davidite which does not respond to leaching with dilute acid in the usual way. The high acid usage is justified by the fact that the ore, mined at a grade of about 0·25 per cent, is concentrated by flotation and heavy media separation to about 1 per cent before acid treatment.

ALKALI BREAKDOWN

Sodium hydroxide is used, either in the molten condition (m.p. 318°C) or as a concentrated solution at about 200°C, for the breakdown of refractory ores such as phosphates or silicates. Usually, the oxide, hydrated oxide or hydroxide of the metal is produced and this can be dissolved in dilute acid for further purification, after first washing free from the other reaction product sodium phosphate or silicate. In exceptional cases, such as the alkaline breakdown of beryl, the reaction is more complex.

In addition to naturally occurring ores, ferroniobium has been used as a source metal for the production of pure niobium, in a process where it is leached with a potassium hydroxide solution as if it were a high-grade ore. In this case the niobium is taken into solution in the alkali, together with its homologue tantalum.

Breakdown equipment

Alkali breakdown is usually carried out as a simple batch operation in mild-steel, cast iron or stainless-steel vessels. The reaction products may assume the form of a viscous paste and suitable agitation is necessary to maintain intimate mixing. The design of stirrer system is simpler than for breakdown by concentrated sulphuric acid since corrosive fumes are not present to attack bearings or motors, etc., and corrosion of the stirrer blades and vessel by the reactants or products is also much less serious. A simple gate stirrer of mild steel or stainless steel is usually satisfactory. The reaction vessel may require to be tipped if the products are solids or viscous pastes, but in other circumstances a bottom outlet might be satisfactory.

Alkali breakdown of monazite

The breakdown of monazite for the production of thorium and rare earths is probably the prime example of the use of sodium hydroxide, and this reagent is tending to displace the more conventional sulphuric acid.

The essential reaction, for thorium, is:

$$Th_3(PO_4)_4 + 12NaOH \rightarrow 3ThO_2 + 4Na_3PO_4 + 6H_2O,$$

although in practice the thorium oxide tends to be hydrated. The thorium oxide is mixed with an excess of rare earth oxides from decomposition of the other components of the mineral, and sufficient sodium hydroxide is necessary for this purpose. For each ton of monazite sand 1·2 tons of sodium hydroxide and 1 ton of water can be used, although the precise quantities vary according to the source and grade of the mineral.

The reaction can be carried out in a stainless-steel vessel, fitted with a slow-speed stirrer, heating jacket and reflux condenser. The concentrated alkali solution is first heated in the breakdown vessel to about 130°C and the monazite, ground to pass a 300-mesh sieve, is added gradually over a period of 30 min. A total reaction time of about 4 hr is then required under reflux at 140–45 °C. Adequate ventilation is needed, as with sulphuric acid breakdown, to remove the radioactive thoron gas under safe conditions. Unlike the acid breakdown process, however, highly corrosive fumes or spray are absent.

The reaction temperature is important; if this exceeds 145°C by more than a small margin, or more particularly if fused sodium hydroxide is used in place of a concentrated aqueous solution, the resulting thorium and rare earth oxides become unreactive. For example, they do not dissolve completely in the nitric acid used at a subsequent stage.

Filtration of the oxides is carried out preferably at an elevated temperature, up to about 110°C, to maintain the trisodium phosphate in solution.[40] Digestion at this temperature is desirable before the filtration stage, to increase the particle size and consequently the rate and efficiency of filtration. When recovery of trisodium phosphate is carried out, it is convenient to dilute the breakdown product with water at the digestion stage before filtration. This allows the major proportion of the sodium phosphate to be recovered as a single crop of crystals from the strongly alkaline liquor, rather than from several subsequent wash liquors. In practice, a very high proportion of the phosphate may be recovered in the form of large crystals by evaporating the filtrate back to a sodium hydroxide concentration of 47 per cent. The residual mother liquor is a fairly pure sodium hydroxide solution, suitable for recycling to the breakdown stage.

The thorium and rare earth oxides, which also contain most of the associated uranium, are washed several times in water to reduce the phosphate content to about 5 or 10 per cent of that of the thorium. Removal of wash liquor is mainly by decantation, except for the last wash, since the filtration rate becomes progressively less as the pH decreases in successive washes. A standard type of plate and frame filter press can be used for the final stage and the rate is sufficiently low to make additional washing of the cake in the press undesirable.

The mixed oxide cake is dissolved in acid, preferably nitric acid, and further purified. Hydrogen peroxide may be added to assist the dissolution.[40] In the early process developed by the American Battelle Memorial Institute,[40] the nitrates are passed directly to a solvent extraction stage (Chapter 4). In their later process[41] and the corresponding process of the U.K. Atomic Energy Authority,[23, 24] the prior precipitation of thorium hydroxide away from the major part of the rare earths is advised, this being accomplished by a basicity separation step using sodium hydroxide at a pH of 5·8 to 6·0.

Rock monazite, obtainable from South Africa, contains a few per cent of the mineral apatite (calcium phosphate) together with a little iron phosphate impurity. The apatite in particular does not respond to the sodium hydroxide breakdown procedure to the same extent as thorium and rare earth phosphates. Consequently, the "oxide" product after washing still contains a quantity of phosphate about equal to the weight of thorium present. This is too high for passing to the final solvent purification stage and it is therefore necessary to eliminate apatite before the alkali breakdown stage. Removal is accomplished by a pretreatment process[23, 24] in which the rock monazite, finely ground, is leached with 8N nitric acid at the boiling-point for 3 hr. This dissolves most of the apatite and about 7 per cent of the thorium, but the latter may be recovered by selective precipitation from the nitrate solution with sodium hydroxide. The resulting thorium phosphate paste, fairly free from calcium phosphate, may be added to the acid-washed monazite for sodium hydroxide breakdown. The breakdown and phosphate removal process is then as successful as when using a high-purity monazite sand.

Alkali breakdown of zircon

Zircon, or zirconium silicate, is the common ore of zirconium. Although it is not appreciably attacked by aqueous alkalis, it responds readily to breakdown by fused sodium hydroxide at temperatures of 550 to 650°C. The reaction varies according to the proportions of the reactants and other conditions but can be represented approximately by the equation:

$$4NaOH + ZrSiO_4 \rightarrow Na_2ZrO_3 + Na_2SiO_3 + 2H_2O$$

A large excess of sodium hydroxide has sometimes been used in the past,[43, 44] but this is hardly justified, since its cost per ton is about twice that of high-grade zircon sand. A small excess represented by the use of 1·2 tons of alkali per ton of sand is sufficient for a breakdown efficiency near to 90 per cent.

A stainless-steel breakdown vessel has been used, although this is not essential, cast iron being satisfactory if it is not subjected to undue thermal shock. A stirrer is not required since satisfactory agitation is usually obtained by the evolution of steam resulting from the reaction. The reactants are both added to the vessel at the start, the zircon preferably on top of the sodium hydroxide flake. It may take several hours for the mixture to reach the reaction temperature and for the sodium hydroxide to melt, using an electric, gas- or oil-fired furnace. The reaction then proceeds sufficiently vigorously for material to be ejected, if the vessel is not fitted with a loose lid. Provided a large excess of sodium hydroxide has not been used, the "frit" which results is porous and friable and on cooling can be removed from the reactor with relative ease. A reaction mixture richer in alkali, however, may require pouring from the reactor in a molten condition near the reaction temperature.

The cold frit is crushed in equipment which is preferably totally enclosed to prevent personal contact with the irritant alkaline dust. Leaching is then carried out with water to remove sodium silicate and excess sodium hydroxide. About 7 tons of water per ton of zircon are appropriate, this quantity being divided between several successive leaching operations. Solid–liquid separation is by decantation between each leach. The sodium zirconate is finally filtered off in a fairly dry condition. It is advisable not to use a larger excess of water or peptization of colloidal zirconium compounds prevents satisfactory decantation or filtration, and in any case the washing out of the last trace of alkali is not essential.

It is more important to remove small amounts of silica from the sodium zirconate but this is retained in close association with the solid, probably as a sodium zirconium silicate, until it is subsequently dissolved in acid. Cold 12 to 16N nitric acid or 10N hydrochloric acid is used, but the dissolution is accompanied by a considerable increase in temperature:

$$Na_2ZrO_3 + 4HNO_3 \rightarrow ZrO(NO_3)_2 + 2NaNO_3 + 2H_2O.$$

The unreacted zircon and impurities can be removed, with difficulty, by filtration and diatomaceous earth filter aids are beneficial.

Removal of silica from the nitrate or chloride solution is desirable before, for example, any final solvent purification process. Methods have been based upon precipitation of zirconium sulphite, sulphate, phthalate, or oxychloride, etc.

Alkali treatment of ferroniobium

A number of processes have been described for the breakdown of niobium and tantalum ores by fusion with alkali,[45] but the low cost of the raw material is balanced by the difficulties associated with the high temperatures which are necessary.

Although not an ore, ferroniobium is produced by a smelting operation from columbite, in reasonably large quantities and at a cost which is sufficiently attractive for it to be used as a source material for the producton of pure niobium. It consists essentially of an alloy of about 60 per cent niobium, 9 per cent tantalum and 24 per cent iron with smaller amounts of tungsten, titanium, manganese and aluminium, etc. Processes have been based upon dissolution of ferroniobium in acids (e.g. a mixture of sulphuric and hydrofluoric acids) or fusion with potassium carbonate,[46] but the most satisfactory method is to dissolve the alloy in a concentrated potassium hydroxide solution.

In the U.K. Atomic Energy Authority's process a 34 kg batch of crushed ferroniobium, at a particle size below 100 mesh, is dissolved in 34 kg of potassium hydroxide and 50 l. of water, at a temperature of 100°C. Hydrogen is evolved according to the reaction:

$$2Nb + 2KOH + 4H_2O \rightarrow 2KNbO_3 + 5H_2.$$

The ferroniobium is added slowly over 2 hr, at a rate sufficient to maintain the temperature of 100°C and avoid excessive froth formation. An extra 2 hr digestion at temperature is allowed after complete addition of the ferroniobium. A reducing atmosphere is necessary to avoid undue oxidation of ferrous iron, since ferric hydroxide is difficult to filter. The hydrogen evolved in the reaction is therefore supplemented in the later stages of digestion by passing a slow stream of the gas through the liquid.

Potassium niobate, together with the analogous tantalate, is soluble, whereas iron and titanium remain in the insoluble residue, along with 3 to 4 per cent of the niobium.

Although the digestion temperature is somewhat below the boiling-point, about 20 l. of water are lost in the reaction and by evaporation. This is made up, together with an additional 100 l., before filtration at 70°C. The residue is reslurried with 100 l. of hot 5 per cent potassium hydroxide solution and filtered again at 70°C before finally discarding. This wash liquor is added to the main filtrate to give a total volume of about 250 l. of potassium niobate/tantalate solution in excess alkali.

The plant required for the above operations is relatively simple; digestion is carried out in a stainless-steel vessel, steam jacketed, fitted with a stirrer, reflux condenser, conical base and bottom outlet. Special provision is made for passing a slow stream of hydrogen into the vessel via a pipe at the base. Filtration is on a Nutsche vacuum filter, a suitable filter medium being paper between two layers of terylene cloth. An additional clarification stage is also used to remove fine suspended particles of iron oxide. A bed of firmly packed paper pulp is satisfactory for this purpose.

Conversion of the potassium niobate/tantalate solution to the corresponding oxides is via the insoluble sodium niobate and tantalate. These are readily precipitated by the addition of a sodium salt, solid crystalline sodium chloride being preferred in economic grounds, i.e.:

$$KNbO_3 + NaCl \rightarrow NaNbO_3 + KCl.$$

A complexing agent, Sequestrol CS, is used to retain traces of iron in the solution. It is added immediately before the sodium chloride. The precipitated sodium niobate settles and filters well. The mother liquor is removed by decantation and the niobate washed by resuspending in 5 per cent sodium chloride solution, before being finally filtered. The final conversion is by means of hydrochloric acid, followed by water-washing to remove the chloride ion, i.e.

$$2NaNbO_3 + 2HCl \rightarrow Nb_2O_5 + H_2O + 2NaCl.$$

The method of performing this operation is important if an excessive filtration time is to be avoided. Thirty litres of 10N hydrochloric acid is in fact added to a suspension of sodium niobate (containing 22 kg of niobium) in 150 l. of water. After stirring for 5 min, the solution is brought to a pH of 5 to 6 by the addition of ammonia. A precipitate made in this manner settles rapidly and the supernatent liquor is therefore decanted, and replaced by 200 l. of water for washing. After four decantation washes at pH 5 to 6, the oxide cake is filtered without difficulty. It is then reasonably free from sodium and chloride ions and can be passed to the tantalum separation stage.

Final purification of the niobium from tantalum is achieved by solvent extraction as described in Chapter 4.

Alkali breakdown of beryl

A process has been described by McKee[47] in which beryl is treated with about three times its weight of a 75 per cent aqueous solution of sodium hydroxide at a temperature of about 185°C. The beryl is first crushed and ground to pass a 300-mesh sieve and is then stirred slowly into the alkali for 20 to 24 hr at temperature. After cooling, the reaction paste is poured into an excess of water at normal temperature. The suspended beryllium oxide is settled and after removal of the supernatant liquor it is extracted with a 10 per cent solution of cold sodium bicarbonate, for about 16 hr. This dissolves principally the beryllium which, after filtration away from other oxides, can be reprecipitated by boiling. In this way a fairly pure hydroxide, contaminated with a little sodium carbonate, can be obtained. Ignition and leaching with water then gives a beryllium oxide of 99 per cent purity.

The excess of sodium hydroxide remaining in the dilute breakdown liquor contains sodium silicate and carbonate, etc. These can be precipitated as the insoluble calcium compounds by the additions of calcium hydroxide, so allowing the sodium hydroxide to be evaporated back to a concentration of 75 per cent and re-used for another breakdown reaction.

DILUTE ALKALI CARBONATE LEACHING

Dilute alkali leaching of ores, principally with solutions of sodium carbonate or ammonium carbonate, is a technique of some commercial importance. In the rare metal field, however, its use is almost entirely restricted to two elements, uranium and vanadium, which form soluble complexes in carbonate solutions. The relatively inexpensive "soda-ash" grade of sodium carbonate is adequate for the purpose.

Comparison with dilute acid leaching

Sodium carbonate leaching regarded as a chemical engineering process has many similarities with dilute acid leaching. Batch, co-current and counter-current methods may be employed in vessels with either stirrers or air agitation for low temperatures and atmospheric pressures. Higher pressure leaching, at temperatures above the normal boiling-point of the solution, resembles acid pressure leaching and was, in fact, originally developed by Forward and Halpern[48, 49, 50] for sodium carbonate systems.

Pre-leaching treatments, as for acid systems, always involve crushing and grinding and the supply of a "pulp" of the correct solids content to the leaching vessel. In carbonate leaching, however, it is often important to grind to a smaller particle size than in acid leaching, since the leaching medium does not appreciably attack the unwanted minerals in the gangue material. These may be surrounding the particles of the desired mineral and effectively shielding it from the alkali if the particle size is insufficiently reduced.

Roasting, either in air or after admixture with salt, is a pre-leaching operation which is employed rather more frequently than with acid leaching, but this is mainly dependent upon the particular chemical properties of uranium and vanadium.

The general post-leaching operations are again similar to those used in acid systems. Filtration and sedimentation rates of most minerals tend to be lower in sodium carbonate solutions than they are in dilute sulphuric acid, but the advent of synthetic flocculating agents has now made this difference of less practical importance in the design of processes. Aeroflox 300 and Separan 2610 have both been used in conjunction with counter-current decantation.

Sodium carbonate leaching has three important general advantages over the acid leaching of ores. The first is that the solutions are less corrosive and plant may therefore be constructed of cheaper materials. Mild steel is often satisfactory for leaching vessels, pumps, piping, filters and decantation vessels. The second concerns ore with a high limestone content: whereas the limestone is quantitatively dissolved by acid media, sometimes with a prohibitive acid usage, sodium carbonate leaching is not greatly affected by its presence. Finally, the use of sodium carbonate is readily amenable to recycling procedures, since one obvious method of recovery of the values is to increase the pH by the addition of sodium hydroxide until the point of precipitation. After removal of the precipitate, the mixed sodium carbonate-sodium hydroxide reagent may then be regenerated by passing carbon dioxide through it, in a standard gas absorption tower. Carbon dioxide is usually readily available on site from flue gases, etc.

There are several disadvantages to sodium carbonate leaching. The leaching rates and efficiencies are often substantially lower than in acid systems. As already mentioned, this may in part be a general phenomenon not related to the rate of an individual chemical reaction, but may arise from the fact that sodium carbonate is a fairly selective reagent and does not easily break down gangue minerals which may be physically shielding mineral values. Higher temperatures therefore tend to be employed in an attempt to correct this deficiency. Sulphide minerals interfere with sodium carbonate leaching, as with acid leaching, in cases where an oxidant is employed, e.g.

$$4FeS_2 + 16Na_2CO_3 + 15O_2 + 14H_2O \rightarrow 4Fe(OH)_3 + 8Na_2SO_4 + 16NaHCO_3.$$

Unfortunately, the resulting sulphate does not in this case supplement the leaching reagent as it does under oxidizing conditions in an acid system, but tends to neutralize the alkali. This is no disadvantage up to a certain amount of sulphide (usually about 1 per cent) in the ore, since a small concentration of bicarbonate in the carbonate solution can often be beneficial. However, an excess of sulphide can seriously reduce the carbonate concentration, with the production of inert sodium sulphate. Arsenides behave similarly. Gypsum (calcium sulphate) or magnesium sulphate minerals have also a harmful effect in reacting with the sodium carbonate to produce inert sodium sulphate and calcium or magnesium carbonate, i.e.

$$CaSO_4 + Na_2CO_3 \rightarrow CaCO_3 + Na_2SO_4.$$

Silicates may be attacked to some extent by sodium carbonate solutions, particularly at high temperatures, i.e...

$$SiO_2 + H_2O + 2Na_2CO_3 \rightarrow Na_2SiO_3 + 2NaHCO_3.$$

Besides decreasing the sodium carbonate concentration, the silicate in solution has an adverse effect upon filtration properties.

Application to uranium and vanadium extraction

Two of the most well-known applications of the sodium carbonate leaching of ores are the extraction of uranium from pitchblende in Canada and extraction of both uranium and vanadium from carnotite, which is mined in numerous localities of the Colorado Plateau area of the United States. The latter deposits were originally worked for their vanadium content but since the 1939–45 war the emphasis has been on uranium, with vanadium a subsidiary product.

Carnotite is a potassium uranyl vanadate, $K_2O.2UO_3.V_2O_5.nH_2O$. Since the uranium is in the fully oxidized condition, leaching can usually be carried out without an oxidant, at a particle size of about 100 mesh. The vanadium dissolves on leaching, to sodium vanadate, and the uranium forms a soluble double carbonate. The reaction may be represented approximately as:

$$K_2O.2UO_3.V_2O_5 + 6Na_2CO_3 + 2H_2O \rightarrow$$
$$2NaVO_3 + 2Na_4UO_2(CO_3)_3 + 2NaOH + 2KOH.$$

Since the leach liquor becomes more alkaline after reaction with the mineral it is advantageous for sodium bicarbonate to be present along with the sodium carbonate leaching reagent. The bicarbonate is partially converted to carbonate during the leaching process, i.e.

$$NaHCO_3 + NaOH \rightarrow Na_2CO_3 + H_2O.$$

In practice, the bicarbonate concentration is usually in excess of that required for reaction with the sodium and potassium hydroxide; concentrations of 10 to 70 g/l. have been used, associated with 50 to 100 g/l. of sodium carbonate.

When a carnotite ore contains more than about 1 per cent of vanadium a "salt roasting" process is found to be beneficial before leaching with sodium carbonate. The ore is mixed with 5 to 10 per cent of its weight of sodium chloride and heated at 850°C for several hours, after which it is rapidly quenched in the leaching reagent. Stephens and Macdonald[51] state that various changes take place during the salt roasting process, and with carnotite the process can be divided into four temperature regions as follows:

1. Up to 350°C the mineral is stable and soluble in sodium carbonate–sodium bicarbonate solutions.
2. Between 350°C and 600°C water of hydration is lost, or decomposition takes place to form a uranium complex which is insoluble in the leaching solution, or both.
3. From 600°C to 850°C sodium vanadates are formed, and these then react with uranium compounds to form sodium uranyl vanadates which are readily soluble.
4. Above 850°C sodium vanadates and sodium uranyl vanadates decompose, or react with silica to produce insoluble silicates.

The third stage is clearly beneficial, but this is flanked by two regions which are undesirable. Also, sodium uranyl vanadate can revert on cooling slowly to sodium vanadate and an insoluble uranium complex. Hence the necessity for a reasonable control of temperature during roasting and a rapid quench so as to preserve the state reached in stage 3. Salt roasting increases the vanadium leaching efficiency but does not improve the extraction of uranium. If carried out without satisfactory temperature control, or under other adverse conditions, the uranium extraction efficiency can even be reduced. Consequently, now that carnotite is being worked principally for uranium, the salt roast procedure is tending to be abandoned.

Copper sulphate and ammonia, added to the sodium carbonate leach liquor, have been found to catalyse the oxidation by air where this is necessary. This process has been used in the large pilot plant at Grand Juntion in the United States.[52]

Direct alkali leaching of uranium alone is used in the Eldorado plant at Beaverlodge, in Canada, where the minerals are pitchblende and uraninite. Since the uranium is partially in the tetravalent state, it is not readily leached by sodium carbonate solutions unless in the presence of an oxidant. Potassium permanganate is very effective for this purpose[53] but air or oxygen under pressure are preferred on economic grounds. The reaction is essentially as follows:

$$2U_3O_8 + O_2 + 18Na_2CO_3 + 6H_2O \rightarrow 6Na_4UO_2(CO_3)_3 + 12NaOH.$$

Sodium bicarbonate is present in addition to sodium carbonate, as with a carnotite ore, to reduce the hydroxyl ion concentration. It has been shown[49] that the rate of leaching is proportional to the square root of the oxygen pressure and the fineness of ore grind, and is independent of carbonate concentrations above 50 g/l.

It has recently been discovered[54] that the roasting of carnotite ore at 850°C in the presence of a few per cent of calcium sulphate, prior to carbonate leaching, enhances both the vanadium and uranium extraction efficiencies. A convenient way of achieving the desired conditions is to blend the ore with another carnotite ore with a high natural calcium sulphate content, when available, rather than waste the beneficial effect of the latter by treating it alone.

Temperatures near 100°C are often employed in the sodium carbonate leaching of uranium, with pressures up to about 100 psi. Leaching times vary over a wide range but the object is to reduce them to only a few hours.

Recovery of uranium from the leach liquor is usually carried out by precipitation with sodium hydroxide solution at a pH greater than 11 for easy recycling of the reagent, i.e.

$$2Na_4UO_2(CO_3)_3 + 6NaOH \rightarrow Na_2U_2O_7 + 6Na_2CO_3 + 3H_2O.$$

Hot precipitation gives the most easily filterable precipitate but at a sacrifice of uranium recovery efficiency. However, cold filtration may be satisfactory if accompanied by an appropriate flocculating agent.

Vanadium may be recovered, together with uranium, as an artificial carnotite or "yellow cake", $Na_2O.2UO_3.V_2O_5.nH_2O$, by the addition of sulphuric acid. Additional acid then precipitates the excess vanadium as V_2O_5 or "red cake".

A more recent method of recovery, which is applicable either to uranium alone, or to uranium mixed with vanadium, is to precipitate the lower oxides by hydrogen reduction.[48, 49, 50] Commercial gaseous hydrogen is used at a temperature of about 150°C and a hydrogen pressure of 200 psi, preferably in the presence of metallic nickel powder as a catalyst. Reactions may be represented as:

$$Na_4UO_2(CO_3)_3 + H_2 \rightarrow UO_2 + Na_2CO_3 + 2NaHCO_3,$$
and $$2NaVO_3 + 2H_2 + 2NaHCO_3 \rightarrow V_2O_3 + 2Na_2CO_3 + 3H_2O.$$

Conditions are not critical and the nickel catalyst can be recovered by electromagnetic separation and recycled indefinitely. The barren liquor, after removal of the uranium and vanadium oxides, can similarly be re-used directly for leaching.

Ammonium carbonate leaching has been developed specifically for uranium extraction from the ore at Grand Junction, Colorado. The technique and plant resembles that used for sodium carbonate pressure leaching. The leaching agent is a 10 per cent solution of ammonium carbonate containing 2 per cent of ammonium bicarbonate and the pulp is maintained at a solids content of about 50 per cent and a pH of 8 to 9. Pressures up to about 125 psi and temperatures just above 100°C are satisfactory for 90 to 95 per cent extraction of uranium, over a period of about 4 hr, in the presence of potassium permanganate as an oxidizing agent. In the absence of an oxidizing agent of this type, oxidation can be carried out by air alone but a pressure of about 700 psi is then required. A static air pressure is essential since a flow of gas would tend to carry away ammonia from the system and cause the uranium to be reprecipitated from solution. One of the principal advantages of this process is that the uranium can be recovered from solution by a simple steam stripping operation in which the pH is reduced to about 7·4 as a result of ammonia evolution. The uranium is precipitated in this manner with an efficiency of about 99 per cent without usage of chemical reagents.

An ammonium carbonate leaching pilot plant has been described [55, 56] which consists of five towers, each 10 ft high by 4 in. internal diameter, connected in series. The slurry of acid and ore is pumped in a co-current manner from the bottom to the top of each tower and then allowed to pass via 0·5 in. piping from the top of one tower to the base of the next. Air is injected at the base and mid-point of each tower. Typical pressures in the first and last towers are 130 psi and 90 psi. The system is fed from an agitated mixing tank, via a positive displacement piston pump located at the base of the first tower. After leaching, the gases are separated off by means of a pressure release valve and the leach liquor then removed from the spent ore in a hydrocyclone.

The steam stripping tower is 7 ft high by 1 ft diameter and contains baffles in the top half. Leach liquor flows down the tower against a counter-current flow of steam. A liquid level is maintained at a height of about 2 ft, and from this reservoir at the base of the tower the liquor and suspended uranium precipitate and pass to a filter.

The plant, including valves, etc., is constructed of mild steel, or preferably stainless-steel, for corrosion resistance to ammoniacal solutions.

CHLORINATION BREAKDOWN
Mineral chlorination technique

Chlorine is a highly reactive reagent which is now available in large quantities relatively cheaply, although it suffers the disadvantage that it must be transported in liquid form under pressure, contained in stout steel cylinders or drums. An ore breakdown method which has been applied in the rare metal field to titanium, zirconium, hafnium and uranium, is to pass chlorine gas at high temperature over an intimate mixture of the mineral oxide with carbon, A mixture of carbon monoxide and carbon dioxide is usually formed and the reactions (for a tetravalent element) can conveniently be represented as

$$MO_2 + C + 2Cl_2 \rightarrow MCl_4 + CO_2 \quad \text{or} \quad MO_2 + 2C + 2Cl_2 \rightarrow MCl_4 + 2CO.$$

The proportions of carbon monoxide and dioxide depend upon the temperature, the excess of carbon and the physical disposition of the reactants. The aim is usually to achieve oxidation to the dioxide as far as possible, by reducing the proportion of carbon to the minimum.

This technique has been extended to minerals other than oxides, e.g. zircon (zirconium silicate $ZrSiO_4$), ilmenite ($FeTiO_3$), monazite (rare earth and thorium phosphates) and beryl ($3BeO.Al_2O_36SiO_2$). The chlorination technique is equally applicable as a second stage where the reaction with carbon or aluminium to remove oxygen has taken place first, e.g. when applied to the alloys ferroniobium or ferrovanadium, obtained by smelting, or to zirconium carbide obtained by electric arc treatment of zircon and carbon. When oxygen-containing materials are present during the chlorination reaction, phosgene is present in the tail gas. This is produced as a result of the reaction $CO + Cl_2 \rightarrow COCl_2$, which is catalysed by the presence of carbon. It is probable that phosgene or carbon monoxide play some part in the mechanism of chlorination, since it is unlikely that the rare metal oxides will be reduced by solid carbon.

Plant constructional materials

In all cases, it is necessary to use a special furnace designed to withstand highly corrosive conditions, usually at temperatures of 700°C to 1000°C. Paradoxically, the materials of construction which have been found most useful for furnace linings of this type are graphite or silica despite the fact that graphite is often a suitable form of carbon for use as a reactant, and silica is a common constituent of ores processed by this technique, which reacts readily to give silicon tetrachloride. Their success as materials of construction is due to their use in separate massive form rather than as an intimate mixture with one another. They are slowly attacked even under these conditions and must be regarded as expendable. The corrosion products, however, produced by the reaction:

$$2SiO_2 + 3C + 4Cl_2 \rightarrow 2SiCl_4 + CO_2 + 2CO$$

are harmless, since they are already present in the reaction products from the mineral itself. Industrial scale furnaces are best lined with pure fused silica bricks rather than with other cheaper varieties of silica refractory containing alumina. Equal care has then to be exercised in the choice of a silicious cement which will provide reasonable resistance.

The silica bricks are normally backed by other, cheaper, refractory bricks to provide mechanical strength and thermal insulation. Silica tubes have been used on the smaller technical scale or for laboratory work, but often appear to be slightly porous to chlorine at high temperatures. Graphite is more commonly used in the form of tube since it can be manufactured in larger diameters. It is more porous than silica and must be backed by other materials to provide an adequate seal.

Plant design

The chlorination furnace is usually of the vertical type, chlorine being passed through a bed of the solid reactants from the base and the volatile products removed from the top. The solid reactants are also added at the top, either batchwise after removal of a lid, or continuously via a star feeder or similar device. This allows reactants to be added continuously or inter- mittently via a deep hopper with only the minimum escape of chlorine and gaseous products through the charge in the hopper. Suitable provision must be made for removal of the non-volatile residue which collects at the base of the furnace. This consists of carbon and unreacted minerals, together with various chloride impurities. A sketch of a typical furnace and condens- ing system as used for the chlorination of zirconium and hafnium is shown in Fig. 2.7. An alternative arrangement, sometimes used for laboratory investigations, is a horizontal tube furnace in which the solid reactants are located on boats; chlorine passes in from one end and carries the products out at the other end. This is clearly less satisfactory since, unless the re- action is very vigorous, the chlorine may by-pass the other reactants, which are not filling the whole cross-section of the furnace. Also, the chlorine efficiency decreases as the reaction proceeds, in what is inevitably a batch process. A horizontal furnace has, however, the advantage for experi- mental work that the condenser can if necessary be integral with the reactor, and all joints can therefore be cooled. Also, it is possible to chlorinate mixtures in powder form rather than as the lumps or briquettes which must be used in the vertical (static bed) system.

The distribution of chlorine and the avoidance of blockages in the chlor- ine inlets require some thought in the normal vertical furnace. It is relatively easy to grade lumps of carbide, for example, to give a suitable voidage for good access of chlorine, both initially and when the lumps are reduced in size as a result of chlorination. It may also be possible to re- cycle any material from the crushed carbide which is too fine for passing to the chlorinator, and allow it to compact again into lumps along with a new batch of carbide. When a mixture of a mineral with carbon is used, it is necessary to prepare it in briquette form before feeding to the chlorinator. The carbon may be in the form of coke, graphite, petroleum coke, charcoal or even coal in one case, and after mixing with the mineral a small quantity of binding agent is added. This is usually an organic material such as pitch, tar, sugar or starch which decomposes on later heating to give a carbon bond. Several types of briquetting machine are available for compacting the constituents at low pressure into pieces which are usually about the size of eggs before the heating operation. Sodium silicate has also been used as a binding agent. In this case the rather adhesive dough which the constituents formed was rolled on to a plate; the slabs were cut into squares by means of a knife and the plates then placed in an oven for drying. Although these briquettes could be made simply and rapidly by manual methods, they had the disadvantage that the sodium silicate tended to be chlorinated before the mineral. This resulted in many breakages of the briquettes during chlorination, with the production of a high proportion of fines in the ash.

Several chlorine inlets are often employed and these sometimes admit the gas first to a semi-permanent bed of carbon granules which is situated at the base of the chlorinator. This reduces the tendency for blockages to

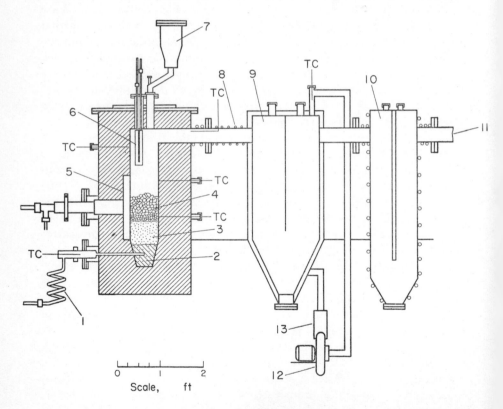

FIG. 2.7. Chlorination furnace: TC, thermocouple positions; 1, chlorine gas preheater; 2, charcoal diffuser bed; 3, resistor carbon; 4, charge of briquettes; 5, graphite electrode; 6, split graphite-pipe top heater; 7, feed hopper; 8, nichrome heater for cross-over pipe; 9, nickel-lined condenser; 10, water-cooled iron aftercondenser; 11, exhaust to scrubbers; 12, condenser heating air blower; 13, nichrome air heater (Stephens, W. W. and Gilbert H. L. Ref. 62).

occur, but the bed may slowly become blinded with unreactive impurities and require occasional renewal.

It is important to be able to detect blockages soon after occurrence, particularly on the outlet side, since high pressures may build up, with the danger of an explosion. Even if an explosion does not occur, the continual production of the volatile chloride without access to its normal escape route may cause it to diffuse back against the chlorine stream and deposit in the cooler inlet lines, so leading to additional blockages. Usually, diaphragm pressure gauges are intalled on the chlorine inlet systems to detect blockages, and bursting discs or other pressure release devices should be connected directly to the furnace chamber. The design of bursting discs may present some difficulty in individual cases, where chlorides condense to solids, since the release systems require heating.

Methods of heating the furnace charge vary, but frequently the chlorination is so exothermic that the charge only requires raising to the initiation temperature and thereafter the reaction is controlled by the chlorination rate and the rapidity with which excess heat can be removed. The initial heat is sometimes supplied by passing an electric current directly through the charge or through a layer of resistor carbon granules, from graphite electrodes. Alternatively, the current may be passed through a heating rod constructed with a saw cut down most of its length. In some cases where the introduction of oxygen is relatively unimportant, a shovel full of the reactants, heated from an external source, may be quickly placed in the chlorinator, the seal made, and chlorination quickly begun. It is not usually feasible to heat the chlorinator externally by gas, electric resistance elements, or oil, etc., owing to the highly effective insulation provided by the thick refractory brickwork. It is often necessary to be able to estimate, if only approximately, the chlorinator temperature, particularly when the reaction is highly exothermic. Limitation of the temperature to the minimum compatible with a satisfactory rate of reaction reduces corrosion of the chlorinator lining and assists in the condensation of the chloride product. A simple optical pyrometer is usually satisfactory where it can be applied to a transparent window, e.g. of quartz or "Perspex", in the cooler part of the system. In the latter case, the cooled window is purged inwards with chlorine or nitrogen.

The type of system used to condense the product depends naturally upon whether condensation takes place to give a solid or a liquid, and the temperature involved. This is best illustrated by the individual examples given later. Condensers have been constructed of mild steel, nickel, monel, aluminium or magnesium, and under anhydrous conditions the corrosion rate is usually quite low. Graphite has sometimes been used for connections between condenser and chlorinator. When condensing a solid, an air-cooled labyrinth shape is often preferred to allow a long path-length for collection of fines, but a cylindrical type fitted with a rotating spiral scraper has also been used. Vibration or intermittent hammering of the walls of a condenser is often necessary when they are not scraped. This allows large flakes of the product to fall away from the walls, renewing the initial heat transfer conditions and economizing on condenser size. However, in some cases it may be advantageous to condense the solid under conditions of poor heat transfer, in order to grow large crystals of high packing density. This may be accomplished by deliberately heating or insulating the condenser walls or allowing a thick layer of product to deposit on the walls before removal. Condensation of a liquid product is achieved by means of a standard type of water-cooled coil or jacketted tube, but when the freezing-point is relatively high careful temperature control may be necessary.

Secondary condensing or trapping systems are usually required. With a solid product these can take the form of either a labyrinth of suitable dimensions to give a low linear velocity, or filters, or electrostatic precipitators. Finally, a sodium hydroxide scrubbing tower is needed to absorb excess chlorine and residual traces of the product chlorides. The tail gases, containing carbon monoxide and possibly traces of chlorine and phosgene, must be discharged to atmosphere through a high stack because of their toxicity. A liquid product can usually be condensed fairly efficiently and the only additional plant required before discharge of the tail gases is an alkali scrubber.

Sometimes it is possible to obtain some degree of elimination of impurities by controlling the condensing conditions, particularly if the chlorides of the impurities are distinctly more, or less, volatile than that of the product. This is commonly achieved in the case of silicon tetrachloride impurity, which is allowed to pass through the condenser by running the latter at a rather higher temperature than would otherwise be desirable. Ferric chloride aluminium chloride and vanadium oxychloride may be removed in a similar manner.

When the chlorination breakdown is carried out on a sufficiently large scale to justify continuous operation and a plant of high capital cost, as in the case of titanium, a fluidization process might be employed. This has, amongst other features, the advantage that the mineral and carbon may be supplied to the reactor in powder form and they do not require briquetting before use. The solid reactants are continuously fed to the fluidized reactor bed and maintained in a suspended condition by means of an upwards flow of chlorine, with or without the presence of an inert carrier gas. Problems of corrosion of the reactor walls are accentuated by the fact that, in a fluidized system, erosion occurs to a greater extent than with a static bed. However, this may be compensated by the good heat transfer properties of a fluidized bed of powder. This tends to mitigate the local overheating which would otherwise be present with an exothermic reaction. Another difficulty of the fluidized system, when a volatile product is removed, lies in the diminution of particle size as the reaction proceeds. Small particles towards the end of their life tend to escape from the bed and be entrained by the outgoing product. This necessitates the use of a hot settling chamber or cyclone before the volatile chloride stream passes to the condensing system, to avoid contamination of the final product.

Chlorination of titanium ores

The principal ore of titanium is ilmenite or ferrous titanate ($FeTiO_3$), and this is the ore mainly used for the production of ferrotitanium by a smelting process. However, its use directly for the production of titanium tetrachloride would be extremely wasteful of chlorine, since a high proportion of this reagent would be used for the production of unwanted ferric chloride. Consequently, chlorination generally involves the less plentiful ore of titanium, rutile, the dioxide (TiO_2), which is found in the form of black river and beach sands. This is mixed with ground charcoal or petroleum coke, briquetted, and volatile material removed by heating to 500 to 800°C. Chlorination can be carried out at 700 to 1000°C in a conventional vertical furnace, and the reaction is sufficiently exothermic for it to proceed without the application of external heat, except to raise the temperature of the reactants initially. The reaction may be represented approximately as:

$$2TiO_2 + 3C + 4Cl_2 \rightarrow 2TiCl_4 + 2CO + CO_2.$$

The more modern fluidization process is used in the U.K. by Titanium Intermediates Ltd.[60] The carbon is in the form of ground coke and the rutile, dried before use, is also present as a fine powder. After chlorination, the gas stream is first subjected to a "de-dusting" operation, to remove finely divided entrained reactants in a labyrinth or cyclone. Ferric chloride impurity is then allowed to deposit in a condenser maintained at 200°C, before scrubbing out the titanium tetrachloride with cold recycled tetrachloride, in a packed column. The principle impurities at this stage are aluminium chloride, ferric chloride and vanadium oxychloride ($VOCl_3$). The first two of these are insoluble in the titanium tetrachloride and are removed as a sludge by decantation and filtration. The soluble vanadium oxychloride is first reduced to the less volatile vanadium trichloride by either organic materials, hydrogen sulphide, or powdered copper, before separation by fractional distillation. The titanium tetrachloride is obtained as a middle fraction boiling at 136·4°C, the lower boiling material containing hydrogen chloride, phosgene, carbon tetrachloride and silicon tetrachloride, whilst the heavy fraction is discarded as a slurry. The purity of the final tetrachloride is about 99·98 per cent and it must be stored under completely anhydrous conditions in the presence of argon, to avoid hydrolysis or the dissolution of atmospheric oxygen and nitrogen. Storage can be in mild steel containers.

Various attempts have been made to use ilmenite as a source of titanium tetrachloride. The most promising of these is based upon the selective smelting of the ore with carbon in an electric arc furnace, using lime and magnesia as fluxing agents. Metallic iron and a slag containing a high proportion of the titanium are obtained. The slag usually contains 70 to 75 per cent of TiO_2 but is not ideally suited to chlorination owing to the formation of molten calcium and magnesium chlorides. However, it is possible under special circumstances to obtain a slag containing more than 90 per cent of titanium oxide, which chlorinates satisfactorily.[60]

Chlorination of zircon

Zirconium is extracted mainly from the silicate mineral, zircon ($ZrSiO_4$), which is found as a beach sand, usually in association with other minerals of commercial value, in Australia, India, Madagascar, Malaya, Ceylon, parts of Africa and the United States. The mineral is obtained in a relatively pure condition by ore dressing methods, except that it is usually associated with about 2 per cent of the isomorphous, and chemically very similar, hafnium silicate. The silicate has been used directly, in admixture with charcoal, for chlorination to zirconium tetrachloride. The reaction can be represented as,

$$ZrSiO_4 + 4C + 4Cl_2 \rightarrow ZrCl_4 + 4CO + SiCl_4.$$

The reaction can be made more exothermic if a little oxygen is introduced to react with a small excess of carbon. It proceeds rapidly at a temperature of 1000°C, although it can be operated satisfactorily down to 800°C. The zirconium tetrachloride contains hafnium tetrachloride in almost identical proportions to that present in the mineral zircon and, for all except nuclear purposes, the hafnium can remain in the zirconium without detriment.

The more expensive baddeleyite (ZrO_2) is sometimes used in place of the silicate, but it is not generally available. The reaction in this case is:

$$ZrO_2 + 2C + 2Cl_2 \rightarrow ZrCl_4 + 2CO.$$

A vertical furnace with a static bed is usually employed and the zirconium tetrachloride sublimes out into an air-cooled mild-steel condenser, together with a high proportion of silicon tetrachloride and 0·1 to 1 per cent of titanium tetrachloride, aluminium chloride and ferric chloride. The sublimation temperature of zirconium tetrachloride under atmospheric pressure is about 330°C and it is an advantage to condense at about 200°C to obtain a high proportion of it as a dense crystalline product. This aids removal of the more volatile titanium, aluminium and silicon chlorides.

The latter, together with some phosgene and dissolved chlorine, can subsequently be condensed to a liquid (b.p. 58°C) by means of a freezing mixture. Its ultimate disposal is potentially hazardous and expensive unless an outlet can be found for it as a reactive source of silicon compounds.

The silicon tetrachloride disposal problem, together with the initial briquetting operation, can be avoided by the conversion of the silicate to carbide before chlorination. This operation is accomplished by heating the zircon with about 25 per cent of its weight of powdered graphite to a temperature of 1800°C in an electric arc furnace lined with graphite, or in a graphite resistor furnace. The reaction involves the liberation of silicon monoxide, which is volatile at the high temperature and is immediately converted to silica on contact with air.

$$ZrSiO_4 + 4C \rightarrow ZrC + SiO + 3CO,$$

and
$$2SiO + O_2 \rightarrow 2SiO_2.$$

It is sometimes considered advantageous to allow atmospheric nitrogen to take part in the reaction and form a mixture of zirconium carbide with nitride, referred to as the "cyanonitride" or "carbonitride". This gives a more exothermic reaction with chlorine than the carbide itself.

The zirconium carbide or "carbonitride" is obtained as a massive material of metallic appearance which tends to be pyrophoric in air, and must therefore be cooled in absence of air and handled with caution afterwards. It usually contains a proportion of unreacted zirconium silicate and carbon. The crude, arc-treated, product is readily broken into small lumps for feeding to the chlorination furnace, but an undue proportion of fines is produced from the cheaper, resistor furnace, carbide. Chlorination takes place at a rather lower temperature than when the mineral is simply mixed and briquetted with carbon (i.e. about 500°C), thus giving a prolonged life to the chlorination furnace lining. Figure 2.8 shows the chlorinator, condensers and scrubbing system used by the United States Bureau of Mines[62, 63] when operating with a feed which is relatively free from silica. They use briquettes which are almond-shaped, approximately $1\frac{3}{8}$ by 1 by $\frac{3}{4}$ in., made from a mixture of 81 per cent zirconium oxide, 14·5 per cent carbon and 4·5 per cent dextrine. These are pressed in a moist condition by means of a "Belgian roll" type briquetting machine and dried at 140°C before use. The throughput of the plant shown is about 50 lb of zirconium chloride per hour when using a chlorinator of 26 in. diameter.

Additional purification of the zirconium tetrachloride is often carried out by sublimation. This leaves involatile oxide or oxychloride behind, which may have been introduced by hydrolysis. If the sublimation is carried out in a stream of hydrogen, iron impurity also remains in the residue, owing to reduction of the volatile ferric chloride to the non-volatile ferrous chloride.

$$2FeCl_3 + H_2 \rightarrow 2FeCl_2 + 2HCl.$$

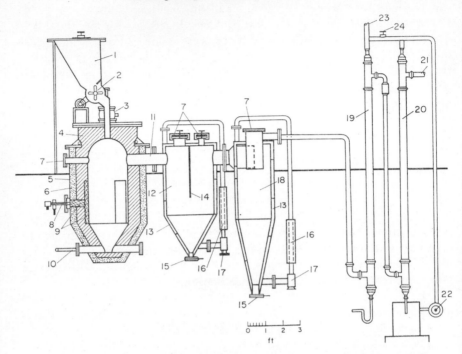

FIG. 2.8. Zirconium Chloride Plant. 1, feed hopper; 2, star valve feeder; 3, ball valve; 4, silica brick; 5, steel shell; 6, insulating brick; 7, clean out; 8, water-cooled copper electrode connector; 9, graphite electrode and nipple; 10, chlorine inlet pipe; 11, nickel cross-over pipe; 12, primary condenser; 13, condenser jacket; 14, baffle; 15, discharge valve; 16, air heater; 17, blower; 18, cyclone-type aftercondenser; 19, water scrubbing tower; 20, caustic scrubbing tower; 21, exit gas outlet to stack; 22, caustic circulating pump; 23, waste water inlet; 24, caustic bleed line (Stephens, W. W. and Gilbert, H. L. Ref. 62).

Removal of the hafnium tetrachloride from the zirconium tetrachloride cannot easily be achieved in a direct manner. However, the addition compounds with phosphorus pentachloride and with phosphorus oxychloride ($3Zr(Hf)Cl_4.2POCl_3$) have been separated by fractional distillation on a small scale.[64, 65] A proposal has also been made to separate the chloride by vapour phase dechlorination with a mixture of chlorine and oxygen,[66] making use of the difference in equilibrium constant for the two reactions:

$$ZrCl_4 + O_2 \rightleftharpoons ZrO_2 + 2Cl_2,$$

and

$$HfCl_4 + O_2 \rightleftharpoons HfO_2 + 2Cl_2.$$

Unfortunately, the zirconium is converted to oxide more readily than the hafnium and it is not therefore practicable to recover the pure zirconium tetrachloride directly, without additional processing.

A method has been described[67, 68] which is more suitable for commercial exploitation in which the mixed zirconium and hafnium chlorides are passed over heated zirconium metal or zirconium dichloride. The reaction

$$ZrCl_2 + ZrCl_4 \rightarrow 2ZrCl_3$$

takes place at about 400°C, giving a non-volatile deposit of zirconium trichloride and leaving the tetrachloride in the vapour phase highly enriched in hafnium. By raising the temperature to 450°C, disproportionation of the pure zirconium trichloride takes place, to give pure volatile zirconium tetrachloride and non-volatile zirconium dichloride ready for the next cycle of operations.

Solvent extraction is regarded as the most satisfactory commercial process for the removal of hafnium from zirconium (see Chapter 4), but it is an indirect route, since it is necessary to re-form the tetrachloride ready for pure metal production. The solvent extracted product is converted from an aqueous solution to the oxide, ZrO_2, which can be mixed with carbon and chlorinated in a similar manner to zircon. However, the high purity of this oxide warrants some changes in the chlorination technique. In the United States (Bureau of Mines) 50 kg/hr plant, the oxide and carbon are formed into briquettes 1 in. wide by $\frac{3}{4}$ in. thick, using sugar and water as a binding agent. After drying at 120°C on stainless-steel trays, they are supplied via a hopper and star feeder to a standard type of chlorinator, lined with pure silica brick. Chlorination takes place at 600 to 800°C, heat being supplied by means of strips of resistor carbon carrying an electric current. Condensers can be made from sheet nickel to avoid contamination of the pure product by iron.

The hafnium is sometimes obtained from a solvent extraction process relatively free from zirconium and in an otherwise pure condition. Hafnium oxide may then be converted to the tetrachloride, preparatory to metal production, in a manner analogous to zirconium. It may be important to carry out the process in separate plant from that used for zirconium, to avoid contamination of the latter with hafnium, which would make it unsatisfactory for nuclear purposes. Equipment which has been used in the U.S.A. for this purpose is shown in Fig. 2.7. The size of chlorinator is smaller than for zirconium, being appropriate to the lower throughput although not in direct proportion, its capacity being 10 lb/hr. A 6in. diameter graphite tube, jacketed with nickel and electrically heated, is required on this scale to convey the chloride vapour to the condenser without blockages. The main condenser is also of nickel with a mild-steel jacket, its temperature being controlled by circulating heated air between the two.

A small air vibrator is used occasionally, to loosen the product from the condenser walls and provide a new condensing surface. As in the case of zirconium tetrachloride, additional purification by sublimation is needed, immediately before metal production, to remove oxide and oxychloride. A rather lower sublimation temperature is used, however, for hafnium owing to the more volatile nature of its oxychloride.

Chlorination of monazite

Monazite, the principal source of both thorium and rare earths, is readily available as the pure mineral, This consists essentially of the rare earth phosphates in which a few per cent of the rare earth content has been replaced by thorium. High-temperature chlorination of the ore with carbon has been suggested as a breakdown technique,[76, 77, 78, 27] but it is not known to be operated commercially for either thorium or rare earth elements. The reaction (for thorium) may be represented apparently as:

$$Th_3(PO_4)_4 + 16C + 16Cl_2 \rightarrow 3ThCl_4 + 4PCl_5 + 16CO,$$

although some phosphorus oxychloride and trichloride may also be present. A temperature near to 1000°C is required for the thorium tetrachloride to be produced and distilled at a reasonable rate. Thorium and rare earth chlorides can be produced slowly at 700°C, but at this temperature they remain undistilled in the chlorination furnace and require separation, e.g. by leaching with dilute hydrochloric acid. In experimental work alumina tubes, silica tubes and graphite reactors have been used. The latter were enclosed in silica envelopes to contain the chlorine, which diffused through the graphite at the high temperatures involved. The reactants are present as briquettes, bonded with starch or calcium chloride. The products range from the relatively volatile phosphorus, aluminium and ferric chlorides, through to the less volatile thorium tetrachloride, ferrous chloride, lead chloride, manganese chloride and copper chloride, subliming below about 1000°C, to the relatively involatile rare earth trichlorides. A high proportion of the rare earth chlorides, eg.. lanthanum and cerium, can be allowed to remain behind in the chlorination residue, particularly if the temperature is about 1000°C. The more volatile components can be removed by condensing at temperatures of several hundred degrees. Purification of the middle fraction, however, to obtain a thorium tetrachloride product, presents some difficulties. Fractional distillation is not very practicable at the temperatures involved. Copper, however, can be reduced to metal by hydrogen above 500°C, and thus eliminated.

Chlorination of ferrovanadium

The direct chlorination breakdown of vanadium ores is not undertaken commercially, since ferrovanadium is available in large quantities for use by the steel industry and, being made by a smelting operation, is fairly cheap. For practical purposes, therefore, when considering the production of the relatively expensive pure vanadium metal, ferrovanadium can be accepted as a feed material and regarded as an ore concentrate.

A typical analysis of ferrovanadium is as follows:[79]

Element	%	Element	%
Vanadium	54·37	Titanium	<0·04
Iron	41·3	Tungsten	<0·2
Aluminium	0·7	Cobalt	<0·04
Barium	<0·01	Platinum	<0·04
Beryllium	<0·04	Molybdenum	<0·03
Bismuth	<0·09	Tin	<0·04
Calcium	<0·2	Zinc	<0·2
Chromium	<0·2	Oxygen	<0·3
Magnesium	0·1	Hydrogen	<0·01
Manganese	0·13	Carbon	0·04
Nickel	<0·03	Sulphur	<0·025
Silicon	1·03		

In practice, batches with a vanadium content as high as 80 per cent can be selected for chlorination. The oxygen content is variable and may be as high as several per cent; this has an important bearing upon the chlorination process since it is converted quantitatively to vanadium oxytrichloride, $VOCl_3$, instead of the desired tetrachloride.

Chlorination of ferrovanadium does not require the presence of carbon and the reaction is highly exothermic. The vanadium is mainly converted to the tetrachloride (a red liquid with a boiling-point of 152°C), i.e.

$$V + 2Cl_2 \rightarrow VCl_4.$$

However, the trichloride and dichloride can be formed if insufficient chlorine is present. In the process operated by the British Magnesium Elektron Company[80] (Chapter 9, Fig. 9.12), a vertical furnace is used, lined with silica bricks and contained in a mild steel shell. Chlorine is fed in at the base through a bed of carbon granules, for good distribution of the gas. A simple inclined charging point is available for addition of fresh ferrovanadium when the chlorine supply is turned off. A "Perspex" observation window is provided, in the form of a blank flange on the end of a cooled pipe leading to the furnace. The pipe is kept free from blockages by an additional flow of chlorine, which also serves to provide an excess of the gas and thus prevent thermal decomposition of the tetrachloride. This allows an estimate of the reaction temperature to be made using an optical pyrometer. In practice, it is necessary to control this below about 1000°C by limiting the chlorine flow rate, to prolong the life of the furnace. The re-

action can be started initially simply by adding a quantity of hot ferrovanadium to the furnace, closing the entry point, and quickly turning on
the chlorine supply.

The volatile chloride products pass from the chlorinator to a separator
unit made of magnesium and attached in the most direct manner possible.
This is a box fitted with baffles and maintained at 150 to 180°C for condensation of the ferric chloride (b.p. 315°C) and other less volatile chlorides.
From the separator, a simple water-cooled tube condenser leads to a magnesium drum which acts as a receiver for the mixed vanadium tetrachloride
and oxytrichloride. Magnesium appears to be an ideal constructional

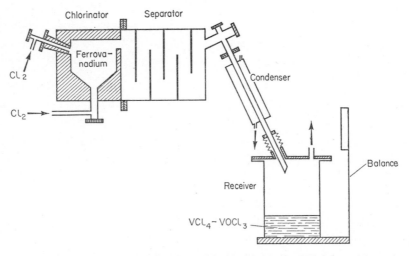

FIG. 2.9. Production of vanadium tetrachloride (Foley, E., Ward, Mrs. M., and
Hock, A. L. Ref. 80).

material for this purpose since, at the temperatures involved, it is completely
unattacked. This is a little surprising since vanadium metal sponge is manufactured by reacting the chlorides with magnesium at rather higher temperatures. A sketch of the plant used for chlorination, iron removal, and
condensation, on a 60 lb batch scale, is shown in Fig. 2.9.

Magnesium equipment is again used for the subsequent purification and
trichloride production stages. The first of these consists of distilling the
vanadium tetrachloride and oxytrichloride (b.p. 152°C and 127°C respectively) away from the small amount of residual, less volatile chlorides,
which have been entrained in the crude product. Afterwards, thermal
decomposition of the tetrachloride is carried out by refluxing in a slow
stream of carbon dioxide, i.e.

$$2VCl_4 \rightarrow 2VCl_3/ + Cl_2.$$

This is normally a slow process, carried out on a 60 lb and a 200 lb scale, over a period of several days, the progress being followed by determination of the loss in weight owing to evolution of chlorine. However, the rate might be considerably increased by the use of a catalyst. A final distillation from the same vessel removes the vanadium oxytrichloride and other volatile impurities such as silicon tetrachloride (b.p. 56°C) and titanium tetrachloride (b.p. 136°C), which may have remained with the product up to this point. This is performed firstly at atmospheric pressure and finally under reduced pressure. The quantity of oxytrichloride removed may be as much as 20 per cent of the total volume, and represents a loss of vanadium.

The pure vanadium trichloride product is a purple solid which decomposes at about 500°C and is best stored in absence of air to prevent oxidation to the oxytrichloride. As made by the above method, the principal metal chloride impurities, those of magnesium and iron, are both reduced to about 0·02 per cent and the trichloride is satisfactory for reduction to metal with magnesium by a Kroll type process.

The overall vanadium efficiency in this process is not high, partly because of the high loss as oxytrichloride, and probably also owing to the absorption of vanadium tetrachloride by ferric chloride when the latter is condensed out in the separating unit. The additional high loss (up to 15 per cent), originally sustained owing to thermal decomposition of tetrachloride taking place prematurely during the first distillation stage, is now reduced to only 1 per cent by incorporating a flash distillation unit in the chlorination equipment. None of these losses are in any case irrecoverable, if the scale of operation warrants the installation of suitable equipment. For example, vanadium oxytrichloride can easily be reduced to vanadium trichloride by passing through a porous carbon plug at 600 to 700°C,[79] and in the presence of chlorine this forms the more volatile tetrachloride, i.e.

$$2VOCl_3 + C \rightarrow 2VCl_3 + CO_2,$$

$$2VCl_3 + Cl_2 \rightarrow 2VCl_4.$$

Chlorination of niobium

As in the case of vanadium, it is convenient to use the ferro alloy as the raw material for a chlorination process, since it is readily available for use in the steel industry. A typical analysis of ferroniobium is as follows:

Element	%	Element	%
Niobium	63	Titanium	1·0
Tantalum	7	Tin	0·2
Iron	24·7	Tungsten	0·3
Manganese	1·7	Chromium	0·2
Aluminium	1·5		

Chlorination of ferroniobium has been carried out by the U.K. Atomic Energy Authority first at the Culcheth Laboratories[81] and later at Springfields, in a development plant with a capacity of about 1 tonne/annum. As with some other chlorination processes, the design and operation of plant for the reaction with chlorine itself is relatively easy, and a major proportion of the effort must be devoted to the production of the niobium pentachloride or trichloride in a pure state. In this case the problem is made particularly difficult by the presence of a high proportion of tantalum in the ferroniobium, an element which bears a very close resemblance to niobium in its chemical properties. The physical properties of its compounds are also similar to the corresponding niobium compounds.

The chlorination reaction is highly exothermic and proceeds to the pentachloride, i.e.

$$2Nb + 5Cl_2 \rightarrow 2NbCl_5.$$

It was first carried out in a horizontal tube furnace on this relatively small scale of operation (10 to 20 kg per batch). The furnace was constructed of stainless steel tubing 4 ft 6 in. long by 6 in. diameter, lined either with a silica tube or a 1 in. thick graphite tube. The latter afforded better protection of the stainless steel from attack by chlorine, since the periphery of the graphite could be machined to be a close fit. A sketch of the equipment is shown in Fig. 2.10. The ferroniobium charge was packed along the length of the tube in the form of small chips between $\frac{1}{4}$ in. and 10 mesh. A nichrome winding around the furnace allowed the charge to reach the initiation temperature of about 550°C, and thereafter combustion was allowed to take place in the chlorine atmosphere at temperatures up to about 1000°C. The chlorine inlet tube was of silica and had a small bore, and it passed completely through the charge to the end nearest the condenser. This allowed the "Roman candle" chlorination technique to be applied, in which the tube is slowly withdrawn as the charge of ferroniobium burns from the condenser end to the inlet end. An excess of chlorine was thus always maintained and caking of the bed by formation of lower chlorides was easily avoided. As might be predicted, the chlorine efficiency was relatively low by this technique, i.e. about 60 to 70 per cent.

The mechanical construction of the horizontal furnace, to allow steady withdrawal of the inlet tube at a suitable rate to match the chlorination, presented some difficulties and a more conventional vertical furnace has therefore since been developed. This is of a more squat shape than the horizontal tube and is constructed of steel, lined with graphite. It is still considered advisable to feed the chlorine through an inlet tube from above and to move the tube down as chlorination proceeds. However, the mechanics of this are simpler than in the horizontal furnace and the chlorine

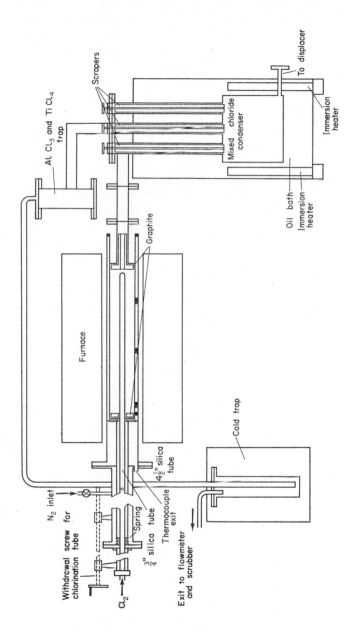

Fig. 2.10. First niobium chlorinator and condenser (U.K.A.E.A. copyright).

efficiency is increased to over 90 per cent, which eases the condensation of the metal chlorides, and subsequent tail-gas scrubbing.

The mixed chlorides from the chlorinator are maintained above 350°C before feeding to the main condensor at 30°C. This takes the form of three steel tubes in parallel, each 2 ft long by 2 in. diameter and fitted with simple scrapers operated through glands. The tubes lead to a 12 in. deep by 12 in. diameter chamber underneath, which collects the loose deposit of niobium and tantalum pentachlorides, ferric chloride and tungsten penta- and hexachlorides. The capacity of this condenser is about 23 kg of chlorides, i.e. a volume of about 8 l. A separate small trap, cooler than the main condenser, collects aluminium trichloride and titanium tetrachloride (b.p. 183°C and 136°C respectively). A series of cold traps and scrubbers is then used to free the tail gas from chlorine and trace quantities of chlorides carried over by entrainment, before release to atmosphere.

Two purification processes have been employed. In one of these the main condenser is immersed in an oil bath, which can be heated to 220°C after condensation, to allow the mixed chlorides to melt and flow to a "displacer" unit. This consists of a vertical steel pipe, also at 220°C, about 5 ft long and 3 in. diameter. A steel cylinder is slowly fed from the upper part of the tube to the lower part, the tube being filled with liquid chlorides, so as to displace the latter at a constant rate. The liquid chlorides are then vapourized, as they flow from the displacer unit through a short section of heated pipe, and passed with hydrogen into a horizontal steel reactor about 4 ft long by 9 in. diameter. This reactor is heated to 350°C and allows the ferric chloride impurity to be reduced to the involatile ferrous chloride, i.e.

$$2FeCl_3 + H_2 \rightarrow 2FeCl_2 + 2HCl.$$

The ferrous chloride collects in the reactor and is trapped by means of a filter of glass cloth and glass wool, whilst the niobium and tantalum pentachlorides pass to the next stage, together with hydrogen chloride and the large excess of hydrogen. Tungsten chlorides are also reduced to less volatile ones with the metal in a lower valency state, and these remain with the ferrous chloride residue.

The degree of purification from iron can be quite high, e.g. down to 0·02 per cent of the niobium, provided the physical action of the filter is effective. Up to 5 per cent of the niobium is lost with the ferrous chloride by reduction to the "trichloride" ($NbCl_{2.67}$ to $NbCl_{3.13}$[82]). Some niobium is also believed to be reduced to the tetrachloride, but this remains volatile with the pentachloride.

Preferential reduction of niobium pentachloride to the "trichloride" by the excess of hydrogen still present is used in the next stage, to separate from tantalum pentachloride, which remains volatile, i.e.

$$NbCl_5 + H_2 \rightarrow NbCl_3 + 2HCl.$$

This is accomplished by raising the temperature to between 500°C and 550°C, and the reaction is carried out in several glass or silica tubes. Horizontal silica tubes, 10 ft long by 7 in. diameter, have been used, packed with lengths of thin glass tubing to provide an adequate surface area for plating out of the niobium trichloride product.

Any niobium tetrachloride which enters this stage is successfully reduced to the trichloride along with the pentachloride, i.e.

$$2NbCl_4 + H_2 \rightarrow 2NbCl_3 + 2HCl.$$

Niobium oxytrichloride is also present, as a result of hydrolysis of the pentachloride or reaction with oxygen at any of the previous stages, owing to the presence of traces of moisture or air, i.e.

$$NbCl_5 + H_2O \rightarrow NbOCl_3 + 2HCl.$$

and $$2NbCl_5 + O_2 \rightarrow 2NbOCl_3 + 2Cl_2.$$

The oxychloride is volatile and enters the second reduction stage along with the pentachloride. At about 500°C it tends to be reduced to niobium oxide, which deposits with the trichloride, i.e.

$$2NbOCl_3 + 3H_2 \rightarrow 2NbO + 6HCl.$$

Unfortunately, the oxide does not reduce further when the trichloride is finally reduced to metal, whatever method is employed for this purpose. Since the oxide forms a permanent contaminant in this way, it is important to reduce hydrolysis to a minimum throughout the process.

A major disadvantage attached to the selective hydrogen reduction process of purification, is the unfavourable equilibrium at the niobium trichloride production stage. With a fivefold excess of hydrogen, a maximum niobium yield of 55 per cent is possible, and in practice a little less than this is obtained. A more favourable equilibrium condition, allowing a maximum yield of 74 per cent is possible if the chlorides are condensed after iron removal, so allowing the hydrochloric acid to be eliminated. Additional hydrogen is then necessary for the niobium reduction stage on revapourizing. Even without intermediate condensation, the process is relatively slow, 8 hr being required for the treatment of an 8 kg batch, with an additional 4 hr for filling the displacer unit. An advantage claimed for this process is the use of a single reagent, hydrogen, for the two chloride reduction stages, and also for the subsequent stage of reduction to niobium metal at 800°C. However, the latter stage is also slow and the reduction efficiency is about 80 per cent in practice. Also, magnesium reduction of niobium trichloride is more satisfactory, as with the chlorides of other metals (see Chapter 6).

It is believed that suitable recycling procedures can be developed for recovery of the niobium lost at the various stages of this process, but the total proportion of recycled material to final product is rather large. For this reason, the selective hydrogen reduction technique has been abandoned in favour of the alternative process of separating the niobium, tantalum and iron chlorides by distillation.

Application to other ores

Beryllium chloride is usually produced by the chlorination of the pure oxide mixed with carbon, the oxide having been obtained via a sulphuric acid or silico-fluoride breakdown of beryl. However, the direct chlorination of beryl has been considered by Sheer and Korman[83]. It is carried out by mixing the ground mineral with about 30 per cent of soft coal and fabricating into electrodes. These are continuously consumed in an electric arc furnace through which chlorine is passed. The chlorides of beryllium, aluminium, silicon and iron, etc., are collected separately, as far as possible, by selective condensation.

Various experiments have been carried out on the chlorination of uranium minerals mixed with carbon, e.g. in Yugoslavia[84] for a very low-grade ore. Using coke as the source of carbon, yields of uranium tetrachloride between about 50 and 90 per cent were obtained at temperatures near $1000°C$, but it is doubtful if the method would discriminate adequately between uranium and other elements capable of forming volatile chlorides. Similarly, American experiments on the chlorination of a Florida ore mixed with carbon, using chlorine or hydrochloric acid, gave yields of over 90 per cent at temperatures of $850°C$ to $1000°C$, but the process was not regarded as economic.[85]

FLUORIDE BREAKDOWN PROCESSES

Several breakdown processes have been used in which the ore is reacted with a fused or sintered fluorinating agent such as potassium hydrogen fluoride or sodium silicofluoride. The most important of these is the Copaux–Kawecki process for opening beryl ore. This is in many ways a unique process and other processes are unlikely to have many features in common with it apart from the problems associated with the handling of toxic fluorides. Since the fluorine is in combination with sodium, as the simple fluoride or as stable complexes with silicon and iron, the severe corrosion conditions inherent in many other fluorination reactions are almost absent in this case.

Fluorination breakdown of beryl

In the original process due to Copaux,[87] each ton of powdered beryl is mixed with 2 tons of sodium silicofluoride and sintered at $750°C$ to $850°C$, the reaction being represented as:

$$3BeO.Al_2O_3.6SiO_2 + 6Na_2SiF_6 \rightarrow 3Na_2BeF_4 + 2Na_3AlF_6 + 9SiO_2 + 3SiF_4.$$

The sodium beryllium fluoride product is soluble in water and can be leached out, together with some aluminium, excess sodium silicofluoride, and small amounts of other impurities. Unfortunately a high proportion of the valuable fluorine is lost as the gaseous and highly toxic silicon tetrafluoride, or as undissolved sodium aluminium fluoride. However, the escape of volatile silicon tetrafluoride can be prevented if a small amount of sodium fluoride is present with the sodium silicofluoride, owing to the reaction

$$SiF_4 + 2NaF \rightarrow Na_2SiF_6,$$

taking place. Since sodium silicofluoride is a product of this reaction and also the principal reactant of the main reaction, a net saving of fluorinating agents ensues.

In effect, the sodium fluoride can also be made *in situ* by making use of the reaction between sodium silicofluoride and sodium carbonate, i.e.

$$Na_2SiF_6 + 2Na_2CO_3 \rightarrow 6NaF + SiO_2 + 2CO_2.$$

A further saving is made under the new reaction conditions owing to the fact that fluorination tends to become more selective for beryllium oxide and less alumina is converted to the fluoride. The improved Copaux process therefore uses much less sodium silicofluoride than the original process, together with a proportion of sodium carbonate, as shown by the following equation:[88]

$$3BeO.Al_2O_3.6SiO_2 + 2Na_2SiF_6 + Na_2CO_3 \rightarrow$$
$$3Na_2BeF_4 + 8SiO_2 + Al_2O_3 + CO_2.$$

After sintering and leaching out the sodium beryllium fluoride with water, beryllium hydroxide is precipitated by the addition of sodium hydroxide, i.e.

$$Na_2BeF_4 + 2NaOH \rightarrow Be(OH)_2 + 4NaF.$$

This hydroxide precipitate can be filtered and passed to later purification stages. The filtrate contains a fairly dilute solution of sodium fluoride which, if completely recovered, could in theory make the process completely self-sustaining in fluorine compounds. A method proposed by Kawecki[89, 90] precipitates sodium ferric fluoride, by the addition of ferric sulphate to the solution, after bringing to a pH of 4 by the addition of sulphuric acid, i.e.

$$12NaF + Fe_2(SO_4)_3 \rightarrow 2Na_3FeF_6 + 3Na_2SO_4.$$

The sodium ferric fluoride can then be used directly to replace sodium silicofluoride in the main breakdown reaction:

$$2Na_3FeF_6 + 3BeO.Al_2O_3.6SiO_2 \rightarrow 3Na_2BeF_4 + Fe_2O_3 + Al_2O_3 + 6SiO_2.$$

In practice higher fluorine and beryllium efficiencies are obtained if a small amount of sodium carbonate is added to the sodium ferric fluoride reaction, as with the silicofluoride reaction, although in the former case it is not strictly required according to the generally accepted equation. It has been suggested, however,[90] that the alkali allows the formation of a basic beryllium double fluoride which is more soluble than Na_2BeF_4.

The essential plant requirements of the fluoride breakdown process are relatively simple and cheap, apart from additional items which are required to satisfy the strict safety regulations now associated with beryllium.

The beryl is ground, wet or dry, to about 200 mesh in a ball mill, and then mixed with the sodium ferric fluoride and sodium carbonate in a wet condition. Briquettes are fabricated from the paste, dried and sintered, e.g. by passing continuously through a gas-heated tunnel kiln with a residence time of several hours at 750°C. A rotary kiln would probably not be very satisfactory since the briquettes are somewhat plastic and would tend to adhere to the lining.[91]

The sintered briquettes are easily ground, e.g. in a wet pebble mill, and leached with water to a beryllium oxide concentration of 3 g/l., up to 95 per cent of the beryllium content of the ore being dissolved. After filtering off the silica, alumina, iron oxide and the fluorides of impurities such as calcium or magnesium, beryllium hydroxide is precipitated. A special technique can be employed at this stage to give a granular product which is easy to filter. Part of the beryllium solution is first dissolved in excess of sodium hydroxide to form sodium beryllate solution. More sodium beryllium fluoride solution is added to this, at 85°C with good stirring, until a crystalline form of beryllium hydroxide is precipitated. This is readily separated in, for example, a filter press, and washed.

In the plant at Milford Haven,[92] formerly managed by Messrs. Murex Ltd. on behalf of the U.K.A.E.A., and now owned by Messrs. Consolidated Beryllium Ltd., a rather high beryllium concentration is achieved (6·5 to 7·5 g BeO/l.) in the breakdown leach liquors, using sodium silicofluoride. This is accomplished by leaching rapidly and so extracting a high proportion of the very soluble beryllium fluoride, rather than the sodium beryllium fluoride complex. Direct precipitation is used, with sodium hydroxide added to the beryllium solution until a pH of 11.3 to 11·6 is obtained. The gelatanous beryllium hydroxide is then filtered in a Sweetland type filter press before purification. The latter involves dissolution in excess sodium hydroxide solution at 50°C and removal of iron and other impurities by filtration. A purer beryllium hydroxide is then precipitated from the "sodium beryllate" solution by boiling.

An alternative fluoride breakdown process for beryl was used during the 1939–45 war by the Sappi Company in Italy.[30] This was based upon the reaction with sodium hydrogen fluoride (NaF.HF) at a temperature of about 680°C. The fluoride reagent is mixed with the ground ore and made into briquettes with a little water, ready for firing in the breakdown furnace. The reaction converts the beryllium to a complex fluoride, believed to be $3NaF.2BeF_2$, without fluorination of the aluminium and silicon components.

The sodium beryllium fluoride is leached out with water after the reaction, leaving an insoluble residue of alumina and silica.

Fluoride breakdown of zircon

A process is operated in the U.S.S.R., on a production scale[93] for the breakdown of zircon by sintering with potassium silicofluoride. The principal reason for the employment of this route is the fact that the product potassium fluorozirconate, is suitable for feeding directly to the Russian fractional crystallization purification process. This removes the 1·5 to 2·5 per cent of hafnium which originates in the zircon mineral.

The sintering reaction is carried out in a rotary furnace at a temperature of 650 to 700°C, the reaction being represented by the equation:

$$ZrSiO_4 + K_2SiF_6 \rightarrow K_2ZrF_6 + 2SiO_2.$$

A proportion of potassium chloride is also present in the reaction mixture and this assists the reaction to go to completion. The efficiency of conversion of the zirconium to fluorozirconate is in fact about 97 to 99 per cent.

The reaction product is obtained from the furnace in the form of free-flowing almost spherical granules, a few millimetres in size. These are crushed to pass a 100-mesh sieve and each ton is leached with approximately 7 tons of water containing about 1 per cent of hydrochloric acid for 1·5 to 2 hr, with stirring, at 85°C. The hot extraction liquor is decanted and the residue washed with water, which is re-used for a later leaching operation, so giving an element of counter-current leaching.

The hot leach liquor is cooled to normal temperature and fairly large, well-formed crystals of potassium fluorizorconate (and the corresponding halfnium salt) are deposited. The crystals are separated and washed with cold water to give a product with the following impurity analysis:

	%
Iron	0·044
Titanium	0·041
Silicon	0·06
Chlorine	0·007

The hafnium to zirconium ratio can be reduced to only 0·01 per cent or less, by 16 to 18 fractional crystallizations in stainless-steel vessels, between temperatures of 100°C and 19°C. At these temperatures the zirconium solubilities are respectively 250 g/l. and 16·3 g/l. Hafnium solubilities are somewhat higher. Since the overall yield, using fresh water for each crystallization stage, would only be about 10 per cent, the mother liquor from each stage is passed back to a previous stage for a later batch. In this way an overall yield of 80 per cent of the zirconium is obtained.

REFERENCES

1. DANCKWERTS, P. V. D. Continuous flow systems, distribution of residence times. *Chem. Engng. Sci.* 2, 1 (1953).
2. SVENKE, E. Recovery of uranium from uranium-bearing alum shale. *Proc. 1st Int. Conf. on the Peaceful Uses of Atomic Energy, Geneva,* 1955. Paper 784.
3. BADGER, W. L. and McCABE, W. L. *Elements of Chemical Engineering,* chap. xi, Extraction. McGraw-Hill (1936).
4. ALMOND, J. N. Treatment of Radium Hill concentrates for the recovery of uranium. Australian Atomic Energy Symposium. Melbourne University Press (1958).
5. GRAY, P. M. J. Acid pressure leaching of uranium ores. *Proc. 1st Int. Conf. on the Peaceful Uses of Atomic Energy, Geneva,* 1955. Paper 986.
6. CREMER, H. W. and DAVIES, T. *Chemical Engineering Practice,* vol. 3, *Solid Systems.* Butterworths (1957).
7. ARDEN, T. V. The concentration of uranium from low grade ores. *Industr. Chem.* 32, No. 376, 202 (May–June 1956).
8. COULSON, J. M. and RICHARDSON, J. F. *Chemical Engineering,* vol. 2. *Unit Operations.* Pergamon Press (1960).
9. McLEAN, C. S. and PRENTICE, T. K. The South African uranium industry. *Proc. 1st Int. Conf. on the Peaceful Uses of Atomic Energy, Geneva,* 1955. Paper 997.
10. ROSENBAUM, J. B. and CLEMMER, J. B. Accelerated thickening and filtering of uranium leach pulps. *Proc. 1st Int. Conf. on the Peaceful Uses of Atomic Energy, Geneva,* 1955. Paper 528.
11. McQUISTON, F. W. Processing uranium ores. *Min. Congr. J.* 36, 28 (Oct. 1950).
12. GAUDIN, A. M., SCHUHMANN, R. and DASHER, J. Extraction process for gold–uranium ores. *J. Metals* 8, No. 8, 1065 (Aug. 1956).
13. FORWARD, F. A. and HALPERN, J. Acid pressure leaching of uranium ores. *Trans. A.I.M.E.,* p. 463 (March 1955).
14. PINKNEY, E. T. A review of uranium leaching practice in South Africa, Symposium *Uranium in South Africa.* The Associated Scientific & Technical Societies of South Africa (1957).
15. PINKNEY, E. T. The chemistry of the uranium leaching process in South Africa. *S. Afr. Industr. Chem.* 10, No. 11, 264 (Nov. 1956).
16. PINKNEY, E. T. The chemistry of the uranium leaching process in South Africa, Symposium *Uranium in South Africa.* The Associated Scientific & Technical Societies of South Africa (1957).
17. MARVIN, G. *et al.* Recovery of uranium from its ores. *Proc. 1st Int. Conf. on the Peaceful Uses of Atomic Energy, Geneva,* 1955. Paper 519.
18. GAUDIN, A. M. Principles and new developments in uranium leaching. *Proc. 1st Int. Conf. on the Peaceful Uses of Atomic Energy, Geneva,* 1955. Paper 529.
19. THUNAES, A. Canadian practice in ore dressing and extractive metallurgy of uranium. *Proc. 1st Int. Conf. on the Peaceful Uses of Atomic Energy, Geneva,* 1955. Paper 2.
20. LENNEMANN, W. L. How to extract uranium from ores. *Engng. Min. J.* 155 (Sept. 1954).
21. WELCH, A. J. E. Some General Chemical Principles in Extraction of Metals from Low Grade Ores. I.M.M. Symposium on the Extraction Metallurgy of Some of the Less Common Metals, London (1956).
22. MARVIN, G. G. and GREENLEAF, E. F. Methods of uranium recovery from ores. *Progress in Nuclear Energy,* Ser. III, vol. 1, p. 3. Pergamon Press (1956).
23. AUDSLEY, A., JAMRACK, W. D., OLDBURY, A. E. and WELLS, R. A. Recently developed processes for the extraction and purification of thorium. *Proc. 2nd Int. Conf. on the Peaceful Uses of Atomic Energy, Geneva,* 1958. Paper 152.
24. BUDDERY, J. H., JAMRACK, W. D. and WELLS, R. A. The extraction of thorium. *Chemistry and Industry,* No. 8, p. 255 (21/2/59).
25. BLICKWEDEL, T. W. Decomposition of monazite. Effect of a number of variables on the decomposition of monazite sand with sulphuric Acid. I.S.C.—66.

26. KAPLAN, G. E. Metallurgy of thorium. *Proc. 1st. Int. Conf. on the Peaceful Uses of Atomic Energy, Geneva*, 1955. Paper 636.

27. SMUTZ, M. *et al.* The Ames process for separation of monazite. *Nuclear Engng.* Part III, vol. 50. Chemical Engineering Symposium Series No. 13. The American Institute of Chemical Engineers (1954).

28. PILKINGTON, E. S. and WYLIE, A. W. Production of rare earth and thorium compounds from monazite, Part I. *J. Soc. Chem. Ind.* **66,** 387 (Nov. 1947).

29. BRIDGER, G. L. *et al.* Separation Processes for Thorium Salts. U.S. Patent 2,815,262 (1957).

30. AUDSLEY, A., LIND, R. and ENGLAND, P. G. The extraction of thorium from monazite. I.M.M. symposium on the extraction metallurgy of some of the less common metals, London (1956).

31. SODDY, F. Separation of thorium and the rare earth group from minerals. U.S. Patent 2,425, 573 (1957).

32. SCHWENZFEIER, C. W. The sulphate extraction of beryllium from beryl, *The Metal Beryllium*, p. 71. The American Society for Metals (1955).

33. SLOMAN, H. A. and SAWYER, C. B. The beryllium industries of Germany and Italy (1939 to 1945). *F.I.A.T. Final Report*, No. 522.

34. POTVIN, R. Production of beryllia and beryllium at Degussa Plants. B.I.O.S. Final Report, No. 158 (1945).

35. WEST, H. W. *et al.* Investigation of beryllium production in Germany and Italy. B.I.O.S. Final Report, No. 550.

36. HUTTER, J. C. and PINGARD, L. Production of pure beryllium oxide. *Proc. 1st Int. Conf. on the Peaceful Uses of Atomic Energy, Geneva*, 1955. Paper 346.

37. KAUFMANN, A. R. and KJELLGREN, R. R. F. Status of beryllium technology in the U.S.A. *Proc. 1st Int. Conf. on the Peaceful Uses of Atomic Energy, Geneva*, 1955. Paper 820.

38. BEAVER, W. W. Technology of beryllium and beryllium oxide. *Progress in Nuclear Energy*. Ser. V, *Metallurgy and Fuels*, p. 277. Pergamon Press (1956).

39. GALVANEK, P. A solvent leaching process for the production of high-purity uranium products directly from low-grade ores. U.S.A.E.C. Report, WIN-31 (1955).

40. BEARSE, A. E. *et al.* Recovery of thorium and uranium from monazite sands. Topical Report, B.M.I.-J.D.S.-151 (1948).

41. BEARSE, A. E. *et al.* Process for recovering thorium and rare earths from monazite. B.M.I.–X–105 (1954).

42. BEARSE, A. E. *et al.* Thorium and rare earths from monazite. *Nuclear Engng.* **50,** No. 5, 235 (1954).

43. BEYER, G. H. *et al.* Caustic treatment of zircon sand. *Nuclear Engng.* Part II, vol. 50, pp. 67–71, Chemical Engineering Progress Symposium, Series No. 12, American Institute of Chemical Engineers (1954).

44. GILBER, H. L. *et al.* Caustic soda fusion of zirconium ores. U.S. Bureau of Mines Report, No. 5091.

45. MILLER, G. L. *Tantalum and Niobium*. Butterworths Scientific Publications, London (1959).

46. DICKSON, G. K. and DUKES, J. A. The selection of a process for development for the production of pure niobium. I.M.M. Symposium on the extraction metallurgy of some of the less common metals, Paper 14, London (March 1956).

47. MCKEE, R. M. Process for the production of beryllium oxide or hydroxide. U.S. Patent 2,298,800 (1942).

48. O'BRIEN, R. N., FORWARD, F. A. and HALPERN, J. Studies in carbonate leaching of uranium ores. *Trans. Canad. Inst. Min. Metall.* **56,** 359 (1953).

49. FORWARD, F. A., HALPERN, J. and PETERS, E. Studies in the carbonate leaching of uranium. *Canad. Min. Metall. Bull.* **56,** 634 (1953).

50. FORWARD, F. A. and HALPERN, J. Developments in the carbonate processing of uranium ores. *Trans. A.I.M.E.* **200,** 1408 (Dec. 1954).

51. STEPHENS, F. M. and MACDONALD R. D. Alkaline leaching of uranium ores. *Proc. 1st Int. Conf. on the Peaceful Uses of Atomic Energy, Geneva,* 1955, Paper 520.
52. BEVERLY, R. G. and CHARLES, W. D. Pilot plant leaching of uranium ores. *Proc. 2nd Int. Conf. on the Peaceful Uses of Atomic Energy, Geneva,* 1958. Paper 512.
53. Alkaline Leaching Process for Uranium Extraction. U.K. Patent Specification 730, 230 (Application 10/12/52, completion 18/5/55).
54. HALPERN, J., FORWARD, F. A. and ROSS, A. H. Effect of roasting on recovery of uranium and vanadium from carnotite ores by carbonate leaching. *Trans. Metall. Soc. A.I.M.E.* **212**, No. 1, 65 (1958).
55. WHEELER, C. M. *et al.* The ammonium carbonate pressure leaching of uranium ores. B.M.I. 282 (1955).
56. WHEELER, C. M., LANGSTON, B. G. and STEPHENS, F. M. The ammonium carbonate pressure leaching of uranium ores. A.E.C.U. 3024 (1955).
57. WHEELER, C. M., LANGSTON, B. G. and STEPHENS, F. M. The alkaline leaching of uranium ores. A.E.C.U. 2946 (1954).
58. MCCLAINE, L. A., BULLWINKEL, E. P. and HUGGINS, J. C. The carbonate chemistry of uranium: theory and applications. *Proc. 1st Int. Conf. of the Peaceful Uses of Atomic Energy, Geneva,* 1955. Paper 525.
59. THUNAES, A. Recovery of uranium from Canadian ores. *Canad. Min. Metall. Bull.* **47**, No. 503, 128 (1954).
60. GREY, J. J. and CARTER, A. *Chemistry and Metallurgy of Titanium Production.* Royal Institute of Chemistry, London (1958).
61. Titanium, zirconium and some other elements of growing industrial importance. Project No. 247, O.E.E.C.
62. STEPHENS, W. W. and GILBERT, H. L. Chlorination of zirconium oxide. *Trans. A.I.M.E.* **4**, No. 7, 733 (July 1952).
63. SHELTON, S. M., DILLING, E. D. and MCCLAIN, J. H. Zirconium metal production. *Proc. 1st Int. Conf. on the Peaceful Uses of Atomic Energy, Geneva,* 1955. Paper 533.
64. HUDSWELL, F. and HUTCHEON, J. M. Methods of separating zirconium from hafnium and their technological implications. *Proc. 1st Int. Conf. on the Peaceful Uses of Atomic Energy, Geneva,* 1955. Paper 409.
65. HUDSWELL, F. *et al.* The separation of hafnium from zirconium. A.E.R.E. C/R 545 (1950).
66. PRAKASH, B. and SURDARAM, C. V. Separation of hafnium from zirconium by vapour phase dechlorination. *Proc. 1st Int. Conf. on the Peaceful Uses of Atomic Energy, Geneva,* 1955. Paper 876.
67. NEWNHAM, I. E. Zirconium for nuclear reactors. *Research,* **10**, No. 11, 424 (Nov. 1957)
68. NEWNHAM, I. E. Improvements in or relating to process for removing hafnium from zirconium. U.K. Patent Specification 778,192 (Application 1952).
69. KROLL, W. J., SCHLECHTON, A. W. and YERKES, L. A. Ductile zirconium from zircon sand. *Trans. Electrochem. Soc.* **89**, 263 (1946).
70. KROLL, W. J. *et al.* Recent progress in the metallurgy of malleable zirconium. *Trans. Electrochem. Soc.* **92**, 99 (1947).
71. KROLL, W. J. *et al.* Large scale laboratory production of ductile zirconium. *J. Electrochem. Soc.* **94**, No. 1, 1 (1948).
72. KROLL, W. J., STEPHENS, W. W. and HOLMES, H. P. Production of malleable zirconium on a pilot plant scale. *Trans. A.I.M.E.* **188**, 1445; *J. Metals* (Dec. 1950).
73. KROLL, W. J. and STEPHENS, W. W. Production of malleable zirconium. *Indust. Engng. Chem.* **42**, 395 (1950).
74. SHELTON, S. M., DILLING, E. D. and MCCLAIN, J. H. The production of zirconium and hafnium. *Progress in Nuclear Energy,* Ser. V, *Metallurgy and Fuels,* vol. 1, p. 305. Pergamon Press (1956).
75. Zirconium, Its production and properties. U.S. Bureau of Mines Bull. **561** (1956).
76. HARTLEY, F. R. and WYLIE, A. W. Preparation of rare earth chlorides by high temperature chlorination of monazite. *J. Soc. Chem. Ind.* **69**, 1 (Jan. 1950).
77. HARTLEY, F. R. The preparation of anhydrous lanthanon chlorides by high temperature chlorination of monazite. *J. Appl. Chem.* **2**, 24 (Jan. 1952).

78. SARMA, B. and GUPTA, J. Studies on the chlorination of Travancore monazite *J. Scient. Industr. Res. (India)* **12B**, 414 (Sept. 1953).
79. TYZACK, C. and ENGLAND, P. G. Processes for the extraction of vanadium. I.M.M. Symposium on the Extraction Metallurgy of Some of the Less Common Metals, London (1956).
80. FOLEY, E., WARD, Mrs. M. and HOCK, A. L. The production of high purity vanadium metal. I.M.M. Symposium on the Extraction Metallurgy of Some of the Less Common Metals, London (1956).
81. McINTOSH, A. B. and BROADLEY, J. S. The Extraction of pure niobium by a chlorination process. I.M.M. Symposium on the Extraction Metallurgy of Some of the Less Common Metals, London (1956).
82. SCHAFER, H. Niobium trichloride—a compound with a large extension of phase. *Angew. Chem.* **67**, 748 (1955).
83. SHEAR, C. and KORMANN, S. *Chem. Engng. News* **32**, No. 24, 2382 (14 June, 1954).
84. GAL. O.S. Extraction of uranium from low grade Yugoslav ores by chlorination. *Proc. 1st Int. Conf. on the Peaceful Uses of Atomic Energy, Geneva,* 1955. Paper 957.
85. Progress Reports for utilization of Florida leach material. Tennessee Valley Authority. R.M.O. 2704, 2705, 2706.
86. McBERTY, F. H. Anhydrous chlorides manufacture. F.I.A.T. Final Report, No. 774, p. 15 (1946).
87. COPAUX, H. Methode de traitement du béryl pour en extraire la Gluciné. *Comptes. Rendus* **168**, 610 (1919).
88. KAWECKI, H. C. The fluoride extraction of beryllium from beryl. *The Metal Beryllium,* p. 63. The American Society for Metals.
89. KAWECKI, H. C. The production of beryllium compounds, metals and alloys. *Trans. Electrochem. Soc.* **89**, 229 (1946).
90. KAWECKI, H. C. Process for extracting beryllium compounds from silicate minerals U.S. Patent 2,312, 297.
91. LUNDIN, H. Production of beryllium oxide. *Trans. Amer. Inst. Chem. Engineers* **41**, 671 (1946).
92. BRYANT, P. S. Beryllium production at Milford Haven. I.M.M. Symposium on the Extraction Metallurgy of Some of the Less Common Metals, London (1956). Paper 17.
93. SAJIN, N. P. and PEPELYAEVA, E. A. Separation of hafnium from zirconium and production of pure zirconium dioxide. *Proc. 1st Int. Conf. on the Peaceful Uses of Atomic Energy, Geneva,* 1955. Paper 634.

6

CHAPTER 3

ION-EXCHANGE PURIFICATION

THE ability to exchange ions from solution by means of certain naturally occuring materials, e.g. "Greensands" and Zeolites, has been known for many years and great use has been made of this property for the purification of water. Natural materials were later replaced by synethetic ones for this purpose, first the aluminosilicates and then various organic polymers or "resins" with much greater capacities. The first of the modern ion-exchange resins was discovered by Adams and Holmes in 1935. Although a high proportion of the various resins are still marketed today for application to water purification, increasing tonnages are being used for other purposes, including the concentration and purification of rare metals. Ion-exchange is usually less attractive commercially for the more common metals where more conventional purification techniques are applicable, or the degree of purification obtained in smelting is satisfactory.

THEORY

Ion-exchange resins may be regarded as insoluble acids or bases, the salts of which are also insoluble.[1] They are composed of macro-molecules in the form of polyelectrolyte chains. These chains are interconnected or "cross-linked" at intervals and also contain a large number of basic or acidic groups which are capable of ionization within the limits of their various ionization constants. The free anions or cations which are thus formed can exchange with other anions or cations in solution. Therefore in the state of dynamic equilibrium which exists the new anions or cations can in general become attached to the basic or acidic groups in place of the original ions.

Ion-exchange reactions are reversible and, for example, for cation exchange, may be simply represented by the reaction:

$$RA^+ + B^+ \rightleftharpoons RB^+ + A^+.$$

The thermodynamic equilibrium constant K may be expressed in terms of the activities of the various species

$$K = \frac{[RB^+]\,[A^+]}{[RA^+]\,[B^+]}$$

The more practical index of affinity of resin for two ions is the "selectivity coefficient" K_c, where

$$K_c = \frac{(RB^+)(A^+)}{(RA^+)(B^+)}$$

the brackets in this case simply representing concentrations of the various species. K_c is usually fairly constant over a range of conditions in the solution.

When concentrations of B^+ and RB^+ are much less than those of A^+ and RA^+, as commonly occurs in the use of say the hydrogen form of a resin for the extraction of a relatively small proportion of a metal ion from an acidic solution, then $(A^+)/(RA^+)(H^+)/(RH^+)$, is effectively a constant. Consequently, the parameter $(RB^+)/(B^+)$ is approximately constant and is often referred to as the distribution coefficient D_B. This is a useful measure of the affinity of a resin for a particular ion.

Relative affinities of ions have often been arranged in series to indicate whether one ion will replace another or not under comparable conditions of concentration, etc., e.g. for sulphonic acid resins, in increasing affinity:[2]

NH_4 $< Rb$ $< Cs$ $< Ag$ $< Tl$

Ni $< Co$ $< Ca$ $< Sr$ $< Pb$ $< Ba$

Li $< H$ $< Na$ $< K$ $< Rb$ $< Cs$ $\ll Ba^{2+}$ $\ll Y^{3+}$ $< La^{3+}$

In general, at low concentrations, the affinity increases with increasing valency and with increasing atomic number.[3, 4]

Series of this type should only be regarded as rough approximations since, for example, they are dependent upon the degree of cross-linking of the polymeric chains. For a highly cross-linked resin, simple ions which tend to cause little swelling of the resin tend to have greater affinities than those which would cause great enlargement of the resin grains. Highly cross-linked resins are therefore in general more selective than those with few cross-linkages.

Highly cross-linked resins, as might be expected, cause resistance to diffusion and thus decrease the rate of absorption of ions. Consequently, such resins are not generally chosen for production purposes unless it is desired to make use of their selective properties.

Practical ion-exchange problems are often concerned with achieving a separation of two species, say two metal ions B^+ and C^+ which may be present in relatively low concentration. The resin itself is frequently associated with a third ion A^+ (often the hydrogen ion) which may also be present in the solution at a higher concentration than the two metal ions. In this case,

$$D_B = \frac{(RB^+)}{(B^+)} \text{ and } D_c = \frac{(RC^+)}{(C^+)}$$

The separation factor D_B/D_C indicates the ease with which the two metal ions can be separated. Clearly, for a simple batch process in which the resin is agitated with a volume of solution containing the two metal ions, little separation is achieved with a separation factor close to unity. Also, with a range of cations present instead of only two, it is unlikely that the desired ion will have a distribution coefficient either much greater or much less than all the others. Consequently, separations are usually achieved by means of multi-stage extraction. This could be carried out by a number of multiple counter-current contacts of resin and solution in a series of vessels in a manner analogous to the operation of solvent extraction processes using mixer-settlers. However, with ion-exchange separations, a column process in which the resin beads remain static is much more elegant. This avoids the difficulties associated with transporting a solid from one process vessel to another, but also it takes advantage of the very small theoretical stage heights which generally prevail in correctly designed ion-exchange columns. This arises principally from the low relative velocities of the two phases, which are possible when one of them is a static solid. An adequate time can be allowed for equilibrium to be reached in each small section comprising a stage, whereas in a solvent extracting column, for example, there is generally no restriction on rate of rise or fall of one phase through the other.

The various steps in an ion-exchange reaction are as follows:[2]

(a) Transport of one ion from solution across a liquid film boundary surrounding the resin bead.

(b) Diffusion of the ingoing ion into the interior of the resin.

(c) Chemical exchange between the ingoing ion and the outgoing ion within the resin.

(d) Diffusion of the outgoing ion to the surface of the bead.

(e) Diffusion of the outgoing ion through the liquid film to the bulk solution.

Since chemical exchange itself is usually rapid, the overall reaction rate is controlled by one of the diffusion stages. The stage principally responsible is dependent upon a number of factors such as the diffusion coefficients in the two phases and resin particle size, etc. These various factors, together with others, must clearly be taken into account in the design of ion-exchange columns. The individual effect of each factor may not be known precisely but their combined effect is expressed in terms of the parameter the "Height equivalent of a theoretical stage" (HETS) as in a solvent extraction or distillation column. Gluekauf[5] discusses the methods of calculation of HETS from the fundamental factors which affect it, and also points out the limitations of this approach. HETS values vary greatly with operating conditions and, for example, at extremely low flow rates figures of $1 \cdot 2 \times 10^{-3}$cm have been observed,[5] being approximately the diameter of a single resin particle as used in the experiment.

The capacity of an ion-exchange resin, i.e. the number of ions which it can take up, is dependent upon the number of functional groups, acidic or basic, which it contains. Ion-exchange reactions are therefore stoichiometric, as in the case of other chemical reactions. Since, however, the size of the "molecule" is indefinite, the "equivalent weight" cannot be expressed in the normal way. Instead, reference is usually made to the number of milli-equivalents per gramme of dry resin or per millilitre of apparent volume (strictly, the number of milligram equivalents). It is necessary to define the form of the resin, e.g. hydrogen or chloride form for a cation resin, since the uncombined resin ion does not exist as a separate entity.

Under complete equilibrium conditions therefore, ion-exchange should not be regarded as a surface phenomenon, and the stoichiometric equivalent is not dependent upon particle size. In this way it clearly differs from conventional chromatographic adsorption. The stoichiometry of ion-exchange reactions has various limitations in practice. Although every functional group is combined with an ion of opposite sign, as in the case of any other salt, it may not be practicable for these ions to be completely exchanged with other different ions. The relative affinities of the two ions and their concentrations (or activities) is the first limitation, and the degree of reaction is limited according to the equilibrium constant in the manner already discussed, as in the case of any other reversible chemical reaction. A second limitation is the ability of ions to diffuse through the resin lattice. Large ions may be unable to penetrate into the interior of a particular resin because of spatial limitations, and this factor is severely aggravated by the existence of cross-linkages. Thus, as has already been mentioned, highly cross-linked resins tend to be selective for small ions only. A third limitation is related to the method of use of the resin, in that it may not be possible or economically advisable to allow enough time for true equilibrium to be obtained, and therefore the desired exchange only takes place incompletely in any given portion of resin. This applies to some degree or other in any ion-exchange column process which is dependent upon the number of theoretical stages. The height of a theoretical stage is therefore a function of flow rate. Within the limits of irregularities due to grain size and lack of piston flow of the solution, the stage height can be decreased to any desired figure by reducing the flow rate. The penalty for low flow rate is obviously a low throughput of the process. This can of course be compensated for by using a column of large diameter or a number of columns in parallel, i.e. an increased resin usage for a given throughput.

For a commercial ion-exchange process, it is important to select a resin with a high exchange capacity per gramme of dry weight, in order to economize on resin usage. It should also have a high exchange capacity per unit wet volume in order to minimize the size of plant and hold-up of solutions.

The capacity (per unit volume) of a resin with few cross-linkages tends to be low because of the ease with which it absorbs water and swells to a large volume. A resin which is highly cross-linked may have a high exchange capacity for ions in general, but not necessarily for large ions, and the rate of attainment of exchange equilibrium is less. Consequently, it may be necessary to compromise and select a resin with intermediate properties. For some purposes, it is possible to use a fairly highly cross-linked resin with a high capacity, at an elevated temperature, say 80–100°C, in order to increase the rate of exchange. Other factors which may require consideration in the selection of a resin are the difficulties which may arise owing to changes in the degree of hydration resulting from contact with a variety of solutions of different ionic concentrations. The resulting volume changes must be accommodated within the column and the expansion should be allowed to take place without undue pressure on the grains which would cause them to adhere together and reduce the surface area or voidage unduly, or even contribute towards blockages in the column. Attrition of the resin may also result from subsequent changes of volume.

METHODS OF APPLICATION

Ion-exchange processes are carried out on columns of resin in several different ways when used for the extraction and purification of metals.

A column is first usually packed with beads of resin which are about 0·1 mm diameter when in the dry state. It is, however, advantageous to fill the column with wet resin which has already swollen, to prevent adhesion of grains or column blockages, etc. It can then be converted to a suitable form for use, e.g. to the hydrogen form by means of dilute acid in the case of a cation-exchange resin. The column may then be washed with water and left flooded ready for absorption.

Frontal analysis technique

The two most direct absorption techniques are "frontal analysis" and "elution analysis". In the former, the feed solution containing the desired ion and various impurity ions is passed down the column of resin at an appropriate flow rate. The ions which are not absorbed, e.g. anions passed through a cation-exchange column, leave the base of the column in the effluent immediately. These are followed by ions which are weakly absorbed and then those more strongly absorbed, until the desired ions begin to break through. (It is usually advantageous in fact to select operating conditions so that the desired ion is the most strongly absorbed.) For any individual ionic species, a graph of concentration in the effluent against successive volumes of effluent has the general shape shown in Fig. 3.1. The "breakthrough point" is p, i.e. where a small amount of the desired species first fails to be absorbed. This is followed, usually fairly rapidly, by the point *s*, where the resin is "saturated" with respect to the desired ion, and the latter passes through to the effluent completely. It is clearly desirable to cease absorption at the breakthrough point, to avoid loss of the wanted material. At this point, the column is full of solution containing essentially the full feed concentration of the desired ion. It would represent a loss if simply washed out by water or a suitable solvent, and it may therefore be

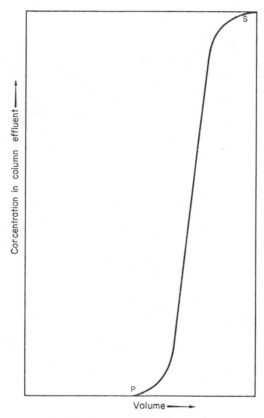

FIG. 3.1. Ion-exchange absorption.

displaced out and into a fresh column. Absorption of further fresh feed solution can then take place on this second column. Often, at the breakthrough point, the lower part of the column has a much smaller concentration of the desired ion than the upper part and capacity is wasted. This can sometimes be overcome by absorbing upon two columns in series and only removing the first one, i.e. most saturated one, on breakthrough. The second column then becomes used as the leading one and is itself replaced by a fresh one. In this way a column is always supplied for elution which is as fully saturated as possible.

If the absorption process is highly specific for the desired ion and no further purification is necessary, elution may be carried out in a relatively crude manner. In this case the product is simply displaced from the column by feeding a solution containing a high concentration of another ion having a great affinity for the resin. The product should also be able to tolerate the presence of a high proportion of the eluting ion.

Elution analysis technique

In many cases simple purification by the "frontal analysis" technique, followed by simple elution, is not satisfactory, since impurity ions would absorb and elute together with the desired ions. It is then necessary to purify the desired ion by "elution analysis". An eluting agent is chosen which will displace the various ionic species down the column at different rates. The rate is in fact inversely proportional to the distribution coefficient in each case. To apply the technique successfully, absorption should have taken place mainly in a narrow band at the top of the column, so leaving the lower part free to allow a high degree of separation between the bands of different ions as they are eluted at their respective rates from top to bottom of the column. This is usually ensured by having the column in two sections, only the top one of which is in fact used for absorption. Alternatively, a portion of loose resin may be allowed to absorb the mixture of ions batchwise and then be placed on top of a fresh column.

A high degree of dispersion between the various bands of ions on elution is best obtained by the use of an eluting agent which exerts a chemical complexing action upon the ions to form covalent compounds. Thus not only does the eluting agent compete with the various ions (all to different extents) for sites on the resin, but it also attracts the ions away from the resin by the formation of non-ionic chemical compounds, or complexes, with them. Each complexing reaction has its own individual equilibrium constant or "complexity constant". Although two individual ions may have similar affinities for the resin and be difficult to separate by normal elution methods, it is unlikely that they will also have similar complexity constants, and these also will have an important bearing upon their relative degrees of elution. The first complexing agent to be used was citric acid mixed with ammonium citrate, the distribution coefficient being very sensitive to pH (or ammonium content) and this system is still commonly employed. Others have proved superior for individual applications, such as tartaric, oxalic, lactic and sulphosalicylic acids, ethyl acetoacetate or acetylacetone.[6] There is some evidence, however, that ethylene diamine tetracetic acid (EDTA) and nitrilotriacetic acid may be of more general applicability than any of these, because of the much more rapid separation which they allow.[2] A classic example of this is the work of Spedding[7,8,9], on the separation of a range of rare earth elements, with their similar affinities for the resin, in which most of these complexing agents were employed.

The eluting agent is passed down the column in the same direction as absorpiton, i.e. from the concentrated to the dilute end of the column. The flow rate is usually quite low in order to allow a short HETS value and therefore a large number of stages in the column. Eluate can be collected in discrete portions and each one analysed subsequently for the various species. Alternatively an instrumental method is sometimes applied which allows the eluate to be diverted from one collecting vessel to another when that portion containing the pure wanted species passes through. In this technique, a large weight of resin must be employed for absorption, in addition to a large volume of eluting agent, which gives a low product concentration. It is therefore only employed for production on a very small scale, with materials where high costs can be tolerated and where the similarity of the chemical properties of the various species makes separation very difficult.

Anionic complexes of rare metals

The most favourable process from a chemical engineering viewpoint is always that in which conditions can be adjusted so that the resin is a specific absorbent for the desired ion alone. One excellent method of achieving this is to form an anionic complex of the desired ion before absorption, in a medium which does not exert any similar complexing action on the ions of the metal impurities. This complex is then absorbed upon an anion-exchange resin by a "frontal analysis" technique. Uranium absorption from sulphate solutions is a good example of this type of process. The $[UO_2(SO_4)_2]^{2-}$ ion and $[UO_2(SO_4)_3]^{4-}$ ion have virtually only the SO_4^{2-} ion to compete with for absorption upon the resin, and the degree of purification from this ion is in any case relatively unimportant. Under conditions of this nature, when the desired ion has a very high distribution coefficient, a high degree of concentration may be achieved simultaneously with purification. Although a "frontal analysis" technique is employed, the resin is often so specific that other ions can be virtually ignored. It is, however, necessary to avoid physical contamination due to impurities, by careful design of washing operations, etc., e.g. between the absorption and elution cycles.

CHEMICAL COMPOSITION AND STRUCTURE OF RESINS
Cationic resins

The early naturally occurring aluminosilicate type of cation-exchange materials were first replaced by a variety of sulphonated natural organic products such as coal, peat or lignite. The resulting compounds contained both sulphonic acid groups ($-SO_3H$) and phenolic groups ($-OH$). Cations can exchange with the hydrogen ions of the former over a wide range of pH, but with the latter exchange is only in alkaline solution. The first synthetic resins of the kind used today may be considered a development of this type of molecule, i.e. they have even more porous structures, which allow ions to diffuse freely through them, and so all the functional groups are able to take part in ion-exchange reactions. The functional groups may be of the sulphonic acid and phenolic type as before, but the properties of synthetic resins can be made more uniform. These resins are made by condensation of phenol, resorcinol, or similar organic compounds with formaldehyde and then sulphonation with sulphuric acid. The condensation reaction may be represented as:

With additional formaldehyde, further methylene bridges are formed between chains, i.e. "cross-linking", as follows:

Numerous —SO$_3$H groups are then introduced by the sulphuric acid treatment.

Later resins of this type, i.e. strongly acidic cation exchangers, have been synthesized directly by condensation of compounds which already contain sulphonic acid groups and phenolic groups, to form polymers, e.g. a mixture of phenol, phenolsulphonic acid and formaldehyde, in the presence of sodium hydroxide as a catalyst.[10, 11]

Assuming the phenolsulphonic acid to be in the meta form only, the first condensation product can be represented as:

which is completely soluble in water.[12] As the formaldehyde usage exceeds one mole per mole of phenolsulphonic acid, cross-linkages begin to form and a gel is produced. The enormous molecule is apparently soluble in a limited amount of water, but as more water is added, the structure is extended to its limit and a separate water phase is formed. By analogy with a phenol-formaldehyde condensation product, the structure may be represented as:

$$
\begin{array}{cccc}
OH & OH & OH & OH \\
\end{array}
$$

$$-\!\!\overset{\displaystyle OH}{\bigcirc}\!-CH_2-\overset{\displaystyle OH}{\bigcirc}\!-CH_2-\overset{\displaystyle OH}{\bigcirc}\!-CH_2-\overset{\displaystyle OH}{\bigcirc}\!-CH_2-$$

$$CH_2 \quad SO_3H \qquad SO_3H \qquad SO_3H \qquad CH_2 \quad SO_3H$$

$$\quad SO_3H \qquad SO_3H \qquad SO_3H \qquad SO_3H$$

$$-\!\!\bigcirc\!-CH_2-\bigcirc\!-CH_2-\bigcirc\!-CH_2-\bigcirc\!-CH_2-$$

$$OH \qquad OH \qquad OH \qquad OH$$

With more formaldehyde, further cross-linkages are formed, in three dimensions, until a hard and tough material with as little as 30–50 per cent of water is formed, and this constitutes the final ion-exchange resin. By its mode of formation, the resin (and ion-exchange resins in general) may be regarded as a solution of phenolsulphonic acid in water, with the organic ions rendered immobile. The hydrogen ions are able to diffuse freely through the "solution", i.e. the resin, and to exchange with other cations. This homogenous theory is in opposition to the alternative idea of a resin as a two-phase structure, i.e. a porous solid containing water held in micro-channels.

Similarly, the commercial resins "Wofatit K" and "Wofatit K.S." marketed by I. G. Farben are made by reacting benzaldehyde-2 : 4-di-sulphonic acid, resorcinol and formaldehyde.[13] Phenol is also present in the production of Wofatit K.S. The final heating stage with formaldehyde is continued until a gel is formed. This is then cooled, washed and dried for several days at 80°C to 90°C, to give a resin which is fairly hard and has an exchange capacity of about 2·8 m-eq/g.[3]

The most important cation-exchange resins are now the ones based upon polystyrene. The functional groups may be present in the molecule before polymerization or may be introduced afterwards. The first resin of this type was prepared by copolymerization of styrene and divinylbenzene, and sulphonation of the product, i.e.:

$$CH{=}CH_2 \qquad\qquad CH{=}CH_2$$

$$n \bigcirc \qquad + \bigcirc$$

$$CH_2{=}CH$$

$$\downarrow$$

$$-CH-CH_2-CH-CH_2-CH-CH_2-CH-CH_2-$$

$$-CH_2-CH-CH_2-$$

The divinylbenzene molecule gives an opportunity for cross-linking to take place and in fact the degree of cross-linking is readily controlled by the proportion of this reagent which is used (normally 8–12 per cent for commercial resins).

In order to obtain the copolymer in a suitable particle size, the polymerization is now usually carried out in suspension in an aqueous medium. The two principal reagents are suspended, together with benzoyl peroxide as a catalyst, with suitable agitation using, for example, polyvinyl alcohol, bentonite, starch or alginates, etc., as suspension stabilizers in the aqueous phase.

The copolymer can have one —SO_3H group introduced into each aromatic nucleus, by treatment with sulphuric acid, chlorosulphonic acid or sulphur trioxide in nitrobenzene. The cation-exchange capacity of the resulting resin is usually about 5 m-eq/g (of dry resin). In addition, these resins are exceptionally stable up to 120°C and resistant to acids, alkalis, oxidizing agents and reducing agents.

Other cation-exchange resins may have weak acid functional groups instead of (or as well as) the strong —SO_3H group, incorporated in their structure. The —OH (already mentioned), —COOH, —H_2PO_3, or —SH groups are the most common. "Wofatit C" is an example of a carboxyl cation-exchange resin. It is produced by the alkaline condensation of 1 : 3 : 5 resorcylic acid with formaldehyde. Another carboxylic resin, but of the polystyrene type, is polymethacrylic acid, made by copolymerization of methacrylic acid with 5–10 per cent of divinylbenzene, i.e.

$$
\begin{array}{c}
CH_3 \\
| \\
nC{=}CH_2 \qquad + \\
| \\
COOH
\end{array}
\qquad
\begin{array}{c}
CH{=}CH_2 \\
\bigcirc \\
CH{=}CH_2
\end{array}
$$

$$\downarrow$$

$$
\begin{array}{ccccc}
CH_3 & & CH_3 & & CH_3 \\
| & & | & & | \\
{-}C{-}CH_2{-} & & C{-}CH_2{-} & & C{-}CH_2{-}CH{-}CH_2{-} \\
| & & | & & | \\
COOH & & COOH & & COOH \quad \bigcirc
\end{array}
$$

$$-CH-CH_2-$$

The weak acid resins generally have lower capacities than strong acid resins and cannot be used satisfactorily in acid or neutral solutions. They are, however, more easily regenerated.

Anionic resins

Anion-exchange resins have been developed in parallel with cationic resins and they are now of greatest commercial importance for the extraction of rare metals. Amines and alkyl substituted amines constitute the functional groups, with the quaternary ammonium compounds as special cases, responsible for the strong base exchangers. The weak base resins do not exchange well in alkaline solutions although they are easily regenerated again by ammonia or sodium carbonate solution. However, the quaternary ammonium compounds are of primary commercial importance, attention being concentrated on the trimethyl ammonium hydroxide group, i.e. $-N(CH_3)_3OH$. This is the source of the exchange capacity of such well-known resins as "De-Acidite FF", "Amberlite IRA-400" and "Dowex 1".

The first anion-exchange resins were made by formaldehyde condensation processes by analogy with cation-exchange resins. An aromatic amine or a polyamine and a phenol were usually mixed and polymerized with the formaldehyde. The more satisfactory polystyrene anion-exchange resins were developed later. The polystyrene matrix is first produced, with a suitable degree of cross-linkage, by polymerization of styrene and an appropriate proportion of divinyl benzene (usually 6–8 per cent) in the presence of a benzoyl peroxide catalyst. This polymer, already in the form of beads, is treated with chloromethyl methyl ether and a Friedel-Crafts catalyst such as anhydrous aluminium chloride, to introduce CH_2Cl groups into the aromatic nuclei, i.e.

$$-CH-CH_2-CH-CH_2-CH-CH_2-CH-CH_2-$$

$$
\begin{array}{cccc}
\bigcirc & \bigcirc & \bigcirc & \bigcirc \\
| & | & | & \\
CH_2Cl & CH_2Cl & CH_2Cl & CH_2Cl \\
& & -CH-CH_2- &
\end{array}
$$

This polymer is then reacted with a tertiary amine such as trimethylamine, $N(CH_3)_3$, to give the strongly basic quaternary ammonium functional groups, i.e.

—CH——CH$_2$——CH——CH$_2$—————CH——CH$_2$—

CH$_2$N$^+$(CH$_3$)$_3$Cl$^-$ CH$_2$N$^+$(CH$_3$)$_3$Cl$^-$ CH$_2$N$^+$(CH$_3$)$_3$Cl$^-$

Variations of this route are possible, by the use of different amines or different cross-linking agents. Some cross-linking may be introduced at the chloromethylation stage for example.

A weak base can be produced by the use of, for example, a secondary or primary amine instead of a tertiary one. Exchange capacities of about 3 m-eq/g are usually achieved with the strong base resins of this type and rather less for the weaker base ones.

Selective resins

Attempts are naturally being made to produce resins which are highly specific for a particular ion species, and this would make them particularly valuable for rare metal purification, where the desired ion is often mixed with ions of a large number of other elements in similar concentration. A crude method of achieving selectivity for small ions is to increase the degree of cross-linking to such an extent that large ions cannot diffuse through the resin. An alternative approach is to use functional groups which act as chelating agents or complexing agents for particular ions, for example resins based upon resorcinol arsonic acid, recently studied by the National Chemical Laboratory.[14]

Commercial resins

A list of equivalent commercial ion-exchange resins is shown in Table 1 compiled by Cook.[15]

Besides the conventional granular or bead form, ion-exchange resins are now marketed in the form of membranes, usually 1 to 2 mm thick. Homogeneous membranes have been prepared by partial polymerization of the resin to a syrup, which is then poured into a mould and finally polymerized *in situ*. Since these are mechanically weak, it is more usual to construct membranes from beads which are held together with a binding agent of polythene, polyvinyl chloride or polymethyl methacrylate. These may contain up to 75 per cent of resin.[1]

PROCESS DESIGN

Before designing an ion-exchange process, it is necessary to decide clearly what the process is intended to accomplish, e.g. which contaminating ions

TABLE 1

EQUIVALENT ION-EXCHANGE MATERIALS

The Permutit Co. Ltd. London	Rohm & Haas, U.S.A.	Chemical Process Co., U.S.A.	Dow Chemical Co., U.S.A.	Farbenfabriken Bayer, Leverkusen	I. G. Farben Wolfen	Type
Zeo-Karb 215	Amberlite IR-1	Duolite C-10 ..	Dowex 30	Lewatit KS (or DN)	Wofatit KS	Sulphonated phenolic resins
Zeo-Karb 315	Amberlite IR-100	Duolite C-3	—	Lewatit PN	Wofatit P	
Zeo-Karb HI	—	—	—	—	—	Sulphonated coal
Zeo-Karb Na	—	—	—	—	—	
Zeo-Karb 216	Amberlite IRC-50*	Duolite CS-100	—	Lewatit C	Wofatit C	Carboxylic resins
Zeo-Karb 226*	—	—	—	—	—	
Zeo-Karb 225*	Amberlite IR-120*	Duolite C-20	Dowex 50* (Nalcite HCR)*	Lewatit KSN*	—	Sulphonated polystyrenes
De-Acidite E	Amberlite IR-4B	Duolite A-2	(Nalcite WBR)*	Lewatit M1	Wofatit M	Weak base anion-exchangers
De-Acidite G*	Amberlite IR-45*					
De-Acidite FF*	Amberlite IRA-400*	—	Dowex 1*	Lewatit M2	—	Strong base anion-exchangers
	Amberlite IRA-410*	—	Dowex 2* (Nalcite SAR)*			
Decolorite	—	Duolite S-30	—	—	—	Porous anion-exchangers
Decalso Y	—	—	—	—	—	Sodium aluminium silicate exchangers
Decalso F	—	—	—	—	—	

* These resins are in bead form.

must be removed and which can be tolerated, and whether the process is intended to concentrate the desired ion in addition to achieving a degree of purification. The aim would normally be to establish conditions suitable for the "frontal analysis" technique to be applied, since the cost of an "elution analysis" process is usually prohibitive for the extraction of rare metals. Conditions should be chosen where the action of the resin is as specific as possible for the desired ion.

If it is necessary to extract the rare metal from an acid or alkaline leach liquor, or similar solution, a resin should be selected which is known to be stable in the leaching reagent. For extraction of the rare metal ion itself, the resin would normally be of the cation-exchange type, unless the rare metal ion could be converted to an anionic complex. However, the possibility of designing a process in which the impurities are absorbed by the resin and the rare metal remains unextracted, should not be neglected. An example of this type has been developed by Ayres,[16, 17] in which iron, titanium, lanthanum and beryllium impurities are extracted from a zirconium nitrate solution by operation at a pH where the zirconium is converted to a non-ionic hydrated oxide sol.

Optimization of absorption stage

The selection of a particular resin is usually by experiment unless adequate information is available from other comparable processes. The physical form of the resin is also important. Spherical beads are normally used. If these are too large, the rate of exchange is low, and if they are too small, the pressure drop across a column of resin is unduly great. In practice, the optimum size is usually about 0·5 mm diameter when in the fully hydrated condition.[3]

Several other fundamental process parameters must then be determined, such as practical resin capacity, flow rate per unit area, length and diameter of columns, etc., and although these may be amenable to calculation in simple cases, a practical development programme is generally essential. This often takes the form of simple absorption experiments in relatively short glass columns of diameter at least ten times that of individual resin beads. Absorption isotherms are then determined at various flow rates and under a variety of chemical conditions which may be of interest. Some of the latter may arise from leaching conditions, but it may be possible to vary others at will, e.g. pH, dilution (if any), or the addition of a complexing agent.

A typical absorption isotherm has the shape shown in Fig. 3.1. The shape is indicative of the fact that, before the breakthrough point, the column has a top layer of "saturated" resin (i.e. where the concentration of the desired ion in the resin is in equilibrium with the concentration in the feed solution, according to the distribution coefficient, D) and also a lower unsaturated layer of resin containing gradually less of the desired ion. There is none at all at the bottom, as in Fig. 3.2, where the amount of resin saturation is indicated by the degree to which the graph is extended to the right. At the breakthrough point, C just reaches the base of the column D, and if the feed is continued beyond the breakthrough point, an increasing proportion of the desired ion is lost into the effluent. Eventually, the effluent reaches the full concentration of the feed solution, when the whole of the resin is "saturated".

For column design purposes, essentially the data shown in Figs. 3.1 and 3.2 are required at the breakthrough point, i.e. when C has reached D. This gives the column loading in terms of weight of desired species per column, but also allows the loading of a longer production column to be calculated, since the section B to C is, to a first approximation, independent of column height. This information can usually be obtained quite readily from an experimental run by pushing the resin through the tube, cutting into sections and analysing the sections individually. Alternatively, if it is sufficiently accurate to assume that the concentration on the resin between points B and C changes linearly with length of column, the length of the section BC can be calculated quite simply from the volumes of feed required to the breakthrough point and to the point of complete saturation.

The more precise McCabe-Thiele graphical method of calculation of solute concentration in terms of the number of theoretical stages in a given length of column can be applied to ion-exchange equally with solvent extraction and is discussed by Pfeiffer.[18]

Ion-exchange columns rarely exceed a few feet in length unless used for elution analysis. An experimental column of say 2 ft in length may therefore be about one-fifth or one-sixth of the height of a fairly large production column (although of much smaller diameter). This is sufficiently similar for the length BC in the experimental column to be applied directly to the production column, provided the flow rate per unit area is the same. In practice, the length BC is highly dependent upon flow rate. At low flow rates, therefore, i.e. when the throughput is low, BC is small and so a high proportion of the resin capacity is employed. At high flow rates, throughput is high and the "saturation" concentration at the top of the resin is the same, but a long section BC represents wasted resin capacity. An optimum flow rate, therefore, exists for the best utilization of a given height of column.

Multi-column processes. In practice the "three-column" method of operation is often employed, and this in effect decides the optimum position for point B, which is in fact such that BC is approximately equal to AB. In this technique, two columns are used for absorption in series and one for elution, numbered initially as in Fig. 3.3. At the breakthrough point, column 1 being fully saturated passes to elution, column 2 is moved to position 1, and the eluted column 3 is placed in position 2. Elution is usually more rapid than absorption (assuming elution analysis is not being used) and therefore the rate of absorption should be increased to the maximum, i.e. the length BC must be increased to the maximum compatible with passing a fully saturated column to elution; thus the point B must lie at the junction of the two columns.

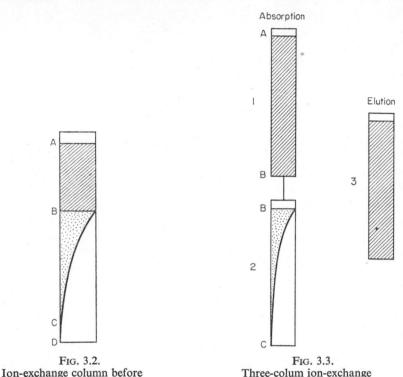

FIG. 3.2.
Ion-exchange column before
breakthrough.

FIG. 3.3.
Three-colum ion-exchange
system.

Similarly with a "four-column" process, three of them are used in series for absorption. The rate of absorption can then be such that only the top one is saturated when the change to elution is made.

It is possible that in some cases an additional worthwhile reduction in the time cycle might be obtained by operating at higher absorption flow rates, with the point B in the top column. When designing a process on this basis, however, the repercussions of passing only a partly loaded column to elution would require examination. In many processes it is important to maintain a minimum volume of eluting agent, to reduce reagent costs and also to achieve the maximum product concentration in the eluate. Elution of a partly loaded column would usually require almost the same volume of eluting agent as a fully loaded column, and therefore the cost per unit weight of rare metal ion would be greater.

Elution optimization

After achieving adequate purification by "frontal analysis" in the absorption part of the cycle, the elution process should be designed simply to expel the rare metal ion as rapidly and cheaply as possible, and in the minimum volume of eluate. A suitable chemical reagent is chosen for this purpose which might be a fairly concentrated acid or salt solution, and consequently of appreciable commercial value. Whenever possible, therefore, the eluate should be recycled, at least up to the point where impurities become undesirable. For example, elution with sodium nitrate solution might produce a solution from which the rare metal could be precipitated with alkali and removed by filtration. If sodium hydroxide or carbonate is employed, the later addition of a little nitric acid to the recovered eluate might allow it to be re-used, Since in theory more sodium nitrate would be available than required for re-use, a proportion could be rejected from each cycle of operations, so avoiding a completely closed system and providing an outlet for impurities.

The elution isotherm should be studied experimentally for optimum design of process. If a high degree of concentration is being achieved in the process, the volume of eluting solution will be much less than the volume of feed to absorption. Further gains in volume would normally be possible by using the available time and carrying out elution at a much lower rate than absorption. This allows the theoretical stage height to be reduced to a low level and therefore a large number of stages (for elution) are contained in the column. Consequently, a sharp concentration change occurs at the tail of the eluting solution, i.e. a high proportion of it is at maximum concentration and therefore the total volume required is low.

In practice, elution is never designed to be complete. Since the last few per cent of rare metal ion may take a disproportionately large volume of eluting agent, it may be allowed instead to remain behind and pass with the resin to the next absorption cycle.

Economy of eluting agent, and increased concentration of the product, may be aided by special techniques such as "split elution". In this, half of the eluate is stored and re-used as eluting agent for the next cycle, thus increasing its rare metal ion content before passing to the precipitation or other recovery section. The eluting agent already has a rare metal ion concentration when it enters the column and therefore elution can never be complete, since a true counter-current effect is not obtained. It is therefore necessary to complete the elution cycle by the use of a second half volume of fresh eluting agent. This then becomes the first eluting agent to be used in the next cycle. The total volume of eluting agent, fresh plus re-used, for two cycles may be rather more than in one cycle of a simple process, so net savings may represent a factor somewhat less than two. Techniques of this kind can only be optimized as a result of laboratory experiment with plant solutions and even then an element of uncertainty always exists because of the variable composition of the plant feed solutions.

Scaling up

Part of the capacity scale factor in passing from a laboratory column to a production version is taken up by increased height of the fully saturated portion. The major factor, however, is dependent upon a large increase in cross-sectional area of the column. As in the scale-up of other processes involving flowing liquids, a linear relationship between capacity and area is generally dependent upon close approach to laminar flow conditions, but in the case of ion-exchange absorption this does not apply to the fully saturated portion of the column. Since equilibrium between solution and resin prevails throughout this section, a degree of turbulence is acceptable. Absence of laminar flow does however tend to lengthen that portion of the column which is not fully saturated. Since flow rates are usually much less in the elution cycle, scale-up of flow rate based directly on areas is closely approached. Length of column must of course also be taken account of when scaling up the total flow of eluting agent. In this respect, a near-linear relationship only prevails if the whole of the column length is filled with saturated resin before elution.

The above remarks apply solely to columns which are correctly packed to an even density with spherical beads which retain their shape, and where the voidage between particles is constant. Under practical conditions, it is not unusual both in laboratory and plant scale units, to find "channels" passing down long sections of column, resulting from unsatisfactory initial packing, or the movement, attrition or adhesion of resin grains as a result of repeated expansion and contraction. These occurrences clearly result in severe abnormalities of column behaviour.

Preservation of resin

The design of an ion-exchange process should take account of resin life, the reasons for failure, and possible remedial action. For example, attrition or chemical attack might be minimized by selection of a more suitable resin, more compatible with the process solutions. Gradual reduction of resin capacity sometimes occurs as a result of a "poisoning" action, i.e. the absorption of a small amount of an impurity in each cycle, which fails to be eluted and gradually takes up the whole of the resin capacity. The remedy may be to include a special elution stage for the impurity after a given number of cycles or after a certain reduction in resin capacity. A related phenomenon is the poisoning action of silica on anion-exchange columns. The silica is deposited as a gel on the surface of the resin beads as a result of ion-exchange action. The silica coating reduces the diffusion rate of ions and so gives an apparent effect of reduction in capacity. In some cases, the silica is known to accumulate to a sufficient extent to cause a physical blockage of the resin. In these circumstances it is necessary to remove the resin from the column hydraulically and deposit it in another vessel where it can be given a batch treatment with sodium hydroxide solution, followed by washing, before returning to the columns.

The volume of an ion-exchange resin varies with the salt concentration of the solutions in which it is immersed and also with the ions which its functional groups are carrying. The design of column must be such that these volume changes can be accommodated. The overall volume must be sufficient to take the whole of the resin in its condition of maximum swelling without distortion of the beads. Where distortion is likely to result from a large height of resin above the swollen beads, it may be advisable to support the column of resin in sections upon a series of grids at different heights.

Process control

Ion-exchange column processes of the type described are discontinuous in nature, i.e. a cycle of operations is necessary; absorption, washing, elution and washing. With a constant feed composition, i.e. constant rare metal ion, acidity and impurity content, constant flow rates and constant resin capacities, it would be ideal to operate each part of the cycle for a predetermined time, and this process can be controlled electronically in an elegant manner. In practice the constant conditions required cannot easily be achieved and the control system becomes complicated by the installation of automatic analysers, etc., to decide the duration of each part of the cycle on an individual basis. Such instruments have been developed for certain ions, but they are not always adequate either in sensitivity, in specificity or reliability for systems of this type to be universally favoured. For systems to be controlled manually, it may be necessary to have available a rapid and reliable analytical service and a certain element of skill and judgement is constantly required by process operators. The design of each part of the cycle must therefore allow an ample margin for the normal errors of judgement or of control analysis.

In order to simplify the operation and control of ion-exchange processes, a number of continuous designs have been proposed, and these have had varying degrees of success. Since in all cases a change from the conventional type of plant using packed columns is necessary, these will be described in the next section. The aim has usually been to remove the resin in a countercurrent manner to the absorption or elution solutions, to make ion-exchange analogous to continuous counter-current solvent extraction.

Design of elution analysis processes

When it is necessary to separate cations of close chemical similarity and the technique of elution analysis must be applied, quite different design principles are employed. The cost of processing and of process reagents usually greatly exceeds the value of the feed material and therefore the efficiency of the absorption stage is relatively unimportant. The essential requirements are a band of saturated resin at the top of a long column of a cation-exchange resin capable of operating with many stages, and a chemical system for elution giving as high a separation factor as possible between the desired and unwanted species. Separation factors (i.e. ratios of distribution coefficients) above 1·2 are satisfactory.[6]

In order to achieve a large number of theoretical stages, the resin particle size may be somewhat smaller than in the case of "frontal analysis" processes. The flow rate is also reduced to the minimum compatible with the avoidance of back mixing resulting from general diffusion effects in solution. The column height may run to over 100 ft, e.g. the 650 ft total length of concatenated columns as used by Spedding[9] et al. for the separation of rare earths. The American resins Dowex 50 and Amberlite 1R 100 have usually been used, but other equivalent cation-exchange resins are available.

The highest separation factors are obtained by using the complexing elution technique and in fact the detailed chemistry of the system is the principal design feature. The complexing agent must compete with the resin for the various species in such manner as to allow the largest possible difference in distribution coefficient between them.

ION-EXCHANGE PLANT

The essential plant items used in an ion-exchange column process are relatively simple, but a number of complications can arise in their operation which demand an element of skill on the part of operating personnel or alternatively the installation of elaborate column control equipment.

Columns

The detailed engineering design of the columns is generally derived from those which have been used in the water purification industry. They are normally fairly squat in shape and constructed as pressure vessels to withstand the hydrostatic pressure of the feed solutions. Typical dimensions of columns used in the uranium extraction industry are 12 ft high by 7 ft diameter as shown in Fig. 3.4. When used for water purification the columns and pipes are frequently constructed of mild steel but lined with rubber to avoid contamination of the solutions by iron. The same materials may be suitable when used for the extraction of rare metals, but in this case to prolong the life of the column in contact with corrosive (usually acid) liquors more than to avoid iron contamination.

The base of each column has a suitable supporting medium for the resin. This may take the form of a grid with a graded gravel and sand bed upon it, or a suitable equivalent specially made from metal, glass or plastic materials

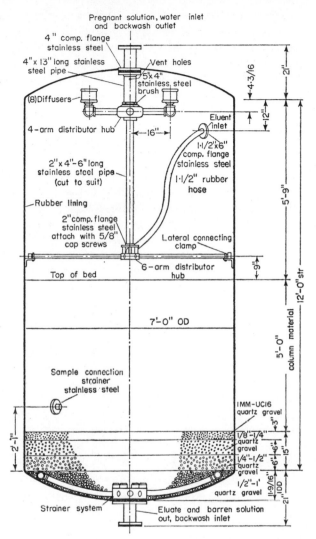

Pregnant solution, water inlet
and backwash outlet

4" comp. flange
stainless steel

4"x 13" long stainless
steel pipe

Vent holes

5"x 4"
stainless steel
brush

(8)Diffusers

4-arm distributor hub

16"

Eluent
inlet

1·1/2"x6"
comp. flange
stainless steel

2"x 4"-6"long
stainless steel pipe
(cut to suit)

1·1/2" rubber
hose

Rubber lining

2"comp. flange
stainless steel
attach with 5/8"
cap screws

Lateral connecting
clamp

Top of bed

6-arm distributor
hub

7'-0" OD

Sample connection
strainer
stainless steel

IMM-UC16
quartz gravel

1/8"-1/4"
quartz
gravel

1/4"-1/2"
quartz
gravel

1/2"-1'
quartz gravel

2"

Strainer system

Eluate and barren solution
out, backwash inlet

4-3/16

2'

12"

5'-9"

9"

5'-0" column material

12'-0" str

3"

6" 15"

1'-6"

21" ID

FIG. 3.4. Schematic drawing of ion-exchange column (Hull, W. Q. and Pinkney,
E. T. *Ind. Eng. Chem.* **49**, No. 1, 7).

which may be resistant to attack by process liquors. Above the support,
the column is packed uniformly with wet resin to the extent of perhaps
50 per cent to allow for swelling and to accommodate the distributor at the
top. The distributor allows liquids to be introduced into the column at fairly
high flow rates, in an even manner, without disturbing the bed. It normally
takes the form of a manifold with a number of radial arms each having
orifices with baffles of a suitable type. The resin and distributor are normally

flooded with water or one of the process liquors. A similar collector in the form of a manifold is located in the liquor below the resin support, since if a single offtake were used short-circuiting to it might result,[19] thus giving channelling through the bed of resin above it.

Columns are used alternately for absorption and elution cycles and it is necessary to wash feed solution out after absorption and eluting agent out after elution, using water or a suitable wash reagent. Piping is required to each column for each of these operations, and in addition it may be necessary to hold the wash-out liquors in suitable tanks for feeding back into the process during the next cycle. Piping is usually arranged to absorb downwards, wash upwards, elute upwards and wash downwards, in that order. Additional connections must usually be provided for "backwashing" the resin, i.e. for the removal of fine solids which may settle on top of the bed after a period of use and cause an increase in pressure drop across the bed. This operation sometimes takes the form of a hydraulic classification inside the column, which allows the fines to be lost but the graded bed and resin to fall back into their respective places. Often, it is more satisfactory to remove the whole of the column contents instead, and to repack, which again requires a suitable facility.

Since the columns must be interchangeable, the full set of connections must be provided on them all, and this involves a fairly extensive set of control valves. Since the start of one feed corresponds precisely with the cessation of another, it is convenient to employ multi-port valves, and various mechanical designs are available. These may be manually operated or may be driven by motors controlled by time switches if operating on a constant time cycle and with constant flow rates. A poppet valve assembly of this type is shown in Fig. 3.5. If each cycle must be unique to cope with variations of feed concentrations, etc., it is possible in some processes to control the motorized valve assemblies by means of automatic analysers on the effluent, eluent and wash streams. Instrumentation of this type can only be installed after very thorough development trials with process solutions under a wide variety of anticipated operating conditions, if reliable operating results are to be obtained.

Various other instruments are normally provided, e.g. pressure gauges to determine pressure drops across columns, and liquid flowmeters or flow controllers, but these are in no way specific to ion-exchange plants.

Continuous counter-current ion-exchange

Ion-exchange processes usually involve a high capital cost per ton of product. Part of this results from the fact that these processes are dependent upon the rate of diffusion of ions through "solids" which is relatively slow and therefore often involves a fairly large hold-up of both product and ion-exchange resin in the process, and a correspondingly large plant. This

FIG. 3.5. Poppet pilot valve assembly (Gilwood, M. E. Ref. 19).

undesirable feature can sometimes be ameliorated in principle by designing processes to operate on a fully continuous basis and make more efficient use of a given quantity of resin. A further possible advantage lies in the simplification of control of a continuous process compared with a batch process having a complex cycle of operations.

Rotating annulus column. One type of continuous process which has been produced by Solms and by Barnebl and Riken[20, 21] departs very little in principle from the normal "frontal analysis" batch procedure. In this, the column of resin is annular in shape and of the same depth as in a conventional column for the same duty. The annulus is divided into segmental or cylindrical compartments, a number of which are used for feed, others for elution, and the remaining ones for washes. The annulus rotates in a horizontal plane under a set of feed solution delivery points, another set for eluting agent and two others for washes. The four types of liquor are collected separately in portions of an annular trough underneath the resin and pumped to their various destinations according to the flowsheet. The collecting channels are slightly out of phase with the feeds to compensate for the time lag required for the liquor to flow through the resin. The feeds and offtakes may be rotated as an alternative to revolving the annular column.

This equipment is not known to have been used on an industrial scale and it probably achieves little which could not be equally well engineered by a conventional column plant controlled automatically to a fixed time cycle, using a system of multi-port valves. It has the disadvantage that a high proportion of the essential part of the plant is continually in motion, with the attendant mechanical engineering problems which this implies.

Systems analogous to solvent extraction. A more satisfactory continuous system from the viewpoint of resin utilization would be based upon the counter-current principle as employed so successfully in liquid–liquid extraction processes. Hutcheon[22] describes a three-column system of this type (Fig. 3.6) for separating two components A and B, independent of the type of plant in which it would be operated. The resin passes down column I and then down column II in counter-current flow with two aqueous solutions. The main one of these is the feed solution which enters at the base of column I, but it is mixed with the "scrub" solution or stripping solution which has passed up column II, again in counter-current flow to the resin. As in a solvent extraction process, chemical compositions of the two solutions are adjusted so that $E_A > 1$ and $E_B < 1$, where E_A and E_B are the "extraction factors" applicable in a solvent extraction process, i.e.

$$E_A = \frac{R}{S}k_A \text{ and } E_B = \frac{R}{S}k_B$$

where k_A and k_B are distribution coefficients (assumed constant) of the two species, whereas R and S are the flow rates of resin and solution respectively.

The resin, containing virtually only species A, leaves the base of column II and enters column III in counter-current flow to the eluting agent, under conditions such that $E_A < 1$. The product A is thus transferred to the eluate and the resin passes back to column I for re-use.

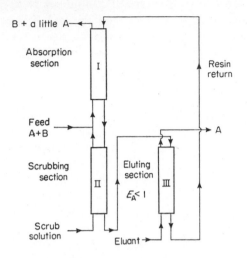

FIG. 3.6. Three-column continuous counter-current ion-exchange (Hutcheon, J. M. Ref. 22).

The ratio of outlet to inlet concentrations (C_0/C_N) of a species in passing through a column of N stages may be deduced by means of the Kremser equation[23] (see Chapter 4), i.e.

$$\frac{C_0}{C_N} = \frac{E^{N+1} - 1}{E - 1}$$

the simplified form assuming the resin entering the column is free of the particular species being absorbed.

Endless belt plant. Attempts have been made to design equipment for counter-current operation in this manner. That due to McCormack and Howard[24] employs a moving endless belt of resin 30 ft in length. This is enclosed in a flexible tube made of a suitable fabric which is not attacked by the solutions. The tube is tied every 6 in. to prevent movement of the resin as the belt passes over two driven pulleys and an idling pulley, shown in Fig. 3.7. The three catenarys thus formed are enclosed by close fitting polythene tubes of a similar shape in each case, and filled with appropriate solutions for absorption, elution and washing respectively. Each catenary has its own feed and exit point for the appropriate solution. When the belt is driven at its normal speed of 6 ft/hr in a clockwise direction, any portion of it passes through each of the three flowing solutions in turn, in a counter-current manner. Flow rates of the solution can be maintained in the usual way by means of, for example, Rotameter type flowmeters. By-passing of the counter-current systems is dependent upon the close fit of the resin bed in the tubes, which is a potential weakness of the design. The process has been used principally for demonstrating the concentration of ions in solution, e.g. copper sulphate by a factor of about 10. The wash section might alternatively be converted into an impurity stripping section as in Fig. 3.6, if its position were exchanged with the regenerating (elution) section and the used strip solution allowed to flow (or possibly be pumped) so as to be added to the main feed solution.

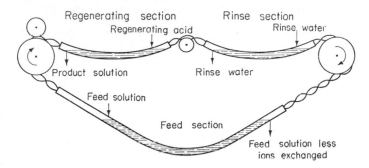

Fig. 3.7. Endless belt type, continuous counter-current ion-exchange unit (McCormack, R. H. and Howard, J. F. Ref. 24).

"Zeo-Karb" and "Nalcite H.C.R." resins have been used. The application of this technique is not necessarily limited to these two resins, but the physical characteristics such as swelling or attrition might be important.

Swinging sieve contactor. Another device for inducing counter-current flow in a horizontal ion-exchange resin stream, relative to a liquid stream, is the swinging sieve contactor developed by Swinton and Weiss of the Australian C.S.I.R.O.[25, 26, 27] This is shown in Fig. 3.8. It consists of a long narrow box with a base in the form of a sieve, suspended on pivots inside a trough. A mechanical device enables the box to be lifted and then dropped, under its own weight downwards and forwards at a rate of 60–200 strokes/min. The vertical amplitude of each stroke is about $\frac{1}{8}$ in. This is sufficient for the resin bed contained in the box to be fluidized by jets of the liquid, contained in both trough and box, passing through the perforations in the base of the box. The box sides fit closely to the sides of the trough and the ends have rubber flaps to close the gaps. These small clearances assist the liquid to pass through the perforations instead of taking the easier path around the box.

At the same time as the resin is fluidized, it has a slight forward motion imparted to it as part of the jigging action of the box. This enables the resin to progress slowly from one end of the box to the other. A resin feed hopper is provided at one end of the box, and at the other end is a weir offtake leading to a sump. Resin can then be lifted from the sump, with a certain amount of associated liquid phase, by means of a suitable slurry pump or

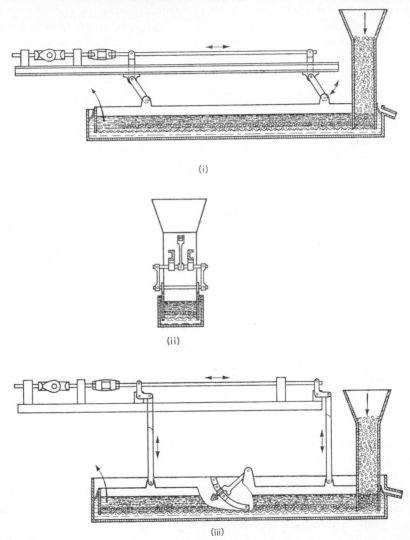

(i)

(ii)

(iii)

Fig. 3.8a.

airlift, etc. A controlled flow of liquid is fed into the box at the opposite end to the resin hopper, and it leaves by means of a small weir under the hopper,

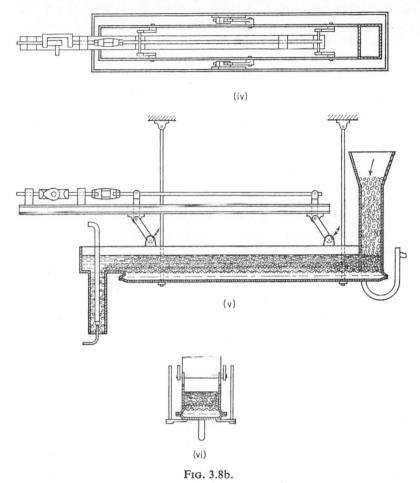

(iv)

(v)

(vi)

FIG. 3.8b.

FIG. 3.8. Swinging sieve ion-exchange contactor (U.K. Patent 731,000, by by permission of the controller, H.M. Stationery Office).

thus travelling counter-current to the resin. A certain amount of resin attrition takes place, and this can be minimized by suitable choice of resin.

This type of unit has been operated on a near commercial scale for the anion-exchange extraction of uranium from sulphuric acid leach liquors. For this purpose it is claimed to operate satisfactorily even in the presence of finely ground particles of ore, thus saving a filtration stage.

Fluid-bed and moving bed plant. A number of column type processes have been developed for continuous ion-exchange. Selke and Bliss[25] have demonstrated the principle of one of these on a laboratory scale using a "fluid-bed" column for absorption and a "moving bed" for elution. They used the principle for the concentration of copper solutions, as an example. In the first (absorption) column, an upwards flow of feed solution was used to fluidize the cation-exchange resin. At a suitably low fluidizing velocity, the column behaves as a hydraulic classifier, with the denser resin beads in the form containing most of the metallic ion, at the bottom, and the less dense beads, in the hydrogen form, tending to remain near the top. Counter-current flow is thus achieved, the column effluent leaves at the top, and fully saturated resin is bled off continuously from the bottom. Fresh resin is fed continuously from a reservoir above. The saturated resin is pumped as a slurry to another reservoir above the elution column. The principle of classification by fluidization clearly cannot be applied in the latter since, for counter-current flow, the upflowing eluate must leave the top of the column in contact with the resin at its maximum degree of saturation with the metallic ion, whereas the denser saturated resin is at the bottom. Consequently the elution column is run as a "moving bed," i.e. the resin is allowed to fall in "piston flow" through the column and leave continuously at the bottom.

Higgins column. Two other column processes with mechanical movement of the resin have been described by Arehart *et al.*,[28] one of them continuous and the other semi-continuous. The semicontinuous process attributed to Higgins [29, 30, 31, 32, 33] involves an absorption column with top feeds of water and metal ions, and a bottom effluent outlet, mounted above a lower elution column with top water and eluting solution feeds, and bottom eluate outlet. Both columns are run flooded and a large valve connects the two columns, which allows resin to flow under suction from the lower to the upper one when opened. This upwards flow of resin from the lower column to the upper one, and out of the top of the latter, is induced as a pulse lasting 3 to 5 sec by means of a pump. The resin sucked out of the top column passes to the top of a vertical limb. When the pumping action ceases, this saturated and washed resin falls down the limb and into a lute leading to the base of the lower elution column. Operation is therefore in a three-stage cycle as shown in Fig. 3.9. The first stage shown is with feeds flowing and the two portions of resin undergoing absorption and elution kept in their separate compartments by means of closed valves. This stage lasts several minutes. The second stage shows the resin valve open and all liquid feeds off, to allow resin movement. The third stage shows the pumped resin falling into place down the vertical limb, with resin valves closed and liquid feeds flowing again. The valves are operated by means of an automatic timing system. This type of plant has been developed on a large scale, in the U.S.A.[29, 32]

Fully continuous column. Arehart's fully continuous process (Fig. 3.10) uses a single column with the processes of absorption and washing in the upper section and elution and washing in the lower section. Resin flows

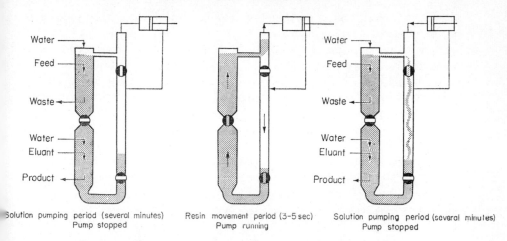

Solution pumping period (several minutes)
Pump stopped

Resin movement period (3-5 sec)
Pump running

Solution pumping period (several minutes)
Pump stopped

Fig. 3.9. Schematic diagram of Higgins continuous ion-exchange contactor, showing mechanism of counter-current solid-liquid flow (Higgins, I. R. U.S.A.E.C. Report TID 7501).

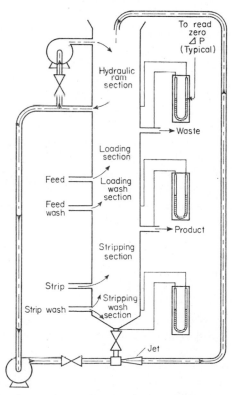

Fig. 3.10. Continuous ion-exchange column (Arehart, J. C. Ref. 28).

down the column as a moving bed and the unsaturated form (i.e. not saturated with metal ions) is pumped continuously in a closed cycle from the bottom to the top. Since the solutions all flow upwards in the column a device described as a "hydraulic ram" is used to prevent fluidization of the resin at high liquid flow rates. This consists essentially of a section of resin at the top of the column down which liquid is pumped and recirculated in a closed cycle. This provides a downward force on the top resin beads which is transmitted throughout the bed, so counteracting the upwards fluidizing force.

A number of other continuous counter-current ion-exchange contactors have been developed[23, 34] based, for instance, upon mixer-settlers, Archimedean screws, etc., but these are likely to involve too high a degree of attrition of the resin or the frequent occurrence of blockages, to be satisfactory in a production plant.

Membrane plants. Some use has been made of ion-exchange membranes in the development of continuous extraction processes. When a resin is in membrane form, it is clearly more suitable than resin beads for forming into an endless belt which can pass successively through absorption, elution and wash stages. Furthermore, additional capacity could be obtained if the "belt" took the form of a large number of closely packed leaves. An advantage of any membrane process of this type is that it can be used almost equally well in the presence of insoluble particles of ground ore, which are more easily separated from membranes than from beads. However, the mechanical strength of some types of membrane at least is in doubt for this type of application.

Another possible use of membranes in this field is the adaptation of an electro de-ionization cell, such as is now used for water purification, to concentrate cations. This type of cell contains a number of parallel compartments with alternate walls made of anion and cation-exchange membranes, the whole pack being between two electrodes. Alternate compartments are interconnected, so that solution fed in at one end and out at the other is in counter-current flow to solution fed to the opposite end, always with membranes to separate the two, In this way, from Fig. 3.11, it can be seen that with the diffusion of anions to the left and cations to the right, one stream will be denuded of virtually all ions and the other enriched. If the latter stream has a low flow rate, and the feed consists of rare metal ions, it may be possible to achieve a fairly high concentration factor in the latter. Such a process is unfortunately not highly specific, and under practical conditions a high proportion of the current would be wasted in transporting unwanted ions.

Comparison with solvent extraction. Although a substantial effort has been devoted to the development of satisfactory continuous counter-current ion-exchange processes for metal extraction, it is debatable whether any of such efforts are logically justified. The object is to use a solid material, which is subject to attrition, as if it were a liquid, and this naturally involves some chemical engineering difficulties. Furthermore, the solids used do not

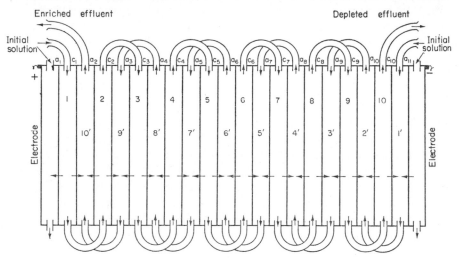

FIG. 3.11. Multiple ion-exchange membrane cell: 1–10, depleted chambers; 1'–10', enriched chambers; a_k, anion exchange membrane; c_k, cation exchange membrane (Amphlett, C. B. Ref. 2).

normally have absorption properties which are specific to the wanted ions, and perfectly satisfactory organic liquids, which are at least as specific, are available for such purposes. In fact, continuous counter-current liquid–liquid extraction processes are tending to replace even the static bed type of ion-exchange process, and satisfactory chemical engineering plants are now available for this purpose. Some of the solvents have in fact been regarded as "liquid ion-exchange agents". High distribution coefficients can be obtained with some solvents, as with solid resins, and this is important for the achievement of a high concentration factor with a dilute feed of rare metal ion. Difficulties may then arise, however, with some types of solvent extraction plant which are unable to operate with a high ratio of aqueous feed to solvent flow rate and therefore cannot take advantage of this concentrating effect. In continuous or static bed ion-exchange processes, on the contrary, a high ratio of aqueous feed to resin is ideal.

URANIUM EXTRACTION BY ION-EXCHANGE

The extraction of uranium from low-grade ores has become an important industry in many parts of the world, and in the overwhelming majority of processing plants the essential purification and concentration stage is accomplished by ion-exchange. In recent years, the quantity extracted has exceeded 50,000 tons per annum.[35] Usually the ion-exchange step is carried out from a sulphate solution following a sulphuric acid leach of the ore, but carbonate solutions have also been employed when sodium carbonate has been used as the leaching agent. In both cases an anion-exchange resin is normally used.

The selective absorption of uranium from sulphate solutions on to a strong base anion-exchange resin was first discovered by American workers at the Battelle Memorial Institute and the Dow Chemical Company in 1949.[36] This was followed very quickly by development of production-scale processes by the Massachussetts Institute of Technology[37] and, in the United Kingdom, the D.S.I.R. Chemical Research Laboratory (now the National Chemical Laboratory). Experimental ion-exchange columns were operated by the collaborating laboratories, Dow, M.I.T. and C.R.L.[38] in South Africa, during 1950, and later in conjunction with the South African Government Metallurgical Laboratory. The first full-scale plant belonging to the West Rand Consolidated Mines Ltd., commenced operation in 1952 and a large number of others were built in the South African goldfields in the next few years. In all the South African plants the grade is very low and the uranium required extraction from leach liquors which contain as little as 0·2 g/l. This is technically feasible and is economically justified by the fact that gold is extracted from the same ore and the cost of mining and grinding operations can therefore be shared between uranium and gold. Later plants, e.g. in the U.S.A., Australia, and Canada, have usually been based upon higher grade ores where feed solutions have contained 1 to 2 g U/l.

Chemistry of absorption

The strong base anion-exchange resins, based upon polystyrene with quaternary ammonium groups attached, are usually employed for uranium extraction from sulphate liquors. Typical examples are the Permutit Company's De-Acidite FF, the Dow Chemical Company's Dowex, and Amberlite IRA-400 manufactured by Rohm and Haas Ltd. Cross-linking with up to 7 per cent divinyl benzene can be tolerated.[39] A newer resin Permutit SK has been specially developed for the extraction of uranium from sulphate solutions. It is reported[40] to have a capacity 5 per cent higher than that of other strong base resins. It has a high absorption rate and its elution is more rapid than usual; elution also gives a more complete removal of uranium. Other features are a high resistance to attrition and good chemical stability in sulphate feed liquors and in eluting agents.

The uranium-containing anions in sulphate solutions are $[UO_2(SO_4)_3]^{4-}$, $[UO_2(SO_4)_2]^{2-}$, and $[U_2O_5(SO_4)_3]^{4-}$, and these replace the sulphate ions SO_4^{2-} and HSO_4^- from the resin. Sulphate solutions are usually employed and a large excess of sulphate is present. The HSO_4^- ions are more strongly absorbed, and therefore less easily replaced, than SO_4^{2-} ions. It is an advantage, therefore, to maintain the concentration of HSO_4^- ions, and hence the acidity, at fairly low levels, and the optimum pH is at about 1·5. At pH values below about 2, absorption is confined to the $[UO_2(SO_4)_3]^{4-}$ ions. Increasing proportions of $[U_2O_5(SO_4)_3]^{4-}$ are formed at higher pH values and this tends to increase the resin loading, but advantage cannot be taken of this in practice because the rate of absorption decreases with increasing pH[41] and also owing to the hydrolysis of various metal ion impurities in solution. The $[UO_2(SO_4)_2]^{2-}$ is believed to play a minor role under practical conditions since high proportions of it are only absorbed on to the resin from rather high uranium concentrations in solution.[42] A standard three- or four-column process is generally employed, with either two or three columns always in use for absorption and one always being eluted. The change from absorption to elution is usually made when about 1 per cent of the uranium passes through the absorption column into the effluent.

Elution

Elution can be carried out with sulphuric acid, i.e. the reverse operation to absorption, although the number of column volumes of eluting agent would usually then be very large. It is more usual, therefore, to use solutions of 1M ammonium nitrate or 1M sodium chloride, the former generally being more efficient but the process economics usually favouring the latter. In either case the eluting agent is slightly acidified with sulphuric acid, to the extent of about 0·1N. Regeneration with dilute sulphuric acid is then necessary to reconvert the resin from the nitrate or chloride form back to the sulphate condition ready for the next absorption cycle.

A standard "split elution" technique is commonly employed which allows each portion of eluting agent to carry out two elutions and thus achieve a high uranium concentration.

Other deviations from a simple elution process can also be beneficial. For example, recovery of eluate is generally a practical proposition, i.e. the uranium is precipitated from sodium chloride solution by the addition of sodium hydroxide, or from ammonium nitrate solution by the addition of ammonia. After filtration of the yellow sodium di-uranate or ammonium di-uranate, the filtrates can be reconstituted as an eluting agent by the addition of hydrochloric or nitric acid respectively.

Reconstitution into satisfactory eluting agents is made difficult by the accumulation of sulphate in the barren eluates. It is found that the major part of the sulphate is associated with about the first 10 per cent of eluate since it tends to be replaced by the advancing front of eluting agent. It has been proposed, therefore,[43] to precipitate the uranium from this portion of the eluate separately and discard the barren eluate after filtration. The remaining 90 per cent of the eluate, after acidification, then makes a more satisfactory eluting agent for the next cycle. Alternatively, it has been suggested[44] that unwanted sulphate can be removed from an ammonium nitrate eluate, before recycling, by reacting it with calcium nitrate or other alkaline earth metal nitrate.

Uranium extraction plant

A typical ion-exchange column for uranium extraction is shown in Fig. 3.4. It consists of a mild steel cylindrical vessel, with dished ends, lined with rubber, 12 ft high by 7 ft diameter. The dished base and bottom 15 in. of the cylindrical section are packed with a graded gravel bed. The gravel varies in size from a maximum of 1 in. pieces at the bottom to a coarse sand at the top. On top of the graded bed rests about 4 ft of resin beads and this is placed in position whilst wet. In the free space above the resin is a diffuser and distributor system for feed solution (or "pregnant liquor") and eluating agent, made chiefly of stainless steel, and these are attached to a single inlet point at the top of the column. Similarly a strainer is located under the gravel bed at the base of the column, attached to a bottom outlet. In this case both absorption and elution are carried out in a downward direction, but the flow is reversible for backwashing operations.

A large number of uranium ion-exchange plants now exist in various parts of the world, and in most cases a standard three- or four-column process is employed, with one column on elution and the others being used for absorption in series. Often, several lines of plant are run in parallel so it is not uncommon to find a dozen columns in the whole plant.

The feed solution is prepared by acid leaching, removal of gross solids by filtration or counter-current decantation, together with a final "polishing" filtration step, often in a sand-bed clarifier. Using such a feed, a typical cycle of operations for a four-column system with split elution is as follows:

1. Absorption through three columns in series for 5 hr at 60 gal/min until the barren liquor leaving the column contains about 1 per cent of the feed uranium concentration. This liquor may be used for pumping the extracted "pulp" from the leaching process to a "tailings dam".

2. A forward displacement wash is given to column 1 at 60 gal/min using one bed volume of 0·1N sulphuric acid. This displaces the residual pregnant liquor to columns 2 and 3.

3. Column 1 is backwashed with two bed volumes of 0·1N sulphuric acid at 120 gal/min, to remove physically entrained impurities. This wash liquor passes to the sump.

4. A forward displacement is given to column 1 at 25 gal/min, using one half bed volume of "returned eluate", and passing it back to the returned eluate tank. This allows the column to contain some chloride

ion ready for the start of elution, but the low uranium content of the liquor does not justify immediate recovery.

5. The first half elution is carried out with 6·5 bed volumes of "returned eluate" at 20 gal/min and the liquor passed to the precipitation stages.

6. A displacement wash is given with one half bed volume of fresh eluting solution, 0·9N in sodium chloride and 0·1N in sulphuric acid, this also passing to precipitation.

7. In the second half elution, six bed volumes of fresh eluting solution are used, at 25 gal/min. This is passed to the "return tank" to become "returned eluate" for use in the next cycle.

8. A displacement wash is given with one bed volume of 0·1N sulphuric acid to remove chloride ion before the next absorption cycle. The resulting solution is passed to the return tank.

The above cycle of operations may be under automatic control. Time switches and sequence adjusting cams are then used to control pumps and valves through a system of relays. The duration of each operation and the pumping rate can of course be varied if required. Since the columns change their function after each cycle, the sequence pattern of valve opening and closing must change automatically. A typical ion-exchange plant and control panel are shown in Figs. 3.12 and 3.13.

Impurities and resin poisons

Although anion-exchange is fairly specific to uranium when applied to sulphate leach liquors of uranium ores, certain impurities such as iron, silica and also titanium and vanadium, if present, do pass into the eluate. They can therefore enter the final "concentrate" which is produced by drying the precipitate obtained by the addition of alkali to the eluate. In addition, other impurities such as sulphate, chloride, nitrate and water are derived from the process reagents. Uranium which is to be used for nuclear purposes must meet a very stringent purity specification and hence it is always necessary for the "concentrate" to undergo considerable further purification. Impurities present in percentage quantities are therefore chiefly important in that they lower the "grade" or the weight of uranium per ton of concentrate. Nevertheless, impurities are important in the ion-exchange process for other reasons. Some of them, such as vanadium, may be present in proportions which justify their recovery as by-products. Others may act as resin "poisons", i.e. they are absorbed by the resin and not completely eluted, so taking up an increasing proportion of the resin capacity from one cycle to the next. The result is that the resin life may be considerably reduced from the 2 years which is normally expected without treatment. For most uranium processes the resin capacity initially approaches 100 g/l. of wet settled resin. The resin must be restored when the loading capacity falls to about half of this value.

One of the resin poisons of considerable importance in the South African uranium plants is the very stable cobalti-cyanide complex, or series of complexes,[45] which form as a result of leaching the ore with cyanide solutions. These are used for the extraction of gold before the final leach with sulphuric acid for uranium extraction. The cobalti-cyanide complex can sometimes be removed from the resin by treatment with 2M potassium thiocyanate solution.[36] This is expensive and not always satisfactory under plant conditions since it is believed that several different compounds are responsible, some of them polymeric complexes[46] and some are retained by the resin to a greater extent than others. The most satisfactory procedure is to prevent the absorption of cobalti-cyanide by removing it from the ore. This is accomplished by means of a water wash of the ore between cyanidation and sulphuric acid leaching. However, cobalt poisoning remains a problem at some of the South African refineries, particularly that at West Rand.[47] The resin is in fact usually replaced when its cobalt content reaches 2·5 per cent.[47]

The South African cyanidation process also gives rise to thiocyanates by reaction of the alkaline cyanide with sulphide minerals.[46] These act as resin poisons subsequently, during the uranium extraction process. Thiocyanate is more strongly absorbed on the resin than the uranium sulphate complex and it also forms a uranium thiocyanate complex which is fairly strongly absorbed. Consequently, during the normal elution process with acidic ammonium nitrate solution, the thiocyanate ion is only partially removed from the resin and also it tends to prevent the elution of a proportion of the uranium. After repeated cycles of operation, the effect on both absorption and elution efficiency can be quite marked. As with cobalti-cyanide poisoning, the remedy is to wash the ore thoroughly with water after gold extraction.

Polythionates, particularly the tetrathionate, $S_4O_6^{2-}$, have also caused poisoning in South African ion-exchange plants. These are formed as a result of oxidation of sulphide minerals in the ore, e.g. pyrites. They have greater affinities for the resin than the uranium complex ions and therefore reduce the uranium loading of the resin. They can, however, sometimes be eluted, after the uranium, by means of the usual 1M nitrate eluting solution, provided the acidity is fairly high, and consequently it is then possible to prevent the progressive build-up of polythionate. The action of the nitrate ion appears to be to destroy the polythionate, oxidizing it to sulphate or sulphur. This is assisted by higher acidity, and in some plants the 0·1N nitric acid +0·9N ammonium nitrate eluting agent has been replaced by 0·33N acid and 0·6N ammonium nitrate for this purpose.[48] Other methods of regeneration involve the use of sulphide, sulphite, cyanide or sodium hydroxide.[47] The latter tends to be favoured at most South African plants since it is also effective in removing silica.

Molybdenum, zirconium and titanium have been reported as resin poisons arising from the use of New Mexico uranium ores. Breakthrough capacity may be reduced to about 30 per cent of normal after 130 cycles.[49] In this case the resins can be restored to their normal capacity by prolonged treatment with complexing agents of the EDTA type, but this is too expensive for use on a production scale. Consequently, cheaper but elaborate multiple-treatment regeneration processes have been devised, using successive acid and alkaline reagents, e.g. moderately concentrated sulphuric acid, sodium hydroxide and sodium carbonate solutions.

Silica often acts as a type of resin poison, but its effect is more mechanical than chemical. Dehydration of the silica, or its production from dissolved silicic acid, leads to its deposition upon the resin beads and to some extent in the interior of the beads.[50] This occurs particularly near the point of entry of the feed solution to the column. This may result in restriction of flow rate or even a complete obstruction to flow, if the voids between beads become filled. In addition, the silica coating upon the resin beads causes the diffusion rate to be reduced. This gives an apparent reduction in the resin capacity. Some minerals give sulphuric acid leach liquors with a higher concentration of silica than others, e.g. the ore from the Mary Kathleen plant in Australia. The reason for this has been stated to be the high degree of silica breakdown which has occurred in the mineral owing to the action of α-radiation.[46]

Silica is usually removed by treatment of the resin with sodium hydroxide solution of about 5 per cent concentration. This cannot easily be accomplished in the column itself and is best performed in a separate vessel. For this purpose, the resin is removed from the column by hydraulic backwashing with water.[51]

Titanium can sometimes behave in a similar manner to silica, i.e. the oxide deposits physically upon the resin beads. This occurs, for example, at the Port Pirie refinery in Australia which uses the Radium Hill Davidite ore containing titanium. The effect has been considerably alleviated by reduction of the acid usage at the ore leaching stage, thus preventing much of the titanium from reaching the resin.

Precipitation

The uranium contained in the chloride or nitrate eluate is recovered by precipitation. This is best regarded as an intrinsic part of the ion-exchange process, since for reasons of economy it must be carried out in such a manner that the barren eluate can be recycled. For example, a sodium chloride eluate can be precipitated with sodium hydroxide or magnesia, in which case after filtration it can be converted to a re-usable form by acidification with hydrochloric acid. However, the sulphate ion in the eluate is not removed, and care has to be taken that it does not build up from one cycle to another so as to eventually seriously impede the elution process. In practice, a larger volume of eluate is present after precipitation and re-acidification then is necessary for the next elution cycle. Consequently, this provides the opportunity for a purge of sulphate ion by discarding a proportion of the liquor each cycle. The discarded eluate must not carry away with it an undue amount of uranium, e.g. in a finely divided colloidal condition; hence the necessity to have good filtration, at least for that portion which is discarded. The complete removal of uranium is less important for the main part of the eluate which is recycled, since any insoluble uranium particles tend to dissolve again in acid and be added to the next cycle.

It is usual to take advantage of the alkali addition to separate off ferric iron and other metallic ions which precipitate at a lower pH than uranium. Furthermore, this can often be done with lime. This is normally the cheapest alkali and also has the advantage that it precipitates the sulphate ion impurity at the same time as the iron. A pH of 3·6 is used for this impurity precipitation, followed by the first-stage filtration. Then the addition of extra alkali, e.g. ammonia, sodium hydroxide or magnesia, to pH 6·7 precipitates the uranium. The second-stage filtration finally removes the uranium from solution as ammonium, sodium or magnesium di-uranates.

The precipitation stages are often carried out continuously. In this case it is advisable to use two or three precipitators in cascade for each stage, so as to maintain good pH control. Filtration can be by means of continuous rotary vacuum filters, but other types of filter have been used, e.g. in South Africa.[51] Usually, in both cases, iron and uranium, the slurry is "thickened" by decantation first. A few parts per million of a flocculating agent is sometimes used to aid settling of both precipitates. From the iron removal stage, both the overflow from the thickener and the filtrate must of course be passed to the uranium precipitation stage. In rotary vacuum filtration, the uranium precipitate is usually washed on the filter drum to remove chloride or nitrate eluting ions. In some cases, e.g. at Port Pirie, in Australia, it is even considered necessary to reslurry the uranium precipitate with water and refilter to remove the chloride iron completely.

Typical plant vessels for these later stages of the process are made of mild steel lined with rubber, connections being made by rigid PVC pipelines. Rotary vacuum filters are invariably of stainless-steel. The string-discharger type has been used, for example in the Rum Jungle plant in Australia. Rubber-lined diaphragm pumps or mono-pumps are used for conveying the slurries.

The discharge from the filters is passed to a drying and calcining stage. It is convenient to use a belt conveyor and feed continuously into a tunnel type of furnace. The dried product can then be drummed directly and automatically at the other end of the furnace.

Ion-exchange from carbonate leach liquors

Ion-exchange can be used for the extraction of uranium from sodium carbonate leach liquors. However, the process economics are usually unfavourable since a fairly pure concentrate can be obtained by direct alkali precipitation from the carbonate solution. The leaching stage in the ion-exchange process also tends to be more expensive than acid leaching, except in special cases where limestone is present. Consequently, little or no commercial use is made of the process at present.

The uranium anion present in carbonate solutions is $[UO_2(CO_3)_3]^{4-}$ and this is associated with few other impurity anions. Absorption capacities as high as 100 to 200 mg/g of dried resin have been obtained on Amberlite IRA-400[52] and Dowex I[53], under conditions where competing anionic impurities such as phosphate and aluminate ions have only absorbed to an insignificant extent. The resin capacity, in both cases, is greatest at low sodium carbonate concentrations. Vanadate ion absorption can take place to an appreciable extent when vanadium is present in the carbonate leach liquor from the ore. It is, however, readily separated from the uranium, e.g. by a preliminary elution with a saturated solution of sulphur dioxide.[2] This removes the vanadium from the resin by reducing it to a lower valency state.

The elution of uranium can be carried out by means of a large volume of sodium carbonate solution, but 1M to 2M sodium chloride or sodium nitrate is preferred owing to the much smaller volume requirement. The addition of a little sodium carbonate to these salt eluting agents appears to improve their elution properties. Sodium hydroxide is also an efficient eluting agent at low concentrations, but its action is to remove the uranium as an insoluble precipitate or a colloidal solution.

One advantage of a sodium carbonate ion-exchange system over an acid system, as for the ore leaching stage, is that corrosion of plant materials of construction is much less severe. Mild steel, unprotected by rubber, could probably be employed in most cases.

Moving bed process

A process using an acid leach liquor from Canadian uranium ore has been based upon moving the resin from one column to another instead of changing feeds from absorption to elution, etc.[54] Advantages claimed are small savings in capital cost, a higher efficiency owing to elution being carried out on more nearly saturated resin, and a lower susceptibility to mechanical blockage of the columns.

Standard types of column are used, but provision is made for withdrawing resin from near the base of each column by means of an inverted funnel, connected through 4 in. piping to other columns. The resin is fed into each column, near the top, via an inverted funnel. The transfer is carried out hydraulically, by feeding water through the gravel bed of the donor column, with all other connections closed except the discharge funnel. Virtually the whole of the resin is transferred from, say an absorption column to an elution column in about 18 min.

A moving bed ion-exchange process of this type has been in operation since March 1958 near Riverton, Wyoming, in the United States.[55]

Resin-in-pulp process

Attempts have been made in recent years to simplify the acid leach, ion-exchange process, by omitting the expensive solids separation stage after acid leaching. Alternatively, the "sands" or coarse ore particles only may be settled out. In a conventional ion-exchange column process, it is important to use a "pregnant" liquor which is clear, and free even from finely divided solids. Processes can be devised, however, in which the relatively coarse resin beads are contacted directly with the leach slurry containing the much finer particles of ground ore, and subsequently separated again. This is referred to as the "resin-in-pulp" technique.[56] It is essential to avoid the containment of the resin in a static vessel or the voids between the beads could quickly become filled with ore particles. This has been accomplished by simply containing a resin, in the form of coarse beads, in wire-mesh baskets which are agitated in the leach pulp.[57] The mesh size of the baskets is sufficient to retain the resin beads but not the ore particles. Agitation may be obtained simply by raising and lowering the baskets. Counter-current contacting can be obtained by pumping the unsettled slurry along a series of tanks with baskets. Elution can be carried out normally by flowing the eluting agent from one tank to another, after washing away any residual ore particles. Attrition of the resin is an important consideration. It was found to be 23 per cent in 8000 hr of operation in a pilot plant.[57]

An American plant of this type is in operation at Moab, Utah, with a capacity of 1800 tons of ore per day. Baskets are 6 ft by 6 ft by 6 ft in size, up to nine or ten being used in series for absorption from the pulp. It has in this case been found advisable to remove all ore particles above 325-mesh size since those in the 200–325-mesh region tended to coat the resin grains, prevent access of the liquor and reduce the resin loading capacity by as much as 25 per cent.

A disadvantage of this type of plant involving baskets is stated[58] to be that the beads of resin tend to blind the wire mesh. This can be overcome by carrying out the absorption in cells with vertical walls of mesh. A stream of air passes upwards over the walls to prevent blinding, and also causes agitation. An alternative method of applying the resin-in-pulp process is to use the "jigged-bed" technique of continuous ion-exchange, as developed principally by the Australian C.S.I.R.O.[59, 60, 61] and used at Rum Jungle.

FIG. 3.12. Two sets of ion-exchange columns used at Port Pirie (Arden, T. V. Ref. 38).

FIG. 3.13. Typical control panel in use at Port Pirie (Arden, T.V. Ref. 38)

A schematic diagram of the process is shown in Fig. 3.14. In this process, the resin is made to flow almost as liquid down a 4 ft diameter absorption column and up a 13 ft by 2·5 ft elution column. Meanwhile the leach liquor, or in this case the "pulp", is pumped up the absorption column counter-current to the resin, and the eluent similarly flows down the elution column. Under suitable conditions, the ore particles remain with the barren liquor and can be pumped away from the plant with it.

The movement of resin in the absorption column is induced by means of a slow gentle pulsating motion applied at a frequency of about 10 strokes/min. The application is from a compressed air supply which is turned on and

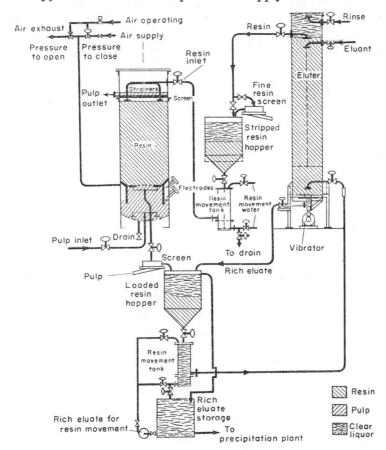

FIG. 3.14. Schematic layout of full scale resin-in-pulp plant (Arden, T. V. *Proc. 2nd U.N. Conf. on the Peaceful Uses of Atomic Energy, United Nations, New York*, vol. 3. p. 406).

then vented away regularly by means of automatic valves. A screen at the top of the resin bed prevents resin from lifting away from the bed. The barren pulp passes through this screen and leaves the column. Fresh resin (recycled after elution) is fed in under this screen. Pulsing of the elution column is done by means of a mechanically-operated diaphragm located under the column. This gives a more rapid pulse of smaller amplitude. Resin is moved hydraulically by pumping it with water into the top of the absorption column and with rich eluent into the base of the elution column. Pumping of resin is carried out intermittently on an automatic cycle for about 1 min out of every 15 min, 2 cu ft being involved in each transfer. Feed valves, etc., are turned off when resin movement takes place.

In order that the resin should not carry large amounts of salt from the top of the elution column to the top of the absorption column, it is rinsed with water at the top of the latter. This water then joins the concentrated eluting agent to bring it to the correct concentration for use in the main part of the column.

At Rum Jungle, the feed to this type of process is provided by passing the normal acid leach pulp through a cyclone classifier system. The "sands" are easily removed and washed at a fraction of the cost of a filtration or decantation system. The residual pulp contains about 20 per cent solids, of particle size mostly between 200 and 300 mesh, and these are difficult to remove before a normal static column ion-exchange process.

A production-scale plant of this type is now in operation at Rum Jungle, and, with an ore where filtration or decantation is difficult, great economic savings are claimed for the process.[60]

One feature of resin-in-pulp processes which is unsatisfactory is the high rate of attrition of the resin beads compared with a static column process. Resin manufacturers are, however, now designing resins specifically for resin-in-pulp processes. The Permitit resin SKB has, for example, been recommended for this purpose.[40]

Another similar continuous system used for uranium resin-in-pulp extraction by the Australian C.S.I.R.O.[61] is based upon a "jigged bed" column for absorption and a horizontal contactor similar to their "swinging sieve" device[62, 26, 27] for elution. The method of agitation or pulsation of the horizontal contactor in this case, however, is based upon the use of a series of diaphragms in the base.

The recently developed "Excer process"[63] of the U.S.A.E.C. aims to extract uranium from low-grade ore, purify it up to nuclear specification and convert to uranium tetrafluoride ready for metal production. The process is shown in Fig. 3.15 and is based first upon a sulphuric acid leach of the ore and anion absorption of uranium from the pulp. Elution is then by 2M sulphuric acid to give a solution containing about 10 to 20 g U/l. The uranyl sulphate is then reduced by metallic iron to uranous sulphate, diluted to an acidity of 0·5M and a second cycle of anion-exchange carried out. Absorption behaves similarly to that with uranyl ion, but ferrous ion is not absorbed. Elution of the tetravalent uranium is again with 2M sulphuric acid. This eluate has the uranium in the tetravalent condition and is free from iron. It is diluted to 0·5M acid and absorbed upon a cation-exchange resin. The uranium is finally eluted with 5N to 6N hydrochloric acid and uranous fluoride precipitated by the addition of hydrofluoric acid to the eluate. The development work has been carried out using a continuous resin-in-pulp technique in Higgins type jigging columns. A full-scale plant would presumably be designed with the same type of equipment.

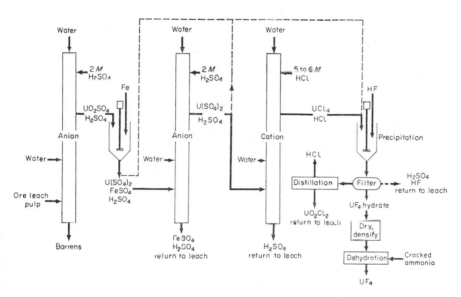

Fig. 3.15. "Excer" process for continuous extraction of uranium (Holcomb, R. R. and Higgins, I. R. Ref. 63).

EXTRACTION OF THORIUM BY ION-EXCHANGE

Thorium is not extracted by ion-exchange on a commercial scale, but several processes have been developed which would probably be successful. It is chemically similar to uranium and, like that element, it can sometimes form anionic complexes in solution. In sulphate solutions, it is absorbed less strongly than uranium, and this can be made the basis of processes for the separation of the two elements, in addition to the removal of other impurities.

Extraction from uranium barren liquor

A process has been described by Arden et al.[67] for the recovery of thorium from the liquors obtained by leaching the Blind River uranium ore. The major part of the uranium is first removed by conventional anion-exchange.

The mixed thorium–uranium sulphate solution, comprising the effluent from the main process, is then passed through a column of the anion-exchange resin De-Acidite FF/530 at a pH of about 2. Both uranium and thorium are absorbed, the latter to a loading capacity of about 4.5 g/l. of resin. The thorium breakthrough point is reached, however, when about half the resin only is saturated, so several columns in series are required. Elution of the thorium from a saturated column is relatively easy with sodium chloride and a little sulphuric acid. The absorbed uranium must then be eluted before continuing with the next cycle. The column loading is adversely affected by the presence of small concentrations of nitrate ion in the feed, originating from the eluting agent used in the main uranium recovery process. The nitrate-rich fractions of the main process effluent are therefore rejected before the effluent is used as the thorium process feed solution, with some loss of thorium.

When thorium is present with rare earth elements after the breakdown of monazite by sulphuric acid, the solution may be partially neutralized, to pH2, and absorption can take place onto the anion-exchange resin Amberlite IRA-400.[68] Cerium is the only rare earth element which might absorb appreciably, but this can be prevented by reduction to the cerous state with sodium nitrite first. The thorium is eluted with 2N hydrochloric acid.

Nitrate and chloride systems

Anion-exchange separation of thorium from uranium in nitrate solutions is possible[69] but the application is almost solely in the field of chemical analysis. Absorption of uranium and thorium takes place from 6N nitric acid as a narrow band at the top of a column. Uranium is eluted first with boiled 4N nitric acid, followed by thorium elution with water.

Another process for the separation of thorium and uranium involves the use of a cation-exchange resin in an acidic chloride or nitrate solution.[70] Hydroxylamine hydrochloride is added to the feed in order to complex the uranium. In such a condition it is less strongly absorbed than thorium. 7 g of hydroxylamine per 5 g of uranium is the optimum usage of the complexing agent, and this might add considerably to the cost of the process in cases where a pure thorium product is required from a mixture in which uranium is the major constituent. Elution of the uranium can be by dilute hydrochloric acid or other mineral acid. The thorium product is obtained from a second elution, and in order to achieve a high concentration it is advisable for the eluting agent to be a complexing agent; 0·5 M oxalic acid or 1·25M sodium bisulphate, are particularly effective for this purpose.

Removal of uranium in a carbonate system

Various thorium purification processes have involved the use of ion-exchange indirectly, e.g. to remove the uranium which is normally associated with thorium in monazite sand. In one of these,[71] the mixed uranium and thorium oxides are dissolved in sodium carbonate solution and the uranium absorbed upon the anion-exchange resin Amberlite IRA-400. The thorium alone passes through the ion-exchange column into the effluent. It is advantageous for the sodium carbonate feed solution to contain some sodium bicarbonate for complete removal of the uranium.[72]

Cellulose phosphate process

A successful process has been developed by the National Chemical Laboratory using cellulose phosphate as a cation-exchange material for the purification of thorium from rare earth elements. Monazite sand is broken with sulphuric acid and extracted with water to give a solution of thorium and rare earth sulphates and phosphates. This is first treated with metallic iron or aluminium to reduce the ferric iron impurity to the ferrous condition. The solution is then fed through a column of cellulose phosphate to absorb the thorium. Some of the thorium is present in solution as a cationic phosphate complex,[73] rather than as simple thorium cations, but both forms are retained by the column to a high degree. Rare earth elements, which predominate in the feed solution, are not appreciably absorbed, and the ratio of thorium to rare earths is increased to about 450.[74]

Elution from the cellulose phosphate column is with 10 per cent ammonium carbonate solution. With as little as 2·5 bed volumes of solution, 99 per cent recovery of thorium can be achieved. Uranium absorbed by the cellulose phosphate is also completely eluted. Three washes are interposed between absorption and elution, with 2N sulphuric acid, water and ammonia respectively. The sulphuric acid prevents hydrolysis and precipitation during the water wash, and the ammonia prevents evolution of carbon dioxide on elution with ammonium carbonate. Washes with water and then 2N sulphuric acid are similarly given after elution to prepare the column for the next absorption cycle. The thorium is recovered from the ammonium carbonate solution by boiling,[75] when a precipitate of hydrated thorium oxide is formed, 99 per cent coming out of solution within 5 min.

For optimum operating conditions, a three- or four-column process is employed, as when resins are used, namely two columns for absorption and one for elution. The columns are never completely loaded, since it is found that this practice improves the ratio of thorium to rare earths absorbed.

The mode of preparation of the cellulose phosphate is of some importance. It is made by impregnating cellulose derived from wood pulp with a solution of 50 per cent urea and 18 per cent phosphoric acid, and curing in air at 130°C. The highest thorium capacity is obtained with a product cured for only a short time, but the physical properties are then unsuitable for satisfactory flow rates through a column of the material. In practice, it is essential to use an overcured product and its properties are modified by storing as an aqueous suspension in the hydrogen form at normal temperature for several days.

Unfortunately, cellulose phosphate is less stable in use than ion-exchange resins, a feature which detracts from an otherwise very promising process. The physical properties of the material deteriorate from one cycle to another, resulting in progressively decreasing flow rates, and a life of ten cycles is considered optimum.

Impurities in the product from ten cycles through a single column[75] are: rare earths 0·2 per cent; phosphate 3·5 per cent; Fe_2O_3 1·5 per cent; TiO_2 0·6 per cent; and U_3O_8 1 per cent.

PURIFICATION OF ZIRCONIUM BY ION-EXCHANGE
Cation-exchange of impurities

A process has been developed by Ayres[16, 17] for the purification of zirconium, in which the various impurities are absorbed upon a cation-exchange resin. The zirconium itself is not absorbed as it is in the colloidal condition. This state is not difficult to achieve with, for example, zirconyl nitrate $ZrO(NO_3)_2$, since it is normally hydrolysed to the highly insoluble hydrated oxide in a neutral or near neutral solution. A zirconium ore is therefore broken in concentrated sulphuric acid and the soluble zirconium sulphate converted to the nitrate by suitable means and passed through a column of resin in the usual manner. Amberlite I.R.-100 has been used, in the hydrogen form. Impurities such as iron, beryllium and rare earth elements are absorbed completely, together with about 80 per cent of the titanium. The resin capacity for zirconium, however, is as low as 0·84 mmoles/100 cm³ of resin, and it is therefore recovered virtually completely in the pure column effluent. The very small amount of zirconium taken up by the resin is probably retained by a surface absorption process rather than true ion-exchange. The zirconium can be precipitated by alkali from the effluent as the hydrated oxide, in massive form, for conversion to other compounds and finally to metal. The resin is regenerated for further use by elution of the cation impurities with, for example, dilute sulphuric acid.

In the above process, hafnium is hydrolysed virtually completely, in the same manner as zirconium. It is not therefore absorbed by the ion-exchange resin and no purification from this element is obtained.

Cation-exchange separation of zirconium and hafnium

It is possible to separate zirconium and halfnium by cation-exchange, but they must both be first absorbed upon the resin and then subjected to "elution analysis" down a column of resin. This process was first described briefly by Street and Seaborg[76] in 1948. They absorbed zirconium and hafnium from the oxychloride solution upon the cation-exchange resin

Dowex 50, by a special technique. In this, the resin in the ammonium form was suspended in 2M perchloric acid and the oxychlorides added slowly with air agitation. About 80 per cent of the zirconium and hafnium were absorbed and this resin slurry was placed on top of a column of resin for elution with 6M hydrochloric acid. The hafnium was eluted first and a fairly good separation of the two elements was obtained.

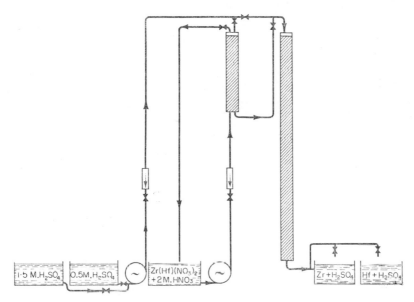

FIG. 3.16. Schematic flow diagram for cation-exchange separation of zirconium and hafnium. (Hudswell, E., and Hutcheon, J. M. *Proc. 1st U.N. Conf. on the Peaceful Uses of Atomic Energy*, United Nations, New York, vol. 8 p. 565).

Lister and McDonald[77] in a comparable process used the cation-exchange resin ZK225 and preferred to elute the absorbed mixture of zirconium and hafnium with dilute sulphuric acid. This is mentioned by Lister and Hutcheon[78] as a method for producing pure hafnium, and was developed for zirconium production on the kilogram scale by Hudswell and Hutcheon.[79] A schematic flow diagram of their process is shown in Fig. 3.16. The mixture of zirconium and hafnium nitrate in 2M nitric acid is allowed to impregnate a small column containing 13·3 kg (dry weight) of cation-exchange resin, until fully loaded. It is next washed, first with 2M nitric acid, and then with water. The short column is then connected in series with the main elution column containing 21·3 kg (dry weight) of resin which has been conditioned with 0·5M sulphuric acid. Elution is also carried out, in the first instance with 0·5M sulphuric acid, to remove the zirconium. When the hafnium content of the eluate becomes unacceptable, 1.5 M sulphuric acid is substituted

9

for 0·5 M acid, for rapid, separate elution of the hafnium and the remaining zirconium. Thirty hours are required for absorption and 130 hr for elution.

The main zirconium fraction is recovered by precipitation and contains 93 per cent of the feed zirconium with a ratio of hafnium to zirconium of 0·035 per cent. The small hafnium-rich fraction contains 98·5 per cent hafnium and can be further purified if pure hafnium is required.

Better separation of zirconium and hafnium by elution from a cation-exchange resin is claimed by Benedict et al. [80] who used 0·09 M citric acid and 0·45 M nitric acid as eluting agent, after absorbing from 0·8 M sulphuric acid. The zirconium eluted first. The elution curve is shown in Fig. 3.17.

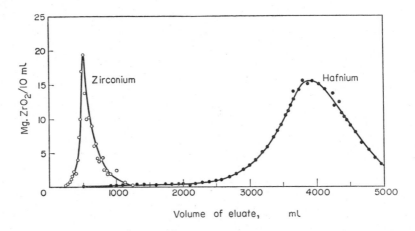

FIG. 3.17. Elution curve for zircononium and hafnium, separated by 0·45M nitric 0·09M citric acids (Benedict, J. T., Schumb, W. C. and Coryell, C. D. Ref. 80. By permission of the American Chemical Society).

Anion-exchange separation of zirconium and hafnium

Anion-exchange has also been used for the separation of zirconium and hafnium but it appears less promising for even a small-scale commercial process. This is based upon absorption of zirconium and hafnium complex fluorides upon, for example, Amberlite IRA-400[81] or Dowex[82] resins, followed by elution analysis with, for example, 0·2 M hydrochloric acid and 0·01 M hydrofluoric acid.[81] The fluozirconate and fluohafniate ions were eluted, i.e. $[ZrF_6]^{2-}$ and $[HfF_6]^{2-}$, the zirconium entering the eluate first.

SEPARATION OF NIOBIUM AND TANTALUM
BY ION-EXCHANGE

Several techniques have been suggested for the separation of niobium and tantalum by ion-exchange, but it does not seem possible for any of them to compete commercially with other methods. A separation scheme based upon elution with mixtures of hydrofluoric and hydrochloric acids proposed by Kraus and Moore[83] is analogous to their process for separating zirconium and hafnium, but it is stated to be more efficient. Loading of a band of anion-exchange resin, Dowex 1, was carried out in 9 M hydrochloric acid which was also 0·05 M in hydrofluoric acid. Elution analysis was carried out with the same medium.

Good separation of niobium from tantalum has also been obtained by oxalate elution from Dowex 2 anion-exchange resin. A 95 per cent yield of niobium was obtained,[84] free from tantalum, by elution with 1 M hydrochloric acid, 0·5 M oxalic acid solution. 85–90 per cent of the tantalum was also recovered, containing 1 per cent of niobium.

EXTRACTION OF VANADIUM BY ION-EXCHANGE
Acid process

Certain American ore deposits contain both vanadium and uranium. An anion-exchange process has been fairly fully developed,[85] using 5 ft by 2 in. columns, for vanadium extraction from Lukachukai ores, which contain about 0·25 per cent U_3O_8 and 1·0 per cent V_2O_5. The ore is first treated with a minimum quantity of fairly concentrated sulphuric acid and a little sodium silicofluoride, to extract the uranium and vanadium, either at normal temperatures, or 100°C, in an "acid pugging and curing" stage. 350 lb of acid, 200 lb of water and 10 to 20 lb of Na_2SiF_6 are usually employed per ton of ore. After breakdown of the ore, it is leached for 1 hr with water at a solids content of 50 per cent, filtered and washed, to give a liquor containing 4 to 5 g of V_2O_5/l.

The uranium is removed from this solution by a conventional anion-exchange process with, for example, Amberlite IRA-400 resin.

A typical analysis of the resulting uranium barren liquor is as follows:

U_3O_8	0·005 g/l.	F	0·93 g/l.
V_2O_5	4·44 g/l.	SiO_2	0·05 g/l.
Fe	3·7 g/l.	CaO	0·80 g/l.
Al_2O_3	10·8 g/l.	MgO	4·35 g/l.
P_2O_5	0·23 g/l.	SO_4	58·9 g/l.

This is first heated to 50°C with a little sodium chlorate to oxidize the vanadium and is then used as the feed for vanadium absorption in a column of a strong base anion-exchange resin. The oxidation equation is:

$$6VOSO_4 + NaClO_3 + 3H_2O + 6NH_3 \rightarrow 3(VO_2)_2SO_4 + NaCl + 3(NH_4)_2SO_4$$

Amberlite IRA-400 and XE-127, amongst others, have been used for this process. The resin is first converted to the sulphate form by means of dilute sulphuric acid. Column loadings over 100 g of vanadium per litre of wet settled resin are often obtained provided the retention time in the column is reasonably long. When loaded with vanadium the resin assumes a bright red appearance. The absorbing anion is probably $[H_2V_6O_{17}]^{2-}$. Two or three absorption columns can be run in series and, with a retention time of 4 min, the vanadium concentration at the breakthrough point in the third column is taken as 0·1 to 0·4 g/l. when the temperatures of columns 1, 2 and 3 are respectively 30°C, 55°C and 60–65°C. In pilot plant runs, 85–92 per cent vanadium recovery has been obtained. After a wash with very dilute sulphuric acid, the fully loaded first column is eluted with water which is saturated with sulphur dioxide, at a concentration of about 50 g/l. The elution process involves an exothermic valency reduction of the vanadium and causes a rise in pH by virtue of the reaction consuming acid.

The eluate is recycled several times through the column and the pH adjusted to between 0·9 and 1·0 each time, by the addition of sulphuric acid. If the pH rises above about 2 when the eluate contains a high concentration of vanadium, hydrolysis takes place to give a deposition of solid in the columns. Normally the eluate is deep blue in colour.

After the main part of the vanadium has been eluted, the remainder is removed by long contact time of 30 to 45 min on the bed. A total of four column volumes of eluate are necessary and the column is then washed with two volumes of very dilute sulphuric acid. A split elution technique has been developed which gives vanadium concentrations of up to 100 g/l. in the eluate. Purification from some impurities, notably iron, appears to be fairly good, although a special primary elution stage for iron with 0·9N ammonium chloride and 0·1N hydrochloric acid can be introduced before vanadium elution when the iron content is high. A few per cent of the vanadium may be lost during the iron elution.

Phosphate, when present, tends to absorb and elute together with the vanadium and can be present to greater than the specification limit of 0·05 per cent of the vanadium oxide. It can, however, be eliminated during the precipitation of vanadium from the eluate by controlling the pH at 1·6. This precipitation is normally carried out at 100°C with slow agitation, in the presence of sodium chlorate and by addition of sodium hydroxide or ammonia for pH control. At pH 1·6 to 2, about 1 g/l. of vanadium remains in solution in the mother-liquor.

Carbonate processes

A series of processes have been patented for the separation of vanadium and uranium by anion-exchange from sodium carbonate solutions resulting from carbonate leaching of carnotite ore. None of them, however, are believed to be operated commercially. Three methods of operation are proposed with a strong base resin. These are (a) selective elution of uranium followed by elution of vanadium, (b) selective elution of vanadium followed by elution of uranium, and (c) the preferential absorption of vanadium on one column followed by absorption of uranium upon a second column, and the separate elution of the two columns.

In method (a) 2M to 3M ammonium sulphate solutions are used to elute the uranium. The vanadium can then be eluted by a number of reagents, of which a saturated aqueous solution of sulphur dioxide is probably the most satisfactory. An example of method (b) is to use saturated sulphur dioxide solution first, for vanadium elution, followed by 0·9M sodium chloride solution which is 0·1N in hydrochloric acid, for elution of the uranium. In method (c) absorption is allowed to proceed beyond the point of uranium breakthrough and is stopped when breakthrough of vanadium occurs, by which time all the uranium on the resin has been replaced by vanadium. The effluent thus contains a higher concentration of uranium than the feed solution when this replacement is taking place. The concentrated uranium in this effluent is absorbed readily upon a second column. Aqueous sulphur dioxide can be used for elution of the vanadium loaded column, and acidified chloride solution for elution of the one loaded with uranium.

REFERENCES

1. PEPPER, K. W. and HALE, D. K. Ion-Exchange Resins. Structure, Synthesis and General Properties. S.C.I. Conference on Ion-Exchange and Its Applications, London (April 1954).
2. AMPHLETT, C. B. Ion-exchange methods and their application to metallurgical problems. *Metall. Revs.* **1**, Part 4, 419 (1956).
3. KUNIN, R. and MYERS, R. J. *Ion-Exchange Resins.* John Wiley, New York (1950).
4. WALTON, H. F. Ion-exchange equilibria. *Ion-Exchange Theory and Application*, edited by F. C. Nachod. Academic Press, New York (1949).
5. GLUEKAUF, E. Principles of Operation of Ion-Exchange Columns. S.C.I. Conference on Ion-Exchange and Its Applications, London (April 1954).
6. SCHUBERT, J. Application of ion-exchange to the separation of inorganic cations. *Ion-Exchange Theory and Application*, edited by F. C. Nachod. Academic Press, New York (1949).
7. SPEDDING, F. H. Large scale separation of rare earth salts and the preparation of the pure metals. *Disc. Faraday Soc.*, p. 214 (1949).
8. SPEDDING, F. H. *et al.* The separation of rare earths by ion-exchange III, Pilot plant scale separations. *J. Amer. Chem. Soc.* **69**, 2812 (1947).
9. SPEDDING, F. H. and POWELL, J. E. The separation of rare earths by ion-exchange. *Trans. Metall. Soc. A.I.M.E.* **215**, 457 (June 1959).
10. BAUMAN, W. C. Improved synthetic ion-exchange resin. *Industr. Engng. Chem.* **38**, 46 (1946).
11. KRESSMAN, T. R. E. and KITCHENER, J. A. Cation exchange with a synthetic phenolsulphonate resin, Part I. Equilibria with univalent cations. *J. Chem. Soc.*, p. 1190 (1949).
12. BAUMAN, W. C. Fundamental properties of ion-exchange resins. *Ion-Exchange, Theory and Application*, edited by F. C. Nachod. Academic Press, New York (1949).
13. TOPP, N. E. The Manufacture of Wofatit Base-Exchange Resins. B.I.O.S. Final Report No. 621. Item No. 22 (1946).
14. *Chemical Age* **82**, No. 2105, 687 (11 Nov. 1959).
15. COOK, W. J. M. Water Treatment and Mixed-Bed De-ionization. S.C.I. Conference on Ion-Exchange and Its Applications, London (April, 1954).

16. AYRES, J. A. Purification of zirconium by ion-exchange columns. *J. Amer. Chem. Soc.* **69**, No. 11, 2879 (Nov. 1947).

17. AYRES, J. A. Zirconium and Hafnium Recovery and Purification Process. U.S. Patent 2567661 (application 31/8/48; completion 11/9/51).

18. PFEIFFER, P. W. A graphical method for calculating ion-exchange columns. *Chem. Engng. Sci.* **2**, No. 2, 45 (April 1953).

19. GILWOOD, M. E. Ion-exchange equipment design. *Ion-Exchange Theory and Application*, edited by F. C. Nachod. Academic Press, New York (1949).

20. SOLMS, J. J. Process for the Continuous Chromatographic Separation of Mixtures. U.K. Patent 786896 (1955).

21. BARNEBL, A. C. and RIKER, W. J. Ion-Exchange Reactor. U.S. Patent 2595627 (1952).

22. HUTCHEON, J. M. Continuous Ion-Exchange. S.C.I. Conference on Ion-Exchange and its Applications, London (April 1954).

23. HIESTER, N. K. *et al.* Continuous countercurrent ion-exchange with trace components. *Chem. Engng. News* **50**, No. 3, 139 (March 1954).

24. McCORMACK, R. H. and HOWARD, J. F. A continuous counter-current ion-exchange unit. *Chem. Engng. Progr.* **49**. No. 8, 404 (Aug. 1953).

25. SELKE, W. A. and BLISS, H. Continuous counter-current ion-exchange. *Chem. Engng. Progr.* **47**, No. 10, 529 (Oct. 1951).

26. McNEILL, R., SWINTON, E. A. and WEISS, D. E. Continuous ion-exchange. *J. Metals* **7**, No. 8, 912 (1955).

27. WEISS, D. E. and SWINTON, E. A. Methods and Apparatus for Obtaining Continuous Counter-current Contact between Solid Particles and a Liquid. U.S. Patent 2,765,913 (1956).

28. AREHART, J. C. *et al.* Counter-current ion-exchange. *Chem. Eng. Progr.* **52**, No. 9, 353 (Sept. 1956).

29. CRONAN, C. S. Ion-exchange column runs continuously. *Chem. Engr.* **64**, 184 (July 1957).

30. HIGGINS, I. R. Mechanical Features of the Higgins Continuous Ion-Exchange Column. ORNL-1907 (1955).

31. HIGGINS, I. R. Counter-Current Liquid Solid Mass Transfer Method and Apparatus. U.S. Patent 2815322 (1957).

32. HIGGINS, I. R. and ROBERTS, J. T. A Counter-current Solid Liquid Contactor for Continuous Ion-Exchange. Chemical Engineering Progress Symposium, Ser. 14, vol. 50, p. 87 (1954).

33. ROBERTS, J. T. Developments in Continuous Ion-Exchange Equipment for A.E.C. Applications. ORNL-2504 (1958).

34. POOLE, K. R. Ion-Exchange Reviewed as a Continuous Process. U.K.A.E.A. Report, AERE–R 3022 (1959).

35. ARDEN, T. V. Modern developments in industrial ion-exchange processes. *J. Roy. Inst. Chem.* **83**, 391 (June 1959).

36. ARDEN, T. V. The Analysis and Recovery of Uranium from Low Grade Ores. U.K.A.E.A. Report, AERE–R 2862 (1959).

37. SCHIF, N. N. Removal of Uranium from Rand Leach Liquors with an Ion-Exchange Resin. U.S.A.E.C. Topical Report, MITG–A93 (July 1950).

38. ARDEN, T. V. The Recovery of Uranium from Sulphate Leach Solutions by Anion-Exchange. I.M.M. Symposium on Extraction Metallurgy of the Less Common Metals, London (1957). Paper No. 8.

39. ROBINSON, R. E., VELTHUIS, R. G. and PINKNEY, E. T. An analysis of the characteristics of anion-exchange resins suitable for uranium recovery from acid leach liquors. *Proc. 2nd Int. Conf. on the Peaceful Uses of Atomic Energy, Geneva*, 1958. Paper, 1113.

40. GREER, A. H. *et al.* New ion-exchange resin for uranium recovery. *Industr. Engng. Chem.* **50**, No. 2, 166 (Feb. 1958).

41. ARDEN, T. V. and ROWLEY, M. Anion-exchange in uranyl sulphate solution. High concentration effects and rate studies. *J. Chem. Soc.* p. 1709 (1957).

42. ARDEN, T. V. and WOOD, G. A. Absorption of complex anions from uranyl sulphate solution by anion-exchange resins. *J. Chem. Soc.* p. 1596 (June 1956).
43. McLEAN, D. C. Elution of Uranium from Resin. U.S. Patent 2877089 (10/3/59).
44. DANEY, W. B. and NYLANDER, A. F. Ion-Exchange Process—Removal of Sulphate Ions from Eluate. U.S. Patent 2900227 (18/8/59).
45. ROBINSON, R. E. and VELTHUIS, R. G. The history of the development of the ion-exchange process as applied to uranium extraction. *Uranium in South Africa, 1946–1956*, vol. 1, p. 332. Johannesburg (1957).
46. EVEREST, D. A., NAPIER, E. and WELLS, R. A. Resin poisons in ion-exchange recovery processes. *Proc. 2nd Int. Conf. on the Peaceful Uses of Atomic Energy, Geneva*, 1958. Paper 101.
47. NUGENT, E. A. The chemistry of the poisons associated with the ion-exchange process. *Uranium in South Africa, 1946–1956*, vol. II, p. 177, Johannesburg (1957).
48. ROBINSON, R. E. The chemistry of the ion-exchange process for the extraction of uranium from Rand leach liquors. *Uranium in South Africa, 1946–1956*, vol. II, p. 68, Johannesburg (1957).
49. GOREN, M. B. A recovery scheme for poisoned ion-exchange resins. *Industr. Engng. Chem.* **51**, No. 4, 539 (April 1959).
50. ARNOT, C. L., BAYLISS, R. K. and NAPIER, E. The Mechanism of Silicia Absorption on Anion-Exchange Resins as Related to Uranium Leach Liquors. D.S.I.R. National Chemical Lab. Report, NCL/AE 174 (1959).
51. AYRES, D. E. R. and WESTWOOD, R. J. The use of the ion-exchange process in the extraction of uranium from Rand ores with particular reference to practice at the Randfontein uranium plant. *Uranium in South Africa, 1946–1956*, vol. II, p. 85. Johannesburg (1957). Also *J. S. Afr. Inst. Min. Metall.*, p. 459 (Feb. 1957).
52. SHANKER, J., BHATNAGAR, D. V. and MURTHY, T. K. S. An ion-exchange process for the recovery of uranium from carbonate leach solutions. *Proc. 1st Int. Conf. on the Peaceful Uses of Atomic Energy, Geneva*, 1955. Paper 871.
53. URGELL, M. *et al.* Extraction of uranium from solutions of sodium carbonate by means of anionic exchange with Dowex 1 resin. *Proc. 2nd Int. Conf. on the Peaceful Uses of Atomic Energy, Geneva*, 1958. Paper 1416.
54. MALTBY, P. D. R. Use of moving bed ion-exchange in the recovery of uranium at Con-Met. Explorations Ltd., Blind River, Ontario. *Bull. Inst. Min. Metall. Trans.* **69**, 95 (Dec. 1959).
55. DAYTON, S. H. Why moving bed-ion exchange system was selected. *Mining World* **21**, 42 (Feb. 1959).
56. McQUISTON, F. W. Recovery of Uranium from the Ores thereof. U.K. Patent 809327 (application 31/12/54, completed 25/2/59).
57. HOLLIS, R. F. and McARTHUR, C. K. The resin in-pulp process for recovery of uranium. *Proc. 1st. Int. Conf. on the Peaceful Uses of Atomic Energy, Geneva*, 1955. Paper 526.
58. U.K. Atomic Energy Authority. Method of Recovery of Uranium by a Resin-in-Pulp Process. U.K. Patent 807094 (filed 13/6/55, completed 7/1/59).
59. Reducing cost of uranium extraction. *S. Afr. Min. Engng. J.*, p. 1341 (June 5 1959).
60. ARDEN, T. V. *et al.* Extraction of uranium from acid leach pulps by jigged-bed ion-exchange. *Proc. 2nd Int. Conf. on the Peaceful Uses of Atomic Energy, Geneva*, 1958. Paper 1096.
61. HERWIG, G. L., STEWART, R. M., SWINTON, E. A. and WEISS, D. E. The "Jigged-Bed" Ion-Exchange Pilot Plant for Uranium Extraction. Australian Atomic Energy Symposium, p. 86 (1958).
62. C.S.I.R.O., Melbourne. Improved Method of Counter-currently Contacting Solids with Liquids. U.K. Patent Spec. 731000 (June, 1955).
63. HOLCOMB, R. R. and HIGGINS, I. R. Development of the Excer Process V: Recovery, Purification, and Iron Reduction of Uranium Using a Sulphate Ion-Exchange System. U.S.A.E.C. Report, ORNL–2554 (1959).
64. KRESSMAN, T. R. E. and MILLAR, J. R. Improvements Relating to the Recovery of Uranium from Solutions. U.K. Patent 812,815 (29/4/59).

65. WEISS, D. E. and SWINTON, E. A. Improvements in and Relating to the Extraction of Uranium, U.K. Patent 813,269 (application 3/1/56, completed 13/5/59). Also Australian Patent 205,608 (application 29/12/55, completed 29/1/57).

66. PAINTER, C. A. and IZZO, T. F. Operation of the resin-in-pulp uranium processing mill at Moab, Utah. *Proc. 2nd Int. Conf. on the Peaceful Uses of Atomic Energy*, *Geneva*, 1958. Paper 500.

67. ARDEN, T. V. *et al*. Recovery of thorium from sulphate solutions by anion-exchange. *J. Appl. Chem.* **9**, Part 8, 406 (Aug. 1959).

68. NAGLE, R. A. and MURTHY, T. K. S. An ion-exchange method for the separation of thorium from rare earths and its application to monazite analysis. *The Analyst* **84**, No. 994, 37 (1959).

69. CARSWELL, D. J. Separation of thorium and uranium nitrates by anion-exchange. *J. Inorg. Nucl. Chem.* **3**, 384 (1957).

70. BANE, R. W. Separation of Thorium from Uranium. U.S. Patent 2,902,338 (application 6/10/49, completion 1/9/59).

71. POIRIER, R. H. *et al*. Ion-exchange separation of uranium and thorium. *Industr. Engng. Chem.* **50**, No. 4, 613 (April 1958).

72. CALKINS, G. D. Recovery of Uranium and Thorium from Aqueous Solution. U.S. Patent 2,838,370 (application 9/4/52, completion 10/6/58).

73. HEAD, A. J. *et al*. The Extraction and Concentration of Thorium from Ores. Part V. Further Studies on the Recovery from Monazite with the aid of Cellulose Phosphate following Sulphuric Acid Attack. D.S.I.R. Report, CRL/AE 166 (1958).

74. HEAD, A. J. *et al*. Ion-exchange on modified cellulose. II. Recovery of thorium from monazite using cellulose phosphate. *J. Appl. Chem.* **9**, Part II, 599 (Nov. 1959).

75. BUDDERY, J. H., JAMRACK, W. D. and WELLS, R. A. The extraction of thorium. *Chemistry and Industry*, p. 235 (21/2/59).

76. STREET, K. and SEABORG, G. T. The ion-exchange separation of zirconium and hafnium. *J. Amer. Chem. Soc.* **70**, 4268 (Dec. 1948).

77. LISTER, B. A. J. and McDONALD, L. A. The Cation-Exchange Separation of Zirconium and Hafnium. U.K.A.E.A. Report, AERE–C/R 703.

78. LISTER, B. A. J. and HUTCHEON, J. M. Preparation of pure hafnium by cation-exchange. *Research* **5**, 291 (1952).

79. HUDSWELL, F. and HUTCHEON, J. M. Methods of separating zirconium from hafnium and their technological implications. *Proc. 2nd Int. Conf. on the Peaceful Uses of Atomic Energy, Geneva*, 1955. Paper 409.

80. BENEDICT, J. T., SCHUMB, W. C. and CORYELL, C. D. Distribution of zirconium and hafnium between cation-exchange resin and acid solutions. The column separation with nitric acid–citric acid mixture. *J. Amer. Chem. Soc.* **76**, 2036 (April, 1954).

81. HOFFMAN, E. H. and LILLY, R. C. The anion-exchange separation of zirconium and hafnium, *J. Amer. Chem. Soc.* **71**, No. 12, 4147 (Dec. 1949).

82. KRAUS, K. A. and MOORE, G. E. Separation of zirconium and hafnium with anion-exchange resins. *J. Amer. Chem. Soc.* **71**, No. 9, 3263 (Sept. 1949).

83. KRAUS, K. A. and MOORE, G. E. Separation of columbium (niobium) and tantalum with anion-exchange resins. *J. Amer. Chem. Soc.* **71**, No. 11, 3855 (Nov. 1949).

84. MILLER, G. L. The separation of tantalum and niobium. *The Industrial Chemist* **35**, 175 (April 1959).

85. McLEAN, D. C. *et al*. Development of an Ion-Exchange Process for the Recovery of Vanadium. U.S.A.E.C. Report, ACCD–63 (1954).

86. BAILES, R. H. *et al*. Anionic Exchange Process for the Recovery of Uranium and Vanadium from Carbonate Solutions. U.S. Patent 2,864,667 (application 16/6/53, completion 16/12/58).

CHAPTER 4

SOLVENT EXTRACTION

THEORY

Most of the rare metals considered in this book can form compounds which are appreciably soluble in both aqueous media and organic solvents. The conditions for high solubility in an organic solvent are often fairly specific to an element, compared with the metal ion impurities with which it may be associated. Consequently, the process of solvent extraction, involving a transfer of a rare metal species from an aqueous to an organic solvent phase, can be used for purification in a relatively simple manner. Multi-stage processes are, however, generally necessary if it is desired to extract a high proportion of the solute into the solvent phase, and further complications arise when impurities also have appreciable solubilities in the solvent.

Solvent systems

The property of solubility of an inorganic salt in an organic solvent is usually associated with a low degree of ionization in the solvent phase,[1] and the non-ionized species is capable of forming addition compounds with the solvent. These are electrically neutral co-ordination compounds and they are soluble in the solvent. Alternatively, compounds of this type may be formed with a small quantity of a complexing agent which is dissolved in a relatively cheap inert organic diluent such as kerosene. The compounds formed with the complexing agent must also be soluble in the diluent. For purely practical purposes, e.g. to avoid high processing losses of the solvent, it is advisable to employ a system where the organic solvent phase is almost immiscible with water. Typical examples are di-ethyl ether, $\beta\beta'$ di-butoxy diethylene glycol, methyl isobutyl ketone, triglycol dichloride, mono-, di- and tri-butyl phosphates, di-octyl phosphate, and higher alkyl amines. The rare metal salt is usually present as a halide, sulphate or nitrate, with an excess of the corresponding halogen acid, sulphuric acid, or nitric acid, at least in the aqueous phase. The range of systems is frequently so diverse that a choice is made on purely economic grounds. An important factor in the economics is usually the material of construction required for the processing plant to withstand corrosion by the acidic solutions employed.

Distribution coefficient

For dilute solutions of the rare metal, the ratio of its concentration in the organic phase to that in the aqueous phase, known as the partition coefficient or distribution coefficient, K, is fairly constant. However, economic solvent extraction processes are always concerned with higher regions of concentration, in order to reduce the usage of organic solvent and the size of plant for a given throughput. Under these conditions, the distribution coefficient often varies with the concentration of rare metal and also with concentration of other species in solution.[2] This deviation from direct proportionality can usually be predicted qualitatively on simple theoretical grounds, and data are often available for quantitative assessment of the influence of the various factors involved. The distribution of uranium between tributyl phosphate (TBP) and an aqueous acidic nitrate phase provides a convenient example. The uranium is mainly present in the aqueous phase as uranyl ions and uranyl nitrate, according to the equilibrium:

$$UO_2^{++} + 2NO_3^- \rightleftharpoons UO_2(NO_3)_2.$$

The uranyl nitrate is hydrated to a certain degree in the aqueous phase but it is also soluble in the organic phase where it associates with two molecules of TBP, i.e.

$$UO_2(NO_3)_2 + 2TBP \rightleftharpoons UO_2(NO_3)_2.2TBP.$$

The equilibrium constants in the two cases are:

$$K_1 = \frac{[UO_2(NO_3)_2]}{[UO_2^{++}][NO_3^-]^2}$$

and

$$K_2 = \frac{[UO_2(NO_3)_2 2TBP]}{[UO_2(NO_3)_2][TBP]^2}$$

Consequently

$$K_1\ K_2 = \frac{[UO_2(NO_3)_2 2TBP]}{[UO_2^{++}][NO_3^-]^2[TBP]^2}$$

The distribution coefficient is defined approximately as:

$$K = \frac{[UO_2(NO_3)_2.2TBP]}{[UO_2^{++}]}$$

and therefore

$$K = K_1 K_2 [NO_3{}^-]^2 [TBP]^2$$

It is clear from this relationship that at fairly low uranyl nitrate concentrations in a neutral aqueous phase, the degree of extraction into the organic phase is proportional to the square of the aqueous uranium (uranyl nitrate) concentration, as shown in Fig. 4.1. A low uranium concentration associated with an excess of nitric acid in the aqueous phase, however, gives a steep and linear graph of organic vs. aqueous concentration, as shown in Fig. 4.2. This is because of the high, and virtually constant, nitrate ion concentration with change of uranium concentration. A different excess of free nitric acid, or for example of sodium nitrate, would give a similar graph but of different gradient.

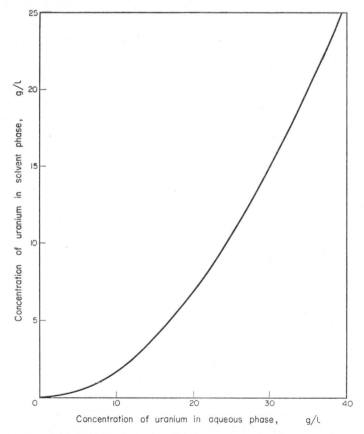

FIG. 4.1. Distribution of uranium between water and 20 per cent TBP.

At high uranium concentrations, large amounts of uranyl nitrate are combined with TBP, so leaving the TBP phase relatively less concentrated in free TBP, and thus the graph of organic phase uranium concentration against aqueous phase concentration shows a gradually decreasing gradient

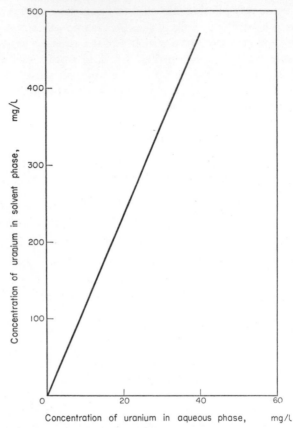

FIG. 4.2. Distribution of uranium between 2N nitric acid and 20 per cent TBP (low uranium concentrations).

as in Fig. 4.3. Finally, when no free TBP remains in the TBP phase, i.e the organic phase is saturated, the graph becomes horizontal.

The presence of other salts without a common ion often increases the distribution coefficient. This is partly explained by the reduction in the free water molecules in the aqueous phase resulting from the hydration of the added salt.[3]

Multiple batch extraction

In principle, it might be possible to effect a reasonable purification of a rare metal in solution by a single-batch extraction, if either the distribution coefficient or the solvent-to-aqueous volume ratio were high. However, a fairly high process cost would usually have been borne by the previous ore leaching or dissolution stages, etc., and this would be sufficient to justify a number of successive extractions with solvent in order to reduce the rare metal concentration in the aqueous phase to an economic reject level. Once the principle of using additional batches of solvent has been accepted, it is clearly necessary to optimize the number of extractions and volume of solvent in each, so as to obtain the maximum amount of product extracted by a given total quantity of solvent.

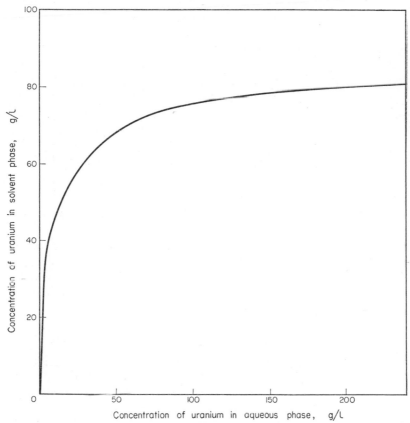

FIG. 4.3. Distribution of uranium between 3N nitric acid and 20 per cent TBP (high uranium concentrations).

Assuming a solute with a constant distribution coefficient,

$$K = \frac{\text{concentration in organic phase}}{\text{concentration in aqueous phase}} = \frac{C_o}{C_A}$$

If V_o and V_A are the volumes of the two phases at each extraction, and $(C_A)_n$ and $(C_o)_n$ the concentrations after n extractions, then,

$$(C_o)_1 V_o + (C_A)_1 V_A = (C_A)_0 V_A$$

i.e.

$$K(C_A)_1 V_0 + (C_A)_1 V_A = (C_A)_0 V_A$$

or,

$$(C_A)_1(V_A + KV_0) = (C_A)_0 V_A$$

Thus,

$$(C_A)_1 = (C_A)_0 \frac{V_A}{V_A + KV_0}$$

Similarly, after two extractions,

$$(C_A)_2 = (C_A)_1 \frac{V_A}{V_A + KV_0} = (C_A)_0 \left(\frac{V_A}{V_A + KV_0}\right)^2$$

and after n successive extractions,

$$(C_A)_n = (C_A)_0 \left(\frac{V_A}{V_A + KV_0}\right)^n$$

Inspection of this equation shows that if the total volume of solvent (nV_0) is constant, then the greatest reduction in concentration is obtained when n is large and V_0 is small, i.e. by means of a large number of small volume extractions.

In practice, it is inconvenient to carry out a large number of successive batch extractions with fresh solvent. There are special cases where a satisfactory degree of removal of solute is obtained by a small number of successive batch extractions and this may be justified by the simplicity of the plant employed, but usually counter-current extraction is preferred.

Counter-current batch extraction

In a counter-current batch process, portions of aqueous phase containing the solute are extracted with successive portions of organic solvent phase in such a manner that the fresh solvent always extracts from the weakest aqueous phase, and the most concentrated solvent extracts from the solute-rich aqueous feed. Similarly, the aqueous solutions of intermediate solute concentration are extracted by organic solvent which already has a moderate solute concentration. The situation is illustrated by Fig. 4.4(a). A stream of solvent portions passes from right to left with respect to a stream of initially solute-rich aqueous portions. At each contact of two new portions, it is necessary to mix throughly to allow solute to pass from one phase to the other and then to settle and separate again, into their separate phases.

A development of this technique is to make the streams of portions, both aqueous and solvent, of infinite length. Such a technique involves the movement of solvent and aqueous portions alternately. When a particular solvent phase portion has reached the extreme left vessel, it is removed and a new portion added to the extreme right vessel. Similarly, when a particular aqueous phase portion has reached the extreme right vessel, it is removed and a new portion added at the extreme left. The system is represented pictorially in Fig. 4.4(b).

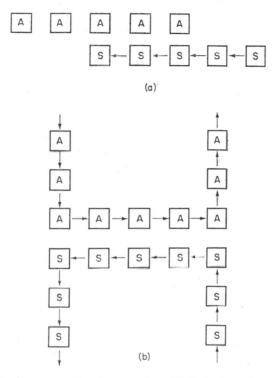

Fig. 4.4. Counter-current batch extraction: (a) limited number of batches; (b) infinite series of batches.

A considerable saving in the number of operations is clearly made by mechanization of mixing, settling and separating. This, however, is only done in the case of certain specialized laboratory applications.[4] Instead, it is more usual to allow the two phases to flow continuously rather than in discrete portions, and a large variety of plant and equipment is now available for carrying out these processes of continuous counter-current solvent extraction on an industrial scale.

Continuous counter-current extraction

Equipment for continuous counter-current extraction takes the form of vertical columns, analogous to fractionating columns except that both phases are liquids, are horizontally mounted mixer-settler extractors. Both types are described in more detail later. In practice, although the flow to a mixer-settler (or some types of column) is continuous, true continuous counter-current operation in not obtained. This type of behaviour is best classed as continuous multiple contact.[5] True continuous counter-current operation is obtained when the two phases pass continuously in opposite directions as in a simple packed or unpacked column.

In order to design a continuous counter-current solvent extraction process, it is important to have an understanding of the elementary chemical engineering theory of solvent extraction, quite apart from considerations of the type of extraction plant to be employed. This, for example, allows a decision to be made regarding the number of theoretical stages which are required to carry out a given extraction operation under defined conditions and efficiencies. The theoretical stage concept for an extraction column can be visualized by analogy with a fractionating column. The "height equivalent to a theoretical stage" may be defined as the height of column such that the organic solvent phase leaving at one end is in equilibrium with the aqueous phase leaving the opposite end, with respect to solute concentration. In the case of mixer-settlers, a practical stage might in fact correspond to a theoretical stage, but it is more usual to economize in the size of unit, and consequently on mixing time, so that the two phases leaving a stage are not quite in equilibrium.

As in the case of multiple-batch extraction already discussed, it is possible to relate mathematically the feed concentrations to the final aqueous (or solvent) concentration in an elementary manner via the distribution co-efficient, the number of stages and the solvent and aqueous volumes or flow rates. As with multiple-batch extraction, however, it is necessary for both distribution coefficient and flow rates to be constant for the calculation to be valid.

In Fig. 4.5., the line OA is a plot of solvent phase concentration against aqueous phase concentration of the solute, i.e. the slope represents a constant distribution coefficient (K). This is usually referred to as the "equilibrium line".

The line BC is an "operating line", i.e. a plot of aqueous and solvent phase concentrations throughout an extraction column, with a slope equal to the ratio of aqueous to solvent flow rates Va/Vs. This can be derived by considering the section of column shown in Fig. 4.6. Let S_n be the concen-centration of solute in the ascending solvent leaving the nth stage of the column, and A_n the concentration of solute in the descending aqueous phase entering the nth stage.

Similarly, S_0 is the concentration of solute in the solvent being fed to the base of the column (usually zero) and A_0 is the solute concentration in an aqueous phase leaving the base.

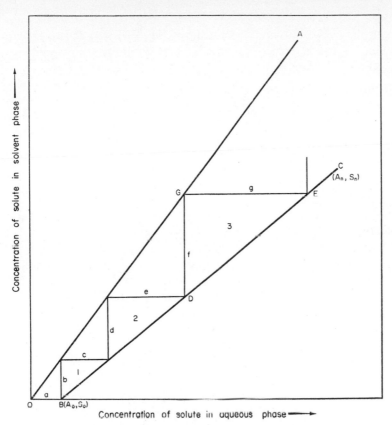

FIG. 4.5. Counter-current stagewise extraction.

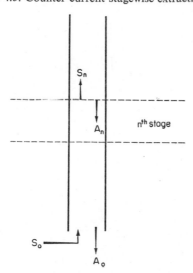

FIG. 4.6. nth stage of column.

With the column at equilibrium, the weight of solute fed to the section of column between these two points is equal to the weight of solute leaving the section,

Therefore
$$V_s S_0 + V_a A_n = V_a A_0 + V_s S_n$$

i.e.
$$V_s(S_n - S_0) = V_a(A_n - A_0)$$

or
$$S_n - S_0 = V_a/V_s(A_n - A_0)$$

This is clearly the equation of a straight line passing through coordinates (A_n, S_n) and (A_0, S_0) of slope V_a/V_s, i.e. the "operating line".

In Fig. 4.5, the individual theoretical stages are shown by a stepwise construction. To take stage 3 as an example, the height of the line GE indicates the solute concentration in the solvent leaving stage 3, and the horizontal distance of the line DG from the vertical axis similarly represents the solute concentration in the aqueous phase leaving stage 3. By the definition of a theoretical stage, these two concentrations are in equilibrium, and the lines therefore meet on the equilibrium line.

If the final aqueous phase (aqueous raffinate) concentration is a, from Fig. 4.5, the initial aqueous feed concentration F_a is $a + c + e + g + \ldots$ But $C = b\,V_s/V_a$, $e = dV_s/V_a$, $g = fV_s/V_a$, etc. (since V_s/V_a is the slope of the line BC).

Also, $b = aK$, $d = cK$, $f = eK$, etc.

(Since K is the slope of the line OA.)

i.e.

$$c = aK\frac{V_s}{V_a}, \quad e = cK\frac{V_s}{V_a}, \quad g = eK\frac{V_s}{V_a}, \quad \text{etc.}$$

or

$$c = aK\frac{V_s}{V_a}, \quad e = a\left(K\frac{V_s}{V_a}\right)^2, \quad g = a\left(K\frac{V_s}{V_a}\right)^3, \quad \text{etc.}$$

or

$$c = aE, \quad e = aE^2, \quad g = aE^3, \quad \text{etc.}$$

(where $E = K(V_s/V_a)$, defined as the "extraction factor").

The aqueous feed concentration therefore $= a(1 + E + E^2 + E^3 + \ldots)$. With n stages, this series continues for $n+1$ terms, and therefore summing the series,

$$F_a = a\frac{(1 - E^{n+1})}{1 - E}.$$

This equation was evaluated by Kremser, who first applied it to absorption.[6] An alternative derivation is given by Klinkenberg.[7]

This equation is quite general in that it applies not only to the feed concentration, but also to any aqueous concentration situated an integral number of stages along the extractor. By similar reasoning it can be deduced that the solvent concentration at any point,

$$F_s = Ka\frac{(1-E^n)}{1-E}$$

The extraction of a solute from an aqueous to a solvent phase is often not a process which is entirely specific to one particular solute. The system is chosen so that the distribution coefficient of the desired solute is fairly

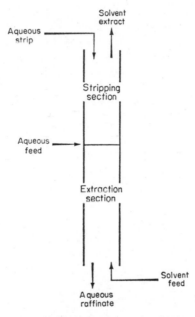

FIG. 4.7. Column with extraction and stripping sections.

high, but other solutes may also have appreciable distribution coefficients and thus tend to extract. In these circumstances, a "stripping section" is commonly employed, as represented in Fig. 4.7. This allows the solvent, before leaving the extractor, to receive a multi-stage wash with a suitable aqueous phase, which then blends with the main aqueous solution passing down the extractor. The flow rate of the strip solution must be selected so that it does not strip back an undue amount of the principal solute. An equilibrium diagram will show the strip operating line on the opposite side of the equilibrium line to the extraction operating line, as in Fig. 4.8. A single equilibrium line can often apply for both extraction and stripping sections, when similar solutions are used for aqueous and strip feeds, as in

Fig. 4.8, but this is frequently only an approximation. For straight equilibrium and operating lines, equations can be evaluated in a similar manner as for the extraction section, to relate the solvent extract concentration to the solvent concentration at the feed point (or any intermediate point).

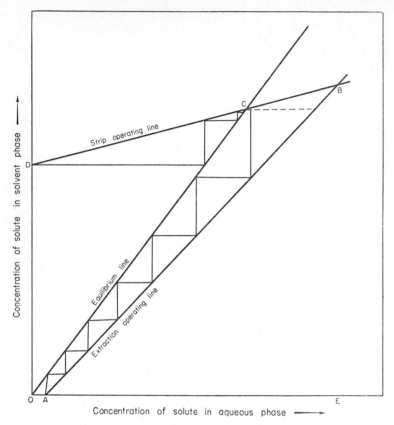

FIG. 4.8. Equilibrium diagram with extraction and stripping.

For example: If S is the stripping factor $(V_a'/V_s K)$, a the solvent extract concentration, and n the number of stages,

$$F_s = a\frac{(1 - S^{n+1})}{1 - S}$$

The solvent concentration at the feed point is common to both stripping and extraction sections provided the centre feed consists of an aqueous phase and not a solvent one.

In a composite column, the point of intersection of the extraction and stripping section operating lines is always at the feed concentration, i.e.

the concentration of solute in the aqueous phase which is fed to the extractor (B).

This follows from considerations of the solute balance throughout the system, and can be deduced by elementary geometry as follows:

Solute input = solute output

i.e.
$$F(V_a - V_a^1) = OA(V_a) + OD(V_s)$$
$$= OE(V_a) - AE(V_a) + OD(V_s)$$
$$= OE(V_a) - EB(V_s) + V_s \left[EB - OE\left(\frac{V_a^1}{V_s}\right) \right]$$
$$F(V_a - V_a^1) = OE(V_a - V_a^1)$$

Therefore $F = OE$.

Equilibrium diagrams

In practice, the equilibrium line (or lines) are not usually straight, i.e. the distribution coefficient is not usually constant throughout the system. This invalidates the simple methods of relating feed to extract or raffinate concentrations by calculation which have been described. Also, the operating lines, being ratios of flow rates, may deviate from linearity as a result of the solubility of one phase in the other, or the transfer of large quantities of solute from one to the other. Consequently, extraction systems are usually designed by the graphical method first used by McCabe and Thiele for the design of fractionating columns.[8]

The "equilibrium diagram" or "Fenske-Varteressian" diagram[9] such as Fig. 4.9. is first drawn from distribution data and the desired flow rates. The flow rates are selected on grounds of economy, compatible with a satisfactory process. It is important to realize that the operating lines represent ratios of flow rates, which intersect at any point along the line EB (in Figs. 4.8 or 4.9). Their exact position is dependent upon the number of stages desired in the stripping and extraction sections, and must be determined by trial and error. Stages are stepped off graphically from the solvent and aqueous exit ends of the two sections. It may be important in individual cases to allow sufficient stages for a low aqueous raffinate concentration, or to have a number of stages in the stripping section which is adequate for stripping back impurities, which can only be decided by reference to the equilibrium diagram for each solute.

Most extraction systems are designed with a "pinch point" in either the extraction or stripping section, i.e. a point of intersection of the equilibrium line with the operating line (point C in Figs. 4.8 or 4.9). For conventional systems where a stripping section serves to wash the solvent free from entrained aqueous phase, or from impurities which have only low distribution coefficients, it is usual to have the "pinch point" in the stripping section, as shown in Figs. 4.8 and 4.9. This introduces an element of stability into the system in that the pinch point absorbs surplus stages and fixes a maximum solvent concentration. This is more satisfactory than the system shown in

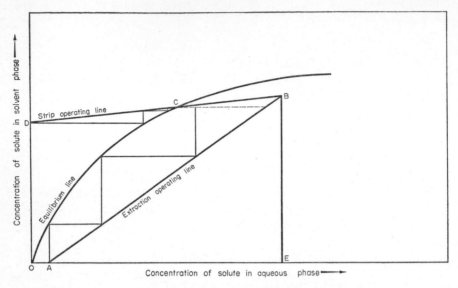

FIG. 4.9. Equilibrium diagram with curved equilibrium line.

Figure 4.10, where any slight fall in the equilibrium line,[10] e.g. as a result of a change of acidity, causes the extraction operating line to move to the right and release additional solute into the raffinate.

As indicated above, the efficiency of a column is determined by the "height equivalent to a theoretical stage". An alternative concept used as a measure of column efficiency, devised by Chilton and Colburn,[11] is the "height of a transfer unit". The number of transfer units is a measure of the difficulty of carrying out a given extraction operation. The height of a transfer unit is the height of a column sufficient to carry out this operation divided by the number of transfer units. A transfer unit only corresponds to a theoretical stage when the equilibrium and operating lines are parallel. In practice, the theoretical stage concept is usually employed for design purposes.

A solvent extraction process must normally have provision for removal of the pure solute from the solvent back into an aqueous phase for further processing. A low distribution coefficient is required, and this can often be achieved by backwashing with a solution of lower acidity than in forward extraction. Water may be suitable if hydrolysis does not take place and cause difficulties.

Figure 4.11 shows a simple back-wash equilibrium diagram with the solute concentration in the solvent reduced in a number of stages from a value of *b* to one of *a*. When additional decontamination from impurities is required,

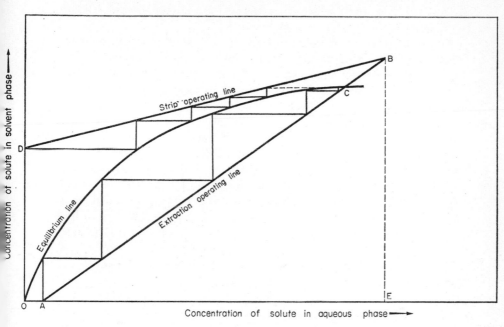

Fɪɢ. 4.10. Equilibrium diagram with pinch point in extraction section.

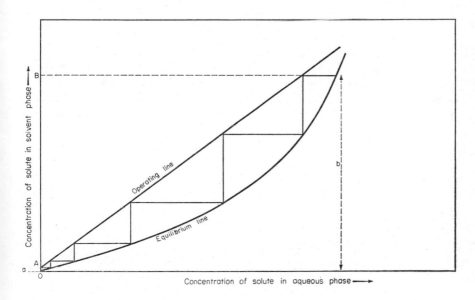

Fɪɢ. 4.11. Equilibrium diagram for backwash extraction.

it is possible to apply a solvent strip to the aqueous extract, but this is uncommon.

Sometimes the solvent contains two principal solutes, one desired and the other unwanted. Separation may then be possible by means of a special "chemical" backwashing of one component, e.g. by changing its valency or complexing with another anion, followed by normal backwashing of the other component. Alternatively, a carefully designed system of separation might be effectively based upon the difference of distribution coefficients. If these are close together, large numbers of stages may be involved and the process may be unduly sensitive to small changes of flow rates or of acidity, etc. Klinkenberg[7] gives a mathematical treatment of this topic which would allow a system to be designed provided the equilibrium and operating lines were straight. Because of these limitations, however, the graphical method is usually employed, operating lines being fitted to the equilibrium lines by trial and error until suitable specifications are found for both extraction and stripping sections.

The solvent which has been almost completely denuded of solute may be suitable for recycling directly back to the first extractor, for re-extraction of more solute. Alternatively, it may require treatment before re-use, e.g. an alkaline wash to remove impurities which have accumulated during its previous contact with acid aqueous phases. It is advisable for any treatment process to be continuous, as are the extraction and backwash processes, to preserve the continuity of operations. The cost of solvent can be an important item of process economics unless it is efficiently recovered. Systems are therefore chosen with low solubilities of solvent in the aqueous phases, and care should be taken to avoid entrainment of solvent, general spillages, etc.

With carefully designed systems involving not more than about twelve extraction stages, efficiencies of over 99·9 per cent are often obtained on the extraction of the main solute into, or out of, the solvent, as measured by the 0·1 per cent or less remaining in the aqueous or solvent "raffinate". Lower efficiencies may be caused by the presence of an inadequate number of extraction stages or, for example, a reduction in stage efficiency of a mixer-settler, or an increase in the theoretical stage height of a column. The system is usually designed with an excess of stages so as to be fairly insensitive to changes of this type.

Solvent-soluble impurities[3] are often reduced by a factor of at least 10^4 (i.e. a "decontamination factor" of 10^4) provided their distribution coefficients are widely different from that of the main solute. Where the impurity is completely insoluble in the solvent, a small proportion may still pass with the principal solute by virtue of physical entrainment of tiny aqueous drops in the solvent phase, but decontamination factors of 10^5 or more have been obtained with some systems, e.g. for the separation of rare earth elements from thorium.

Incidental to its use as a purification process, solvent extraction may lead to a desirable increase in concentration of the solute. This arises when the distribution coefficient on forward extraction is high enough for the solvent-to-aqueous ratio to be less than unity, or alternatively the backwash distribution coefficient may be sufficiently low for the solvent-to-aqueous ratio there to be greater than unity. When high concentrations are obtained in an extraction system, it may be necessary to guard against the deposition of crystals of the solute or of a third phase, solid or liquid, containing the solute. For example, with some designs of extraction system it is possible for say the aqueous-phase solute concentration at the feed point to be higher than the concentration in the feed to the extractor. This arises when the equilibrium line for the stripping section has a lower slope (i.e. a lower distribution coefficient prevails) than in the extraction section, as shown in Fig. 4.12.

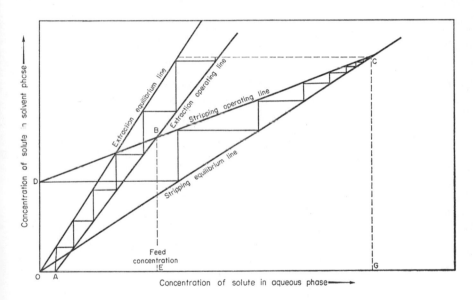

FIG. 4.12. Equilibrium diagram for concentrating system.

SOLVENT EXTRACTION PLANT

A wide variety of solvent extraction equipment has been developed for use in counter-current, liquid–liquid extraction processes. In general they divide into vertical and horizontal types, referred to as "columns" or "mixer-settlers" respectively. In both cases, the object is to obtain suitable conditions for the transfer of solute from one phase to the other as rapidly and efficiently as possible.

Extraction mechanism

The mechanism clearly involves diffusion inside one phase to the "phase boundary", across the "phase boundary", and into the second phase, but it is sometimes complicated by a chemical reaction such as a solvation step[12] at the "phase boundary". Neglecting chemical reactions, the Whitman two-film theory of gas absorption[13] is applicable to liquid–liquid systems. This suggests that the "phase boundary" should be considered as a film of phase A in contact with another film of phase B. Diffusion through the boundary films is controlled by an equation of the type:

$$\frac{dW}{d\theta} = k_A(C_1 - C_2) = k_B(C_2 - C_3)$$

where $dW/d\theta$ is the rate of mass transfer, and the concentrations C_1, C_2 and C_3 respectively apply to the exterior of film A, the point of contact of the two films and the exterior of film B.

The dispersion of one phase in the other as droplets shortens the diffusion paths inside the two phases and increases the interfacial area. Once droplets of dispersed phase have been formed, great benefit is often derived from the eddy diffusion effects[14f, 15] arising from turbulence resulting from various types of motion in the system. The frequent coalescence and re-formation of droplets aids mass transfer considerably.[16] The decrease in droplet size below a certain level may have disadvantages, since it might reduce the degree of internal recirculation within the droplets, would decrease the free rising velocity of the droplets and in any case would require a greater power usage.   Optimization of droplet size is therefore advisable for any particular system.

Extraction columns

The static types of column may be filled with packing in a similar manner to fractionating columns, or contain, for example, sieve-plates or "perforated trays"[17] throughout their length, the object in every case being to reduce the height of a theoretical stage below that in a simple unpacked spray column. Stage heights are reduced in other ways by, in effect, increasing the delay time of the two phases in passing through the column. This may be accomplished for example by rotating a vertical shaft in an unpacked column, so as to increase the path length of the ascending bubbles of solvent. Alternatively the contents of a column may be "pulsed", i.e. a rapid oscillating motion applied to the liquids as they flow through packing or sieve-plates, or the oscillation may be applied to horizontal sieve-plates moving vertically through the liquids.[17] In each case the effect is to cause increased dispersion of one phase in the other, and in some designs, the column becomes divided alternately into relatively calm zones for partial settling and agitated zones where redispersion takes place.

Packed columns. The packed column has the virtue of simplicity and freedom from mechanical maintenance. Considerable headroom may be required, however, if large numbers of stages are involved, since the height of a theoretical stage is rarely less than a few feet. A multi-column system, involving gravity flow of liquids from one column to another in series, might be 100 or 200 ft in total height. The interposition of feed pumps between columns may allow them to be installed at the same level, but the engineering of the plant then becomes more complex.

The principles of construction of solvent extraction columns have similarities with those of gas absorption towers or distillation columns. Similar packing materials have been used, e.g. Raschig rings, Lessing rings, Berl saddles, gauze rings and "Spraypak" expanded metal. The optimum design of column for a particular solvent extraction system is usually based upon fairly extensive development experiments. These allow the most suitable packing to be selected to obtain the maximum throughput from a column of minimum diameter. The type of packing also has an influence upon the height of a theoretical stage. The expanded metal type is now probably at least as satisfactory as any other, in most cases. The size is chosen as a result of experiment, guided by certain rules on its relationship to the column diamater, e.g. the packing size should not be greater than one-eighth of the column diameter. [18, 19] With most types of packing, it is difficult to prevent "channelling" of the solvent drops into a particular path as they ascend the column through the aqueous phase. This reduces the effective area of contact between the two phases over a given height of column, and thus increases the stage height. It is often minimized by fitting redistribution plates at regular intervals up the column. These take various forms, a metal plate containing a network of holes and covering the cross-section of the column being fairly effective. Several feet of packing are supported immediately above each plate, and a few inches of column space is left unpacked immediately below the plate.

Most column extraction processes operate with a solvent of lower density than the aqueous phase and discrete solvent drops are usually allowed to ascend in the continuous aqueous medium, with an interface near the top of the column. Aqueous phase enters just below the interface and solvent phase is fed via the first distributor at the base of the column. "Flooding" of the column takes place at certain critical flow rates. This phenomenon[5] arises when, for example, the flow rate of the dispersed phase is unduly increased with a constant flow of continuous phase. The additional column hold-up of dispersed phase leaves less space for continuous phase and therefore the linear velocity of the continuous phase is increased. A tendency to drag the dispersed phase droplets in the direction of the continuous phase thus arises. When the flooding point is reached, the dispersed phase is discharged along with the continuous phase and counter-current flow ceases.

For a given diameter of column, flooding can take place as a result of excessive flow rate by either phase, and particularly by both phases simultaneously. The flooding rate is dependent upon the chemical nature of the system and the difference of density between the two phases, in addition to the mechanical characteristics of voidage and nature of packing. It is usual to operate at about 70 per cent of the flooding rate to allow a reasonable margin for variations of conditions within the system. Temperature, composition of phases, and the presence of finely divided solids in either phase, affect the flooding rate. In particular, the accumulation of solid impurity material at the interface may become so severe as to prevent normal operation. The remedy may be to empty the system completely of liquid and wash out at intervals between periods of normal operation.

Attempts have been made to place the design of packed columns on a sound theoretical basis[14, 19] to avoid the large amount of empirical work with which it is frequently associated. The theory is often only approximate and cannot therefore be used as the sole guide for design purposes. It does however at least allow valuable qualitative or semi-quantitative predictions to be made, which reduces the development requirement.

Rotary columns. The rotary annular column,[17, 20, 21] as shown in Fig. 4.13, has been outstandingly successful in reducing the height of a theoretical stage, often to as little as 1 or 2 in. In principle, it depends upon the shearing effect of a cylinder rotating at high speed inside an unpacked column. An annular space of the order of 1 or 2 mm only remains, and a rotary motion is imparted to bubbles of solvent phase ascending in this annulus. The shearing effect causes the surface layers on both sides of the bubble boundaries to be renewed frequently, which aids the transfer of solute. To this must be added the additional effect of the very long path length for the bubbles.

Unfortunately, since the preferred width of annulus is fairly constant for any diameter of column, the throughput of a rotary extractor is approximately proportional to its diameter, whereas that of other types is more nearly proportional to the square of the diameter. Consequently, the use of this type of extractor is limited to small-scale processes, and it has also been applied in a highly successful manner as an analytical tool, i.e. for the purification of continuous samples from process streams prior to analysis. The high precision engineering required for the construction of rotors capable of high-speed rotation also militates against their use on a larger production scale.

A similar principle is used in the rotating disc extractor, Fig. 4.14. In this case the vessel diameter is much greater and a comparatively narrow vertical rotor is fitted with horizontal discs at intervals of a few inches. Annular discs are also attached to the internal vertical wall of the stator, opposite the spaces between the rotor discs. The rotor revolves at fairly high speeds and so increases the path lengths of the two phases that theoretical stage heights can be reduced to a few inches. Scale-up of this type of extractor is approximately proportional to area and so is more favourable than for a small annulus type rotary column where it is more nearly proportional to circumference (or diameter).

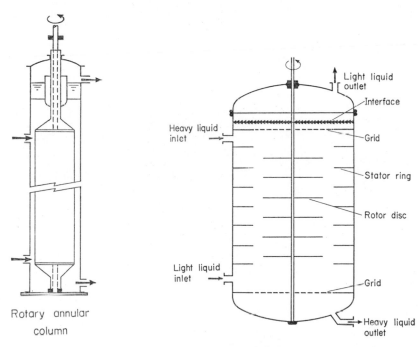

FIG. 4.13. Rotary annular column (Thornton, J. D. Ref. 46).

FIG. 4.14. Rotating-disc extractor. (By permission from *Nuclear Chemical Engineering* by Benedict, M. and Pigford, T. H. copyright 1957. McGraw-Hill.)

The Scheibel column. In the columns so far described, the two phases flowing counter-current to one another are completely dispersed during the whole of their passage through the column. The Scheibel column[22] Fig. 4.15, is designed differently. It consists of a vertical column containing a rotating shaft, upon which are carried a number of small impellors. Between each impellor and across the whole diameter of the column (except the shaft) is placed a mass of wire mesh packing, to form a calming zone. The result resembles in some ways a series of mixer-settlers one above the other. In the region of the impellors, one phase is dispersed in the other to give fairly complete mixing. When the two-phase mixture enters the calming zone, it separates, the lighter (usually organic solvent) phase rising and entering the upper mixer and the heavier phase passing into the lower mixer. It is clear that if mixed phases pass in both directions from the mixing region, a considerable amount of internal recycling takes place in each stage, i.e. solvent or aqueous phase passing in the "wrong" direction and returning to the same mixer. Whilst this aids the achievement of a low theoretical stage height, it limits the throughput of the unit.

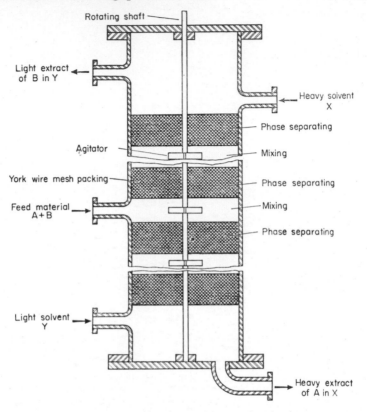

Fig. 4.15. Scheibel column. (By permission from *Nuclear Chemical Engineering* by Benedict, M. and Pigford, T. H. copyright 1957. McGraw-Hill.)

Pulse columns. Pulse columns (or "pulsed" columns), originated by Van Dijck,[23] are now becoming accepted as the most satisfactory general purpose type of column for liquid–liquid extraction (See Fig. 4.16). Mechanical pulsing or air pulsing may be used. They can also be divided into two types in another way, i.e. those which are "packed" throughout their height in a similar manner to static packed columns, and others which have "sieve-plates" located at regular intervals from top to bottom. In both cases, the principal advantage of a pulse column over a simple packed column is a reduction in stage height, and therefore in overall column height, by a factor variously stated as about 3,[24] or 5 to 10.[25] In addition, the sieve-plate type is particularly successful in carrying out liquid–liquid extraction operations where solid particles are present, thus saving a filtration stage or avoiding the necessity for plant wash-outs. It also tolerates a high volumetric throughput before the onset of flooding, which may be 50 to 100 per cent greater than that of a static packed column of the same diameter.

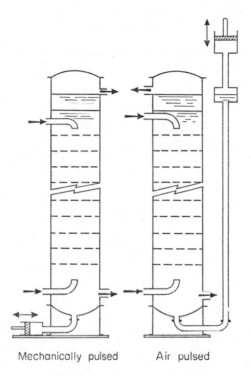

Mechanically pulsed   Air pulsed

Fig. 4.16. Pulsed columns (Thornton, J. D., Ref. 46).

A sieve-plate pulse column is fabricated from precision-bore piping, in sections, with bolted flanged ends if necessary. The plates can be welded in position but a more convenient method of construction is to slide the plates into the column down a central stringer, alternating each plate with a spacer to keep successive plates a constant distance apart (sometimes as little as 1–2 in.). It is important that the plates are a good fit in the piping to avoid gaps which would lead to "channelling" of one of the liquid phases during operation.[24] For the same reason, the plates must be sufficiently stout and well supported to be in a horizontal position. A disc plate with a special gland has been developed[26] to minimize leakage. The gland consists of a skirt to the plate, with a circumferential groove packed with asbestos cord. Each plate has a number of orifices of fairly small diameter such that they would prevent the flow of one liquid through the other in the absence of pulsing. The diameter of each orifice is usually of the order of 0·1 in. and the number is such that the free area is up to 20 per cent or more, although a fairly wide range of orifice diameters and free areas have been used for various purposes. Better distribution is obtained when every fourth or fifth plate is conical instad of flat.[27]

Pulsing is applied to the column via one of the feeds or outgoing streams, or a special pulse line to the base of the column, in such a manner that the whole of the liquid contents of the column moves first in one direction and then in the reverse direction, a distance usually of the order of 0·5 in. The pulsing is repeated at a frequency which varies with the individual design but is often as high as 60 c/min[28] and sometimes several hundred per minute.[29] During each pulse cycle, the dense phase is forced through the orifices in each sieve-plate, in a downward direction, as droplets and these partially coalesce again on the top of the next lower plate. When the pulse stroke is reversed, the lighter phase is forced through the orifices in an upwards direction and partially coalesces again under the next plate above, ready for the subsequent cycle.[12]

It is claimed[30] that some advantage is gained if the top of each sieve-plate is made of a material which is wetted by the dense liquid and the bottom made of a material which is wetted by the lighter phase. Fluorothene or polythene are suitable for organic liquids and stainless-steel for aqueous phases, the plastic being used either in the form of a separate adjacent disc or as a spray coating on the metal.

Pulsing units for the smaller plants may take the form of diaphragm pumps from which the non-return valves have been removed, so allowing the liquids to surge first in a forwards and then in a backwards direction. Alternatively, a large diaphragm or a bellows may be used where a greater amplitude is required, and these can be actuated by a cam mechanism[12] as shown in Fig. 4.17. Reliable bellows are available, e.g. of stainless-steel, which have a long life. In one design of pulsed column,[31] the pulsing action is supplied by feeding solvent and aqueous phases intermittently and alternately in pulses. The mechanism consists of solenoid valves on the feed and outlet lines, controlled by a timing unit.

The height of a theoretical stage for a sieve-plate pulse column may be below 1 ft; examples of operating characteristics are given by Cohen and Beyer.[12] Up to a certain point the HETS is decreased by increasing the pulse energy, since this increases the degree of dispersion of one phase in the other. At high pulse frequencies, where large heights of liquid are pulsed, pressures below the vapour pressure of the liquid may be obtained, giving rise to cavitation.[29] The sieve-plates act as redistributors, and consequently the throughput is fairly well proportional to cross-sectional area, which makes scaling up relatively easy.

Pulse columns containing conventional types of random packing have been found to have similar theoretical stage heights to those with sieve-

FIG. 4.17. Teflon bellows pulse generator. Fernald refinery (From C. D. Harrington and A. E. Ruehle, *Uranium Production Technology*, copyright 1959. D. Van Nostrand, Princeton, New Jersey).

plates. There is, however, a tendency for the packing to orientate[19] owing to the pulsing action and this increases the stage height a little. The maximum flow rates (limited by flooding) in a pulsed packed column need be very little lower than when the same column is run without pulsing,[21] although a large reduction in height of a theoretical stage is obtained.

It is usual to operate either type of pulse column with the interface near the top, as with a static column, i.e. with the aqueous phase continuous. It is sometimes advantageous, however, to run with the solvent phase continuous, e.g. when it is particularly important to avoid the carry-over of solids from the interface into the solvent phase. The interface height is achieved in the normal manner, i.e. by balancing the column against a limb of aqueous phase which is leaving it and is vented to atmosphere. Adjustments to the height of the balancing limb would allow the interface to be in any desired position.

Mixer-Settlers

A large number of designs of horizontal liquid–liquid contacting equipment are available for solvent extraction purposes. Most of these can be classified as "mixer-settlers". A single stage of a mixer-settler consists of one vessel or part of a vessel in which the two solvent phases are agitated together so as to produce a turbulent and reasonably fine dispersion of one phase in the other, and a second vessel or zone which is sufficiently calm for the two phases to separate out again. The mixing may be accomplished, for example, by means of a rotary or reciprocating stirrer, a stream of air, or a device which injects intermittently pulses of the liquids into the main body of the two-phase dispersion. The settling chamber may contain baffles, or packing, or be elongated to assist separation of the two phases, and in some devices it is even considered necessary to assist separation by the use of centrifugal force.

When a series of mixer-settler stages are connected to form a counter-current extraction plant, means must be provided to allow the two liquids to flow in opposite directions. External pumps have been used between stages,[32] but this is rarely considered necessary. It is more usual either to utilize the pumping action of the mixing device to assist flow, or simply to rely upon the difference in densities of the two phases.

In-line mixer-settlers. If a vertical unpacked extraction column is allowed to lie horizontally, and the two immiscible solvents fed to different ends from elevated feed vessels, a single interface would be produced along the whole length, across which the transfer of a solute might be allowed to take place. The extraction would be extremely inefficient owing to the trivial interfacial area involved. The interfacial area might be improved by the use of a series of mixers at intervals, allowing gentle agitation in localized zones, with calm settling zones between. Unduly vigorous agitation in the mixing zones would, however, provide too great a resistance to flow and "flooding" would take place. This device might be regarded as a mixer-settler extractor of the "in-line" type, and more refined versions have been patented by Van Dijck,[33] Lowes[34] and Tanner.[35] One of these[35] consists of an elongated box divided into alternate mixing and settling chambers by means of baffles as shown in Fig. 4.18. Mixed phase is ejected in both directions from any individual mixer, into the two adjacent settlers. On settling into two phases in any stage, the phase which is passing in the "wrong" direction must reverse its flow and pass back again into the same mixer, along with other material of the same type from further along the extractor. A considerable degree of internal recirculation thus takes place in an "in-line" mixer-settler, and imposes a severe limitation upon its throughput, particularly when more than a small number of stages are involved, and it is only suited for certain special types of process where this arrangement is necessary.

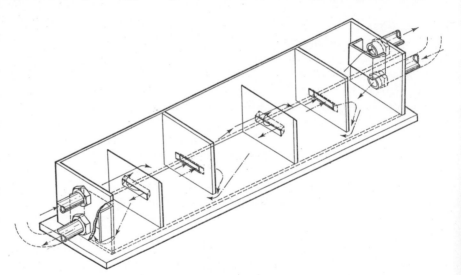

FIG. 4.18. In-line mixer-settler. (Lowes, L. and Tanner, M. C. U.K. Patent 835,282. By permission of the Controller of H.M. Stationery Office.)

A more usual mixer-settler flow pattern is obtained when the stages are arranged in a double bank (e.g. Ref. 36) as shown in Fig. 4.19; this avoids the high degree of internal recirculation. With this arrangement of mixers and settlers, a strict counter-current flow is not obtained at all times as in a column, since the two phases flow together from each mixer to its own settler, but this is unimportant in practice. The same flow pattern is sometimes obtained without the particularly geometrical arrangement shown in Fig. 4.19. It may be obtained with an in-line arrangement by the use of suitable external or internal pipes or channels.[34]

Mixer-settlers with both phases lifted. The engineering construction of mixer-settler stages varies enormously, but there are also important differences of principle between models. In one class, the two phases leaving a mixer are lifted or pumped into a settler, from which they leave in opposite directions by overflowing weirs. This principle is illustrated by means of the screw lift mixer-settler[4, 37] in Fig. 4.20 although this type is more suited for laboratory-scale processes than for full-scale plant. The airlift mixer-settler is almost identical to this, except that the mechanical screw mixer device is replaced by an airlift tube; this has been operated on a substantial production scale for the extraction of uranium. Figure 4.21 shows an airlift mixer-settler in which mixing is carried out at the same time as the lifting

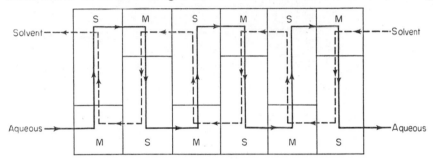

FIG. 4.19. Flow pattern through mixer-settlers arranged in a double bank.

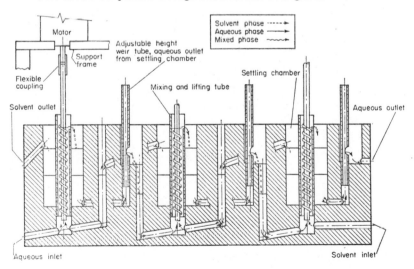

FIG. 4.20. Screw lift mixer-settler (U.K.A.E.A. copyright).

operation in the airlift tube, the two liquid phases being fed simultaneously with the air. The mixing residence time in this case depends upon the size of the tube and is rather small, but it is adequate for most purposes and has given stage efficiencies of about 90 per cent. If a longer residence time is required, a design similar to that in Fig. 4.22 can be adopted.[38] The mixing chamber A contains an air inlet tube B, passing inside and almost to the base of an outer tube C, which in turn approaches the base of the chamber.

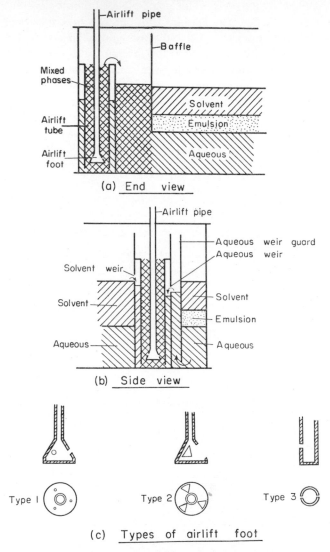

FIG. 4.21. Airlift mixer-settler stage: (a) end view; (b) side view; (c) types of airlift foot (U.K.A.E.A. copyright).

In operation, part of the air escapes from both tubes and serves to mix the two phases in the mixing chamber, whilst the remainder passes up the annular space between the two tubes and lifts the mixture into the upper chamber *D*. From here it flows via the port *E*, into the settler. After settling, the solvent phase flows through the port *F* into an adjoining mixer, and the

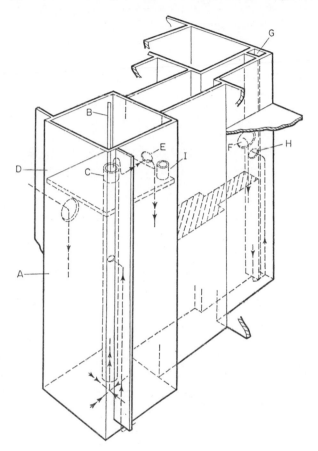

Fig. **4.22.** Airlift mixer-settler stage with long mixing residence time. (Jamrack, W. D. and Walker, H. A. U.K. Patent 774554. By permission of the Controller of H.M. Stationery Office.)

aqueous phase passes under a weir *G*, and through the port *H*, in the opposite direction. Disentrained air from the mixing chamber passes through the chimney *I* and mixes with the waste air from the lift tube, after which it can be piped away through the lid of the extractor. Stages in this model are close-packed with a narrow settler, so that a relatively large mixer can be employed, appropriate to a long residence time.

Airlift mixer-settlers have the advantage that they do not have moving mechanical parts in each stage requiring maintenance, but disadvantages sometimes arise owing to evaporation or the necessity to scrub the air free from traces of the rare metal solute before discharge to atmosphere. The amount of air can however be reduced in some designs to as little as five times the flow rate of the combined liquid phases. There is little or no saving in power by using air in place of mechanical stirrers, since the power is supplied to a compressor plant instead.

Mixer-settlers with dense phase lifted. A second class of mixer-settlers are used in which flow between stages is assisted by the pumping action of the mixer on the denser phase. This phase is lifted into the lighter phase, mixed, and passed into the settler. The level of the dense phase in the settler is controlled by the pump in the next stage. These designs are usually variants of the American "pump-mix" mixer-settler.[39, 40, 41] An early model [40] is shown in Fig. 4.23.

Stages are arranged in a double bank as for other mixer-settlers. Each mixing chamber contains a small centrifugal pump or impellor in the form of a hollow shaft fitted with a disc which has holes round its periphery, each hole being connected, to the hollow shaft. Rotation of this impellor immersed in a liquid sucks the liquid up the shaft and ejects it through the holes, thus causing mixing in the vicinity. Mixing may be assisted by fitting small turbine blades to the periphery of the disc between the holes.[40]

The mixing chamber runs flooded with mixed phase except for a small layer of heavy phase on the base, which in normal operation just reaches the lower tip of the impellor. The impellor thus accepts both mixed phase and dense phase, as long as it continues to be supplied with the latter. The dense phase is in fact supplied from the adjacent settler as shown, i.e. it flows under the baffle, over the weir and into the mixing chamber. The interface level in the settler is therefore controlled at a height depending upon the level of the impellor tip in the adjacent mixer. In practice, all impellors are usually at the same level, thus giving a constant interface level throughout the extractor. It is necessary for a simple weir to be employed on the aqueous outlet end of the extractor since the first settler is not followed by an impellor.

Light phase flows from the adjacent settler on the opposite side of the mixer, from a higher level. Its flow is impeded by a baffle which is intended to prevent mixed phase from accidentally leaving the mixer in the opposite direction.

The mixed phases leaving the impellor are further stirred in the mixing chamber and then leave it by flowing between the baffles protecting the mixed phase port. These baffles are arranged to accept liquor from the pump with the minimum of "by-passing", and rotation of the pump in the opposite direction is distinctly less satisfactory.

It will be noted from Fig. 4.23, that the lower end of the impellor protrudes through a hole in a horizontal plate. The size of the remaining annular gap, though not critical, is of some importance in controlling the degree of internal recirculation in the mixer, which affects the stage efficiency to some extent. Stage efficiencies of about 95 per cent can be obtained in practice.

The stirrers can be driven individually by small electric motors, or power can be taken from a single large motor by means of belts, gear trains, or flexible drives as required. The optimum speed of rotation varies with the

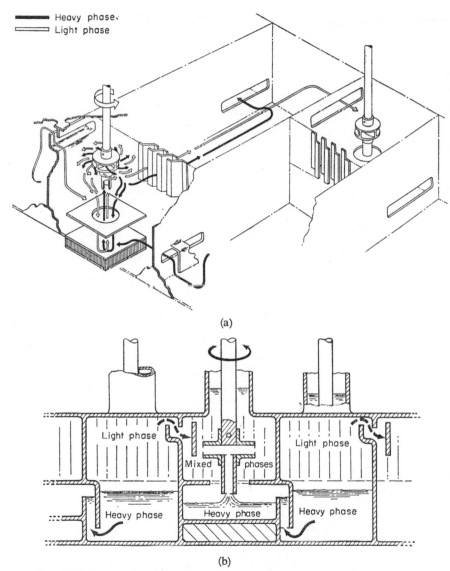

FIG. 4.23. Pump-mix mixer-settler: (a) Schematic drawing showing direction of flow; (b) Elevation showing three adjacent stages (Coplan, B. V., Davidson, J. K. and Zebroski, E. L., Ref. 40).

solvent extraction system but is usually in the range 300–600 rev/min. A higher speed does not necessarily increase the mixing efficiency and might cause such a fine dispersion of one phase in the other that the rate of settling is reduced.

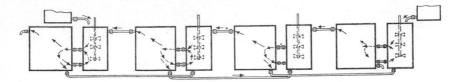

Fig. 4.24. Holley Mott Extractor (Davis, M. W., Hicks, T. E. and Vermeulen, T., Ref. 43).

Simple stirred mixer-settlers. The flow of liquors in some mixer-settlers is by gravity only and is not dependent upon any pumping action of the stirrers. The Holley Mott extractor[42] was probably the first of this type, but it is primarily suited for a process with a long residence time and therefore a small throughput for a given size of unit. The mixers and settlers are separate cylindrical vessels connected by pipes, the mixers being agitated by multi-bladed stirrers, as shown in Fig. 4.24. The light phase is fed into a mixer at one end and the mixed phases pass through a pipe at an intermediate level into the first settler. From here the light phase overflows to the second mixer and the series of operations is repeated at each stage down the system. The dense phase enters the mixer at the other end, mixed phases pass along the pipe leading to the appropriate settler, and the dense phase leaves, via a pipe at the base of the settler, for the next mixer up the system, the cycle of operations being repeated again at each stage. In this manner, a rather slow, almost counter-current flow is achieved throughout the whole extractor. Light phase leaves the settler at one end via an overflow pipe, and dense phase leaves the settler at the other end via a pipe at one end with an adjustable valve. Since many of the original applications of the Holley Mott extractor involved the use of a very high solvent-to-aqueous ratio, an internal recirculation pipe was added to each stage at a low level, between every settler and its corresponding mixer. This allowed a proportion of the dense phase to flow back from the settler to the mixer from which it came, with the object of increasing the stage efficiency and maintaining a solvent-to-aqueous phase ratio lower than the ratio of feeds.[43] The proportion of dense phase recirculation was adjustable by means of valves, one on each recirculation line.

The mixer-settler developed by the U.S. Standard Oil Development Company[43] is similar in principle to the Holley Mott extractor, but a box type of construction is adopted with a double bank arrangement, as used by the later mixer-settlers in which pumping is used to aid flow. Unlike the Holley Mott extractor, the Standard Oil model is able to use ports instead of pipes, for the flow of mixed phases from mixer to settler and of the separate phases from settler to adjacent mixers. This allows greater throughputs, but baffles are necessary to prevent the agitation in the mixers from interfering with settling in the settler compartments. Antechambers are provided to prevent back mixing of the two phases before they enter the mixer, i.e. the transfer of mixed phase back into the two settlers feeding any individual mixer. The flow of dense phase leaving one end of the extractor also is not controlled by means of a valve but is led over a weir. The height of this weir controls the interface in the end settler, the other interfaces depending upon the height of the mixed phase port.

Many other individual mixer-settlers are now in effect modelled upon the Standard Oil type of extractor, including, for example, those used for the extraction of uranium in the U.K. Atomic Energy Authority's Springfields Works.[44] The aim in these, and other modern mixer-settlers, is to reduce the engineering design to its simplest terms,[45] e.g. the problem of backmixing is overcome by the use of a baffle and without the use of an antechamber, despite experience to the contrary elsewhere.[43] A simple mixer-settler is illustrated in Fig. 4.25 and the essential principles of design, assuming negligbible pressure drops across the ports, can be deduced from Fig. 4.26. These are listed as follows:[45]

1. *Mixer and settler liquor levels.* A difference in total liquor level exists between mixers and settlers so that the light phase can flow over a weir from a mixer. This can be deduced simply from the hydrostatic balance about the mixed phase port A between a mixer and its own settler,

i.e. $$\rho_m h_1 = \rho_L h_2$$

but since ρ_2 is less than ρ_m, then h_2 must be greater than h_1. The total liquor level in the settlers is therefore fixed by the height of the light phase ports or weirs B, and the level of mixed phases in the mixers is related to this, depending upon the proportion of the two phases in the mixture and their densities.

2. *Ratio of phases in mixers.* The phase ratio in the mixers is equal to the ratio of the two feeds to the extractor under steady-state conditions. This must apply since, with complete mixing, the proportions of the two phases leaving each stage are the same as those entering each stage, and entering or leaving the extractor as a whole, otherwise an outlet would be required for the surplus of either phase.

3. *Settler interface levels.* The interface level in the end stage where the dense phase leaves the extractor is simply controlled by means of a dense phase overflow weir. This is set at a suitable height to maintain the interface below the level of the mixed phase port.

The level of the interfaces in the other settlers may be calculated, Fig. 4.26, assuming negligible change of density from stage to stage, and

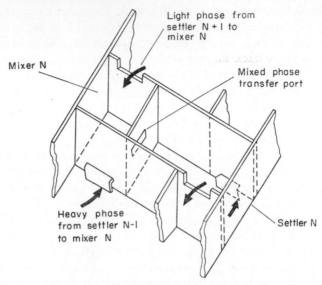

FIG. 4.25. The mixer-settler box contactor (Page, H., Shortis, L. P. and Dukes, J. A., Ref. 44).

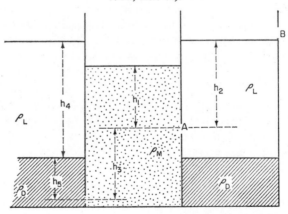

FIG. 4.26. Interface levels in simple mixer-settler.

negligible pressure drops across the dense phase and mixed phase ports.

Taking a balance over the dense phase ports,

$$(h_1 + h_3)\rho_m = h_5\rho_D + h_4\rho_L$$

but

$$h_4 + h_5 = h_2 + h_3$$

Therefore

$$h_1\rho_m + h_3\rho_m = h_5\rho_D + h_2\rho_L + h_3\rho_L - h_5\rho_L$$

Taking a balance over the mixed phase port,

$$h_1\rho_m = h_2\rho_L,$$

Therefore

$$h_3(\rho_m - \rho_L) = h_5(\rho_D - \rho_L)$$

i.e.

$$h_5 = h_3\left(\frac{\rho_m - \rho_L}{\rho_D - \rho_L}\right)$$

But

$$\rho_m(F_L + F_D) = \rho_L F_L + \rho_D F_D$$

(where F_L and F_D are the flow rates of the light phase and dense phase respectively)
Therefore

$$h_5 = h_3\left(\frac{\dfrac{\rho_L F_L + \rho_D F_D}{F_L + F_D} - \rho_L}{\rho_D - \rho_L}\right)$$

$$= h_3\left(\frac{\rho_L F_L + \rho_D F_D - \rho_L F_L - \rho_L F_D}{(\rho_D - \rho_L)(F_L + F_D)}\right)$$

$$= h_3\left(\frac{\rho_D F_D - \rho_L F_D}{(\rho_D - \rho_L)(F_L + F_D)}\right)$$

$$h_5 = h_3\left(\frac{F_D}{F_L + F_D}\right)$$

$$h_5 = h_3 f_D$$

(where f_D is the volume fraction of the dense phase), i.e. the interface levels are dependent upon the height of the mixed phase ports and the fraction of aqueous phase in the total flow to the extractor. Since the latter by definition is less than unity, the interface levels will be lower than the height of the mixed phase ports.

When density changes take place from stage to stage as a result of mass transfer of a heavy solute from dense to light phase, the interface is lowered, and conversely it is increased by mass transfer from the light to the dense phase. In practice appropriate corrections must also be applied to take account of pressure drops across the transfer ports.

The type of stirrer used in a simple stirred mixer-settler is relatively unimportant provided it mixes the two phases adequately. It is clearly not necessary for it to have any pumping action. Neither is it essential for any individual stirrer to be operable at any particular time, since the effect of a breakdown in a single stage is merely to lose the extraction effect of that stage. An interface will form in the faulty mixing chamber at the level of the mixed phase port and both phases will take their normal paths, except without mixing.

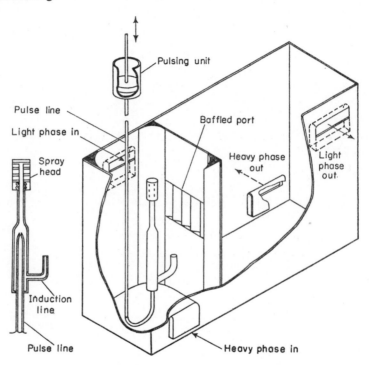

FIG. 4.27. Pulsed mixer-settler (Thornton, J. D. Ref. 46).

A novel type of mixing device for use with the simple gravity-flow type of mixer-settler consists of a pulsed ejector[46] as shown in Fig. 4.27. An external pulsing unit, e.g. a piston type pump without non-return valves, is connected to a jet in the mixing compartment. This is shrouded by an induction pipe which, on the compression stroke, draws dense phase from the bottom of the mixer and disposes it through a small spray head. Mixing thus takes place during half the pulse cycle, whilst the unit fills again during the other half cycle. It would be possible to run two units in the same mixing chamber, 180° out of phase, possibly both actuated by opposite ends of the same piston, to give continuous mixing. Advantages claimed for this include freedom from mechanical breakdown of the mixer-settler extractor, since the only moving parts are associated with the pulsing unit, which can be located away from the mixer-settlers. This is useful when processing poisonous or radioactive materials.

Centrifugal extractors

Centrifugal extractors have been employed for liquid–liquid extraction processes, some resembling columns and others having similarities to mixer-settlers. These often have a high throughput and short residence time and are therefore useful for the extraction of, for example, biochemical materials which tend to decompose quickly. They have not usually been considered economic for use in the rare metal extraction field in view of their very high cost when fabricated in stainless-steel, or other corrosion resistant materials, in the large sizes which would often be necessary.

The Podbielniak extractor[16, 46] consists of a long narrow passage coiled in the form of a spiral around a shaft which is capable of rotating at 2000 to 5000 rev/min. The dense phase is fed through one end of the shaft and into the centre of the spiral, whilst the light phase is fed through the other end of the shaft to the exterior of the spiral. The centrifugal force, equivalent to several thousand times that of gravity, causes the dense phase to pass towards the outer coils of the spiral, and the light phase to the inner coils, in a counter-current manner. The performance of the unit is equivalent to a column of a few theoretical stages with a diameter of several feet.

The Luwesta extractor[16, 47] is a development of the Coutor extractor.[47] It is essentially a three-stage mixer-settler in which separation is carried out by centrifugal means, in a similar manner to a cream separator. Mixing occurs by means of a spray disc or alternatively when the two phases are collected simultaneously, in a collector disc. Light phase flows through the three stages in succession in one direction, and the dense phase in the opposite direction.

Auxiliary equipment

Apart from the extraction equipment itself, columns, mixer-settlers, or centrifugal extractors, the remainder of the plant is usually fairly conventional. It is usually necessary to provide vessels for "conditioning" the feed solution to the correct acidity or for correcting the concentrations of the principal solute or other salts. This may be carried out continuously or in special batch conditioning vessels. In the latter case, batch feed vessels will also no doubt be required.

The flow of the various feeds to the extraction system may be by gravity from elevated feed vessels via, for example, rotameter type flowmeters. It is now becoming common practice to feed from tanks at a similar level to the extractors, via metering pumps. The accuracy required depends upon the design of the particular extraction system, but a sufficient margin is normally present to allow variations of a few per cent either way.

In multi-cycle processes, conditioning vessels are usually required between each solvent cycle, and an evaporator may also sometimes be introduced in order to keep the feed concentration to the second cycle at a low value and therefore economize in the size of the second-cycle extraction plant.

After extraction, the expended aqueous raffinate stream may have an undue proportion of the organic solvent entrained in it, sufficient to warrant the use of a phase separator. This is normally only a delay vessel with provision for removal of the two phases separately. With normal care in design and operation, entrainment losses of solvent can be reduced below 0·1 per cent of the solvent usage, for each circuit of the plant.

Since the aqueous raffinate is often strongly acidic, it may require neutralization before discharge, and plant for this may be provided *in situ*, to minimize corrosion of drain lines, etc., through which the liquor passes subsequently.

The recycled solvent is usually pumped to a feed stock tank for re-use, after appropriate counter-current washing, if required. Stable solvents can usually be selected which do not require replacement, except to make up for process losses.

PURIFICATION OF URANIUM BY SOLVENT EXTRACTION

Solvent extraction can be used at two stages in the refining of uranium. The low-grade ore, after leaching at the mine head, usually with dilute acid or alkali, can be purified with solvent as an alternative to ion-exchange, to form a "concentrate" of above 50 per cent uranium content. This is suitable for shipping to the plant where metal is to be produced, and a further solvent extraction stage can be employed there, in order to achieve the very high purity required for nuclear purposes. The second solvent process is at much higher uranium concentrations than the first and consequently there are large differences in the type of process used in the two cases.

Extraction from ore leach liquors

A solvent to be used for the extraction from ore leach liquors, which may only contain uranium to the extent of about 1 g/l., must be relatively inexpensive in view of the large quantity used per tonne of purified product. It is usual, therefore, to select an organic compound which has an extremely high distribution coefficient for uranium, usually over 100, and to use it in the form of a very dilute solution in a cheap inert diluent. The distribution coefficient for uranium with the diluted solvent may be below 10.

The early organic solvents to be developed for uranium extraction at higher concentrations were for use with nitrate solutions, and were therefore unsuitable for extraction from the typical dilute sulphuric acid ore leach liquors. Two series of solvents have however been developed specially for this purpose, and they can be classed generally as higher alkyl amines (primary, secondary and tertiary), and alkyl organophosphorus compounds. The latter include[48] mono-, di- and tri-alkyl phosphates, alkyl phosphoric acids and their esters, alkyl phosphites, phosphine oxides and alkyl diphosphates and diphosphonates. Examples of both types are given by Brown *et al.*[49] in Table 2 on pages 164 and 165 and also by Moore *et al.*[50]

These solvents are available from American sources. A highly satisfactory amine solvent, tri (3 : 5 : 5 trimethylhexyl) amine, is also marketed in the U.K. by Imperial Chemical Industries Ltd., and a process using it has been developed by the National Chemical Laboratory at Teddington.[51]

Kerosene, a heavy aromatic naphtha,[52] or petroleum products with a high aromatic content such as "Amsco G", "Solvesso 100", etc., have been used as diluents. A small proportion of a long chain alcohol such as tridecanol,[52] or nonanol,[51] is sometimes added also, to increase the solubility, in the case of amine solvents. It is also claimed to improve aqueous-solvent phase separation.[49] $0 \cdot 1 M$ amine and $2 \cdot 3$ per cent alcohol are typical concentrations.

The diluted solvent must be fairly selective for uranium, stable under the conditions of use, and relatively insoluble in aqueous systems.

Selectivity for uranium increases in general from primary to tertiary compounds in the amine class[53] and is highly dependent upon structure in the organophosphorus compounds. It is very difficult to prevent any ferric iron present from extracting with the uranium in the case of the phosphate solvents. Consequently, it is necessary to remove the ferric iron before extraction, the usual method being to reduce it to ferrous ion by the addition of scrap iron.

Amine extraction. The amine extraction mechanism can be described in two different ways.[52] In a sulphuric acid medium, the amine (tertiary) will be present in the acid sulphate form $(R_3NH)_2SO_4$, and this can be assumed to form an addition compound with the uranyl sulphate, i.e.

$$UO_2^{++} + SO_4^{--} \rightleftharpoons UO_2SO_4$$

$$(R_3NH)_2SO_4 + UO_2SO_4 \rightleftharpoons (R_3NH)_2UO_2(SO_4)_2$$

Alternatively, the sulphate ion of the amine sulphate may be assumed to exchange with the anionic uranyl sulphate complex which is known to be present in solution, i.e.

$$UO_2^{++} + 2SO_4^{--} \rightleftharpoons UO_2(SO_4)_2^{--}$$

$$(R_3NH)_2SO_4 + UO_2(SO_4)_2^{--} \rightleftharpoons (R_3NH)_2UO_2(SO_4)_2 + SO_4^{--}$$

The compound present in the solvent phase is identical by either mechanism. The second mechanism is essentially the same as that involved when

TABLE 2

STRUCTURES AND SOURCES OF AMINE AND PHOSPHATE SOLVENTS

ADM   Archer-Daniels-Midland Co., Minneapolis, Minn.
Armour   Armour Chemical Division, Chicago, Ill.
Carbide Union Carbide Chemicals Co., New York, N.Y.
CS   Commercial Solvents Corp., Terre Haute, Ind.
EK   Distillation Products Industries, Eastman Kodak Co., Rochester, N.Y.
GM   General Mills, Inc., Kankakee, Ill.
Gulf   Gulf Oil Corporation, Pittsburgh, Pa.
Monsanto Monsanto Chemical Co., St. Louis, Mo.
R and H Rohm and Haas Co., Philadelphia, Pa.
Shea   Shea Chemical Corp., New York, N.Y.
VC   Virginia-Carolina Chemical Corp., Richmond, Va.

AMINES

Tri-iso-octylamine (Carbide, Gulf),

$$N-[-CH_2CH_2\overset{CH_3}{\underset{|}{C}}HCH_2\overset{CH_3}{\underset{|}{C}}HCH_3]_3$$

"Iso-octyl" = mixture of dimethylhexyls and methylheptyls, etc., principally 3,5-, 4,5-, and 3,4-dimethylhexyl

Trilaurylamine (ADM, Armour),

$$N-[-(CH_2)_{11}CH_3]_3$$

Tri-fatty Amine RC-3749 (GM),

$$N-[-(CH_2)_nCH_3]_3$$

Mixed n-octyl and n-decyl alkyls

Di(tridecyl)amine (Carbide),

$$HN-[-CH_2CH_2-C_{11}H_{23}]_2$$

"Tridecyl" = mixture of 13-carbon alkyls from tetrapropylene

Amine 9D–178 (R and H), (Amberlite LA-1)

$$CH_3CH_2CH_2\overset{CH_3}{\underset{\underset{CH_3}{|}}{C}}CH_2CH{:}CHCH_2-\overset{H}{\underset{|}{N}}-\overset{CH_3}{\underset{\underset{CH_3}{|}}{C}}CH_2CH_2\overset{CH_3}{\underset{\underset{CH_3}{|}}{C}}CH_3$$

N-Dodecenyl (trialkylmethyl)amine; trialkylmethyl = homologous mixture, 12–15 carbon atoms

Amberlite LA-2 (R and H),

$$CH_3(CH_2)_{11}-\overset{H}{\underset{|}{N}}-\overset{CH_3}{\underset{\underset{CH_3}{|}}{C}}CH_2\overset{CH_3}{\underset{\underset{CH_3}{|}}{C}}CH_2CCH_3$$

N-Lauryl(trialkylmethyl)amine; trialkylmethyl = homologous mixture, 12–15 carbon atoms

Amine S-24 (Carbide)

$$HN-\left[-CH\overset{\displaystyle CH_2\overset{CH_3}{\underset{|}{C}}HCH_2\overset{CH_3}{\underset{|}{C}}HCH_3}{\underset{\displaystyle CH_2\overset{CH_3}{\underset{|}{C}}HCH_3}{}}\right]_2$$

Bis(1-isobutyl-3, 5-dimethylhexyl)—amine

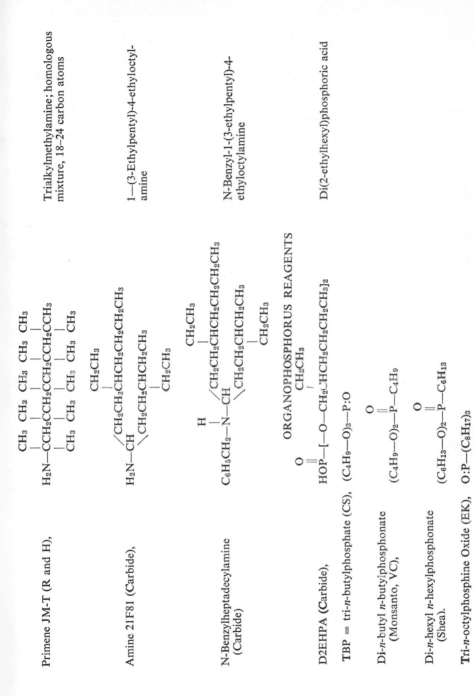

Primene JM-T (R and H),

Trialkylmethylamine; homologous mixture, 18–24 carbon atoms

Amine 21F81 (Carbide),

1—(3-Ethylpentyl)-4-ethyloctyl-amine

N-Benzylheptadecylamine (Carbide)

N-Benzyl-1-(3-ethylpentyl)-4-ethyloctylamine

ORGANOPHOSPHORUS REAGENTS

D2EHPA (Carbide),

Di(2-ethylhexyl)phosphoric acid

TBP = tri-n-butylphosphate (CS), $(C_4H_9—O)_3—P:O$

Di-n-butyl n-butylphosphonate (Monsanto, VC), $(C_4H_9—O)_2—P—C_4H_9$

Di-n-hexyl n-hexylphosphonate (Shea). $(C_6H_{13}—O)_2—P—C_6H_{13}$

Tri-n-octylphosphine Oxide (EK), $O:P—(C_8H_{17})_3$

From BROWN, K. B. et al., Proc. 2nd U.N. Conf. on the Peaceful Uses of Atomic Energy. United Nations, New York, vol. 3, p. 485.

uranium is absorbed by an ion-exchange resin, and for this reason the amine extractants have been referred to as "liquid anion-exchangers."[54]

Backwashing of uranium from an amine solvent may be carried out by exchange of the uranyl sulphate anion with another anion, nitrate or chloride usually being employed, for example 1N sodium chloride, 0·1N sulphuric acid solution, i.e.

$$(R_3NH)_2UO_2(SO_4)_2 + 2Cl^- \rightleftharpoons 2R_3NHCl + UO_2^{++} + 2SO_4^{--}$$

An alternative method is to hydrolyse the amine salt by means of sodium carbonate:

$$(R_3NH)_2UO_2(SO_4)_2 + 4Na_2CO_3 \rightarrow 2R_3N +$$
$$+ Na_4UO_2(CO_3)_3 + 2Na_2SO_4 + H_2O + CO_2$$

The complex carbonate is soluble and consequently does not precipitate in the backwash extractor. Other alkalis have been used which form precipitates, e.g. backwashing can be carried out with a slurry of magnesium oxide, i.e.

$$2(R_3NH)_2UO_2(SO_4)_2 + 5MgO \rightarrow 4R_3N + MgU_2O_7 + 4MgSO_4 + 2H_2O.$$

In this case it is advisable to carry out backwashing of the solvent extract either batchwise or in a suitable extractor, such as a pulsed column, which will handle slurries satisfactorily.

Amine solvents tend to be expensive and therefore losses must be reduced to the minimum on each cycle. In general, it is advisable to select an amine with a solubility below about 50 mg/l. in the aqueous phases with which it is in contact. In most processes, the overall loss per cycle from both solubility in the raffinate and backwash liquors, and entrainment in both liquors, can be maintained below 0·05 per cent, which is satisfactory.

A generalized flowsheet for amine extraction, known in the United States as the "Amex process", is shown in Fig. 4.28. Three to five stages suffice for 99·5 per cent extraction of uranium into solvent with a solvent to aqueous ratio of about 0·25. No impurity stripping section is used. The backwashing extractor ("stripping" in U.S. terminology) contains one to four stages and, depending upon the reagent selected, the aqueous to solvent ratio is about 0·1 to 0·2. The solvent can be recycled directly or may pass through a single-stage regeneration extractor. The latter is particularly advisable if a chloride backwashing system is employed, in order to prevent the amine carrying chloride to the first extractor, which may not be constructed to withstand corrosion by hydrochloric acid. This type of flowsheet achieves a fairly high overall product concentration, i.e. from 1·2 g/l. to 20–40 g/l. besides providing a product with a uranium concentration in excess of 75 per cent.

A number of plants are operating on Amex flowsheets of the above type in the United States and Canada. Mixer-settler extractors are usually favoured, designed individually for each plant, as, for example, at the Port Radium plant of Eldorado Mining and Refining Ltd., the Ambrosia Lake Plant in New Mexico and that at Lakeview, Oregon. The Texas-Zinc Company plant at Mexican Hat, Utah, is however based upon Podbielniak centrifugal extractors. Transfer rates are fairly rapid, mixer residence times being about 0·3 min each in forward extraction and 1 min in backwash extraction. One large Amex plant with a capacity of 1,150,000 gal/day has mixers each of 2600 gal capacity and cylindrical settlers 40 ft in diameter.

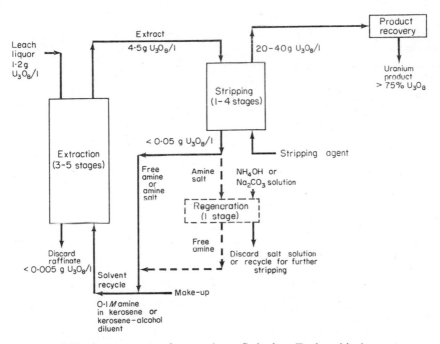

FIG. 4.28. Amex process for uranium. Stripping (Backwashing) agents: (a) Na_2CO_3 sol'n, e.g. 0·75M Na_2CO_3; (b) Chloride sol'n, e.g. 1·0M NaCl–0·05M H_2SO_4; (c) Nitrate sol'n, e.g. 0·9M NH_4NO_3–0·1M HNO_3; (d) MgO slurry, e.g. 20 g MgO/1. (Brown, K.B. *et al. Proc. 2nd U. N. Conf. on the Peaceful Uses of Atomic Energy, United Nations, New York,* vol. 3., p. 477).

An amine process has been devised for the simultaneous extraction of uranium and thorium from the ore in the Bancroft area of Ontario in Canada.[55] A sulphate leach liquor is extracted in four mixer-settler stages, with 5 per cent tri-iso-octyl amine and 2 per cent *n*-decyl alcohol in kerosene, to remove uranium. Thorium is then extracted from the raffinate by means of 5 per cent di-tridecyl amine in another four-stage mixer-settler. Uranium and thorium are backwashed separately by 10 per cent sodium carbonate solution and precipitated with sodium hydroxide. Recovery efficiencies are 99 per cent for uranium and 95 to 99 per cent for thorium.

Phosphate extraction. Of the phosphate solvents, two in particular have achieved prominence for the extraction of uranium from low-grade ore leach liquors, monododecylphosphoric acid (DDPA) and di (2-ethylhexyl) phosphoric acid (D2EHPA), both being readily available in commercial quantities. The compounds are weak acids which exchange hydrogen ions for uranyl ions in the solvent phase, the distribution coefficient decreasing at high acidities. Increased sulphate ion concentration also depresses the distribution coefficient owing to its complexing action on the uranyl ions, making them less readily available for reaction with the organic solvents.

Backwashing of the phosphate solvents can be a reverse of the extraction procedure, i.e. a high hydrogen ion concentration may be provided by a fairly concentrated acid solution, so depressing the distribution coefficient. Sodium carbonate or ammonium carbonate solutions are alternative backwashing reagents which are more satisfactory from the standpoint of plant materials of construction. Their action is to complex the uranium by forming the aqueous soluble double carbonates, which are insoluble in the solvent phase.

The forward distribution coefficient of D2EHPA can be increased out of proportion by the addition of relatively small quantities of other organic phosphorus compounds, such as tributyl phosphate or tributyl phosphine oxide, etc. Values of several thousand are obtained at the low uranium concentrations prevailing in ore leach liquors.

The solubilities of the phosphate solvents in the aqueous phases with which they are in contact are quite low, of the order of a few tens of parts per million, being greatest in the carbonate backwash solutions. Overall solvent losses, including those due to entrainment, are about 0.05 per cent, as for "Amex" process.

A generalized flowsheet for the phosphate extraction process or "Dapex" process is shown in Fig. 4.29.[49] The flowsheet is broadly comparable with the "Amex" flowsheet but uses 0·1M D2EHPA mixed with 0·1M TBP in a kerosene diluent. 99·5 per cent extraction is achieved in 3–6 stages and an aqueous to solvent ratio of about 0·25, but with a feed solution which has first been reduced with scrap iron to reduce the ferric iron. Again, no impurity stripping section (U.K. terminology) is considered necessary. 2–3-stage backwashing (U.S. terminology: "stripping") with a relatively small volume, and 10–20 per cent excess, of 1M sodium carbonate solution, gives a product of 50–65 g/l., somewhat higher than by the "Amex" process. This is neutralized with sulphuric acid before precipitation of uranium with ammonia, as a 75 per cent concentrate. The used solvent can be recycled as the sodium salt directly, without treatment. Processes of this type using

D2EHPA mixtures have been installed by various companies in the United States, at Shiprock in New Mexico, Grand Junction, Rifle and Gunnison in Colorado and Riverton in Wyoming. DDPA in kerosene is used in the Vitro Uranium Company's plants at Salt Lake City[56] and Canonsbury. In the former, at least, a trimethyl nonanol additive is employed. Backwashing is with hydrochloric acid, which is afterwards recovered by evaporation in Karbate or Teflon lined plant.

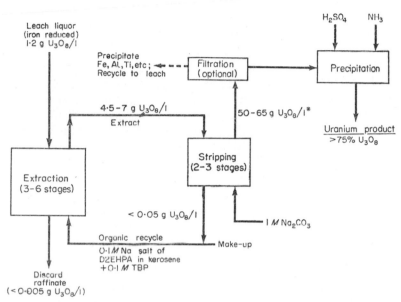

FIG. 4.29. Dapex process for uranium. *Owing to transfer of water to the solvent, the aqueous volume decreases during stripping which raises the uranium concentration above that expected from the initial flow volumes (Brown, K. B. *et al. Proc. 2nd U.N. Conf. on the Peaceful Uses of Atomic Energy, United Nations, New York*, vol. 3, p. 481).

Mixer-settler type plants are favoured, designed with residence times of about 2–5 min in each forward extraction mixer stage and 1 min for each backwash mixer, longer times than are considered necessary in the "Amex" process. In both cases, the residence times in the settlers is insufficient to prevent entrainment in most of the stages, but it is kept to a minimum of about 0·02 per cent by the use of special settlers with longer residence times for the end stages where the outgoing streams leave. Settling may also be accelerated by passing the raffinate through coarse filters of cloth or glass wool, etc., to promote coalescence of the solvent droplets. It is sometimes necessary with "Dapex" (or "Amex") solvents to ensure water-in-oil rather than oil-in-water dispersions since the latter tend to be too stable with some leach liquors. It is claimed[49] that water-in-oil dispersions can easily be obtained by starting the mixers running in solvent only, before supplying the aqueous feed. Thereafter, more than 50 per cent solvent is preferred in the solvent-to-aqueous mixture contained in the mixing chambers. This does not always allow employment of the simple gravity type of mixer-settler, where the phase ratio in the mixers is dependent upon the ratio of the feeds.

Design data for a "Dapex" plant to handle 200 tons of ore per day have been quoted.[49] The leach liquor at 100,000 gal/day would pass, with solvent, through mixers each of 350 gal capacity and fitted with 10 h.p. drives. Settlers would be about 12 ft in diameter. In the backwash extractor, mixer capacities would be 50 gal each, with 1·5 h.p. drives, and settlers 5 ft in diameter.

In order to avoid the expensive filtration stage immediately prior to solvent extraction, the extraction is sometimes carried out directly on the leach liquor slurry, where conditions are favourable. The "Dapex" process is then used, since the amine solvents are sorbed readily on to solid surfaces, and entrainment of amines is excessive. Pulsed columns of the sieve-plate type are considered ideal extraction plant in this case, although mixer-settlers have also been employed. [57, 58, 59]

A logical step further is to use a "non-aqueous extraction process". For example, in one of them[57] the ore is pugged with sulphuric acid, wetted with a little ammonium nitrate solution and then percolated with 5 per cent TBP in kerosene. Solvent losses are excessive, even after recovery by means of a kerosene wash, although a high purity product is obtained after backwashing.

A similar non-aqueous process has been decribed [60] using iso-octyl phosphoric acid, monododecyl phosphoric acid or monoheptadecyl phosphoric acid as solvents, none of which require the ammonium nitrate addition. Methyl ethyl ketone, other ketones, or kerosene are suitable diluents. The sulphuric acid usage is much less than that normally required for, for example, a dilute acid leach of the carnotite ore used, since the high proportion of lime present in the ore is not taken into solution. Hydrochloric acid is preferable for backwashing the uranium.

The carnotite ore of the Colorado Plateau area contains a workable proportion of vanadium in addition to uranium, and processes have been devised for the simultaneous recovery of both elements by solvent extraction methods. The Shiprock plant in New Mexico, for example,[61] extracts first the uranium from a sulphate leach liquor, by means of a solvent containing 10 per cent D2EHPA with 2·5 per cent TBP, in kerosene. A second solvent cycle, with different proportions of the two phosphates, then extracts vanadium from the first cycle raffinate. Sodium carbonate is then used for backwashing the uranium and 10 per cent sulphuric acid for the vanadium.

The purity of the uranium produced by any of the above solvent extraction processes is fairly high with respect to most elements, and it is usually superior to the product from ion-exchange. However, a few elements such as iron often extract along with the uranium in percentage quantities, whilst many others are present in the resulting concentrate to the extent of tens or hundreds of parts per million. This type of material does not meet the exacting specifications which are imposed upon uranium to be used as a nuclear fuel, and a final purification is required, again by solvent extraction, at the refinery associated with the metal production plant.

Final solvent purification of uranium

Obsolete ether process. The refining of reactor grade uranium, both at the U.K. Springfields Works[62, 63] and the U.S. Mallinckrodt Works at St. Louis,[64] originally involved a solvent extraction stage using di-ethyl ether. Springfields for about 10 years used a high-grade pitchblende from the Belgian Congo, concentrated by physical means, as its principal feed material. This was ground and dissolved in sulphuric acid, filtered to remove radium and other impurities, precipitated either as uranium peroxide or ammonium di-uranate, redissolved in nitric acid, evaporated to a composition of $UO_2(NO_3)_26H_2O$ and filtered before ether purification. Ether extraction was carried out at about 35°C in a simple co-current extractor. This involved a single stage in which a stream of hot uranium solution continuously contacted a stream of cold ether. Consequently, a high proportion of the uranium remained unextracted with the impurities, and was recycled. A single-stage warm water strip removed further impurities, along with a further high proportion of the uranium. The ether was finally backwashed, again in a single stage, with a rather larger volume of cold water. The two impurity fractions were recycled back to the evaporator feed point for recovery of uranium, but the first of these was subjected to a prior peroxide precipitation to provide a purge for the impurities. Virtually the whole plant was fabricated of stainless-steel. Ion-exchange concentrates from Australia, South Africa and the Belgian Congo, etc., were also processed via this route in the later years, although the degree of purification available by the process was often more than necessary.

Typical chemical analyses of uranium concentrates from various sources[65] see Table 3.

A similar batch ether process was operated on a scale of 1 ton/day by the U.S. Mallinckrodt Works as early as 1942.[66] It was, however, modified in 1946 to a counter-current "acid ether" process using 40 ft high columns of about four theoretical stages. These columns had centrifugal pumps and jet mixers at 4 ft intervals, and relatively calm zones between. Advantage was taken of the increased uranium distribution coefficient in the presence of excess nitric acid, to reduce the solvent-to-aqueous flow ratio and achieve a

TABLE 3

Impurity	Concentration in various concentrates (%)			
	South African	*Australian*	*Canadian*	*American*
Uranium (U_3O_8) . .	75	65	70	65
Sulphate (SO_4) . .	7	1	1·5	0·01
Phosphate (PO_4) . .	0·06	1	1·5	0·08
Silicon (SiO_2) . .	1·2	3·5	5·4	1·7
Calcium (CaO) . .	0·4	0·8	0·5	0·3
Magnesium (MgO) . .	0·4	5·5	0·2	0·2
Vanadium (V_2O_5) . .	0·3	0·02	0·5	5·2
Molybdenum (MoO_3). .	0·01	<0·001	<0·001	<0·001
Iron (Fe) . . .	0·25	2	0·4	0·03
Aluminium (Al_2O_3) .	0·30	1	1	0·04
Nickel (Ni) . .	0·33	0·2	0·05	—
Chromium (Cr) . . .	—	0·5	—	—
Sodium (Na) . . .	—	0·2	8	7·7
Ammonium (NH_3) . .	1–3	0·01	—	0–3·5
Moisture (120°C, 2 hr) .	2–5	7	0·8	14
Chlorine (Cl) . .	1·16	1	0·04	0·03
Fluorine (F) . . .	—	0·03	—	0·06
Loss on ignition (750°C) .	15·25	15	5·8	16·8
Loss on ignition (1000°C) .	15·26	16	6·1	16·8

high extraction efficiency without recycling. The whole of the product, however, was required to pass through a neutral ether extraction process afterwards, in order to remove certain impurities such as molybdenum, from which the acid ether process does not give adequate decontamination. A typical analysis of the final product was as follows:

	ppm
Iron	11
Molybdenum	< 1
Silver	< 0·1
Chromium	2
Copper	< 1
Nickel	3
Lead	< 1
Tin	< 1
Boron	< 0·15
Nitric acid insolubles	10

New TBP process. The introduction of a more elegant multi-stage counter-current TBP extraction process at Springfields was delayed because of the successful operation of the ether process. Although ether is a potentially hazardous solvent, precautions were always adequate to prevent completely any fire incident. The present TBP process[44] is designed to use principally ion-exchange concentrates as feed materials which may be sodium, ammonium, or magnesium di-uranates, although it is also suitable for high-grade pitchblende with only minor modifications to the feed stage and the introduction of radiation shielding facilities.

Concentrates containing up to 80 per cent uranium are first dissolved by nitric acid in stainless-steel, steam-heated, stirred vessels. The slurry is then fed to a bank of rotary vacuum filters where silica and small amounts of other insoluble impurities are removed. These filters are of the pre-coat type, the filter medium being a $2\frac{1}{2}$ in. layer of diatomaceous earth filter-aid, supported on cloth and removed to the extent of a few thousandths of an inch at each revolution. Washing takes place on the drum, the washings being mixed with the main filtrate to provide a clear liquor for TBP extraction at a uranium concentration of 300 g/l. and a free acidity of up to 3N.

The TBP solvent is used as a 20 per cent solution in odourless kerosene, and extraction takes place in a simple mixer-settler where flow is controlled by gravity only, as shown in Fig. 4.30. Eight extraction stages and eight

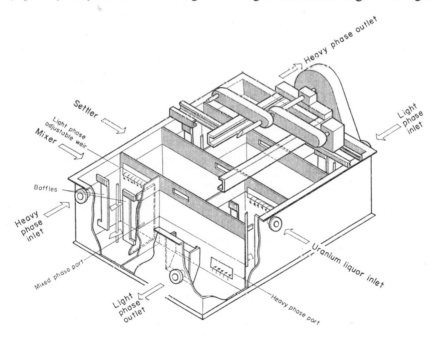

Fig. 4.30. Mixer-settler for TBP extraction of uranium (U.K.A.E.A. copyright).

stripping stages are used, which constitute an adequate excess to deal with the various types of feed material. The uranium equilibrium lines are in fact all of the same general form as pure uranyl nitrate/nitric acid but slightly displaced into the region of higher distribution coefficients owing to the presence of sodium, ammonium or magnesium nitrates, and other impurities. Backwashing is carried out in a second extractor of twelve stages, with a very dilute aqueous solution of nitric acid. The trace of acid is present in order to assist settling and as a precaution against hydrolysis to insoluble colloidal uranium compounds. In all stages except those at the uranium-weak end there would in any case be an adequate excess of acid since a little is carried by the solvent from the first extractor. Backwashing is carried out at an elevated temperature, about 60°C, since this depresses the uranium distribution coefficient and allows a lower aqueous-to-solvent ratio to be used, so giving a more concentrated product requiring less subsequent evaporation. Concentrations of up to 100 g/l. can in fact be achieved.

The solvent is normally recycled directly from the backwash extractor for further use in the forward extractor, although a third extractor of a few stages is available for washing with dilute sodium carbonate solution and water. The alkaline wash is present since by analogy with other extraction processes it is known that traces of TBP can degrade by acid hydrolysis to dibutyl phosphate, monobutyl phosphate and phosphoric acid. The first two of these tend to remain in the solvent and form strong complexes with uranium, which tend to be retained on backwashing. In practice this effect is normally negligible, or the traces of hydrolysis products are removed from the system as rapidly as they are formed, by dissolution in the first extractor aqueous raffinate or second extractor product solution. The overall uranium extraction efficiency is about 99·99 per cent based upon raffinate losses, and the purity reaches the high standard required for a nuclear reactor fuel. Solvent losses are so small that they are difficult to measure precisely, but the total loss by solubility, entrainment and degradation is of the order of 0·1 per cent per cycle.

The uranium product solution, after evaporation, is suitable for precipitation of ammonium di-uranate and conversion to uranium oxide. The major proportion at the present time is evaporated to uranyl nitrate and converted to oxide by thermal denitration, and then to fluoride, using a fluidization process.

The later methods of uranium refining in the United States similarly involve TBP extraction. The National Lead Company's plant at Fernald[65] came into operation during 1954. This uses a 3N nitric acid feed solution prepared from chemical concentrates or high-grade pitchblende with a uranium concentration of 200 g/l. The solvent is 33·5 per cent TBP in a purified kerosene diluent. Phosphoric acid is added in quantities up to 15 per cent on a uranium basis, in order to complex any thorium impurity and prevent its extraction into the solvent.[66] Three separate sieve-plate pulse columns are employed for extraction into solvent, stripping of impurities and backwashing of uranium. These columns are each about 35 ft high with 25 ft occupied by plates 2 in. apart and each with 23 per cent free area. (In practice the first and third columns are duplicated to match a single strip column.) Two types of pulsing unit are in use, either the piston type or that based upon the distention of "Teflon" bellows. The pulse amplitude is $\frac{3}{4}$ in. and the frequency 60 c/min. The solvent washing system comprises a two-stage mixer-settler operated with 1 per cent sodium carbonate solution and with water. A portion of the solvent regularly by-passes the washing system and passes through a continuous centrifuge in order to reduce the quantity of "interface crud", i.e. finely divided solids which interfere with settling and would cause undue entrainment of impurities if allowed to build up.

Another single-stage mixer-settler is used for the kerosene extraction of dissolved and entrained TBP from the first-column raffinate. The quantity of entrained solvent before this treatment is rather high, sufficiently so for there to be a tendency for explosions to occur during subsequent distillation of the raffinate for nitric acid recovery. After treatment, the TBP content is reduced to 0·2 g/l. The recovered TBP is withdrawn from the plant at a concentration of 10 per cent in the kerosene wash, and made up to 33·5 per cent with fresh TBP for re-use in the extraction process.

The advantage claimed for the U.S. pulse column process is that it operates with a high proportion of solids in the feed,[67] i.e. a slurry with up to 15 per cent solids still extracts satisfactorily. This avoids a filtration stage for the feed liquor. However, a small proportion of finely divided solids passes through the whole extraction system by entrainment and makes it necessary to incorporate micro-filters in the system for the product liquor. These are pressure filters made from sintered stainless-steel of 20 μ pore size. Three filter units are necessary, one on load, one being cleaned and one installed spare.

The latest U.S. refinery at Weldon Springs, Missouri, operated by the Mallinckrodt Chemical Works, came into operation in 1957 and it incorporates a number of improvements over the earlier Mallinckrodt and Fernald Plants.[68,69] It processes chemical concentrates only, since there is no provision for shielding from the γ- emitting radium decay series present in pitchblende or other ores. It is based upon 30 per cent TBP extraction but n-hexane[70] is used as the inert diluent instead of kerosene. This allows faster mass-transfer and reduced times for phase separation, owing to its lower density and viscosity, thus reducing the size of plant for a given throughput. In addition, it is free from the small proportions of impurities which are present in kerosene and tend to react with nitric acid to form compounds which stabilize emulsions and form complexes with uranium.

Five mixer-settlers of the "pumper-decanter" type are employed for extraction of uranium into the solvent. These consist of centrifugal pumps acting as mixers and supplying the mixture to very large adjacent settling tanks. The mixture enters the tanks tangentially and is therefore subjected to a swirling motion as in a cyclone. A facility is provided on each settler or "decanter" to recycle some of its settled solvent phase back to its own mixer, so giving a high internal solvent-to-aqueous ratio. This tends to produce a suspension of aqueous solution in a continuous solvent phase rather than the reverse, and this is known to improve the rate of settling and minimize carry-over of solids suspended at interfaces. Stripping is carried out with pure water in a sieve-plate pulse column, as is back-washing, but in the latter case a larger volume of water is necessary, and at a temperature of 120–40°F (49–60°C). These pulse columns have plates with a larger free area than normal because of the use of hexane as a diluent. This allows the columns to have a throughput almost three times as great as would apply with a kerosene diluent.[69]

A similar 40 per TBP process is also used at Bouchet in France.[71] Two packed columns are used with Raschig ring packing, each 5 m in height, one for extraction into the solvent and the other for backwashing. Further purification is necessary, e.g. by peroxide precipitation, presumably because a stripping section is not employed in the primary extraction column.

PURIFICATION OF THORIUM BY SOLVENT EXTRACTION

Solvent extraction processes for thorium tend to resemble those for uranium in some ways. A thorium ore is, however, considered to be work-able when the grade is in the region of 5–10 per cent, unlike uranium, where grades of over 1 per cent are exceptional and figures of about 0·2 per cent are more likely. In the case of thorium, therefore, only 10–20 tons of ore per ton of metal requires transporting to the processing plant, against about 500 tons of ore per ton of uranium metal. There may be two solvent extraction stages for uranium, one at the minefield for the production of an easily transportable "concentrate" and another in association with the metal production plant. There is no parallel with this for thorium, where most solvent extraction processes are based upon a feed produced by the break-down of the monazite ore, and they may be located in countries far removed from the minefields. Thorium solvent-extraction plants thus usually tend to resemble the second stage of uranium extraction rather than the first, by virtue of the fairly high solute concentrations involved.

U.K. process

The tributyl phosphate purification process,[72] [73, 74] developed by the U.K. Atomic Energy Authority can accept feed solutions containing thorium which have been produced in a number of ways.[73, 74, 75] Monazite may be broken with sulphuric acid, the thorium selectively precipitated as oxalate from the major part of the rare earth constituents and dissolved in nitric acid. Alternatively, an alkali breakdown of monazite will give a mixture of thorium and rare earth oxides, which are dissolved in acid and the thorium precipitated with alkali. The resulting hydroxide dissolves in nitric acid to give the feed solution. A third method produces a feed solution essentially by the direct nitric acid leaching of thorite ore. Another process uses a column of cellulose phosphate to absorb selectively the thorium from a monazite-sulphuric acid liquor. The thorium is then eluted with ammonium carbonate and the resulting solution acidified with nitric acid. In all cases the solution fed to the solvent extraction process (after evaporation if necessary) contains about 200 g Th/l, a 4N excess of free nitric acid and usually a quantity of rare earth (or zirconium) impurity approximately equal to the thorium. Smaller amounts of iron, uranium and phosphate are also present. If phosphate is present in stoichiometric excess over the iron, it tends to depress the thorium distribution coefficient, and this can be quite marked at low thorium concentrations. The distribution coefficient can, however, be restored by the addition of extra iron to form a soluble complex with the phosphate.[76]

When the rare earth element cerium is present, it is necessary to change its valency from the extractable tetravalent to the inextractable trivalent condition, by reduction with a little hydrogen peroxide.

Since all sources of thorium are associated with a certain amount of uranium, the first solvent-extraction cycle is designed solely to eliminate this element. The proportion of uranium to thorium can vary, but is often of the order of 5 per cent. The uranium distribution coefficient into tributyl phosphate is much higher than that of thorium under comparable conditions,[73] e.g. 20 and 0·5 respectively for 40 per cent TBP/xylene or 6 and 0·04 respectively for 5 per cent TBP/xylene. The more highly diluted solvent is used for the uranium separation cycle in view of the higher ratio of the two distribution coefficients, or "separation factor". Xylene is chosen in preference to, for example, odourless kerosene owing to the danger of formation of a third phase rich in thorium with the latter diluent.

The two solvent cycles are shown in Fig. 4.31.

Extraction of uranium takes place in nine forward extraction stages and five stripping stages. The object of the stripping section is to minimize the extraction of thorium, and 1N nitric acid is used. The ratio of feed: solvent: strip flow rates is 1 : 1 : 0·2. The second extractor backwashes the uranium into an equal volume of 0·02N nitric acid, in five stages, and the solvent is recycled back to the first extractor. The uranium-to-thorium ratio is reduced from 5 per cent to less than 1 ppm and the loss of thorium in this cycle is only a fraction of one per cent.

Thorium is extracted into 40 per cent TBP/xylene in the second cycle. The first extractor has nine extraction stages and six stripping stages, stripping being with 2N nitric acid in order to keep the rare earth contamination at a low level. The ratio of feed: solvent: strip flow rates is $1 : 3\cdot3 : 0\cdot6$ in this case. Backwashing resembles that for uranium, an equal volume of $0\cdot02N$ nitric acid being used in five stages, the depleted solvent being recycled to the first extractor. The thorium product solution contains about 1 ppm of cerium (on a thorium basis) and even smaller proportions of the other rare earth elements. The overall recovery efficiency can be more than $99\cdot7$ per cent. Conversion to oxide is via oxalate precipitation, ammonia precipitation or thermal denitration, according to the required physical properties of the product.

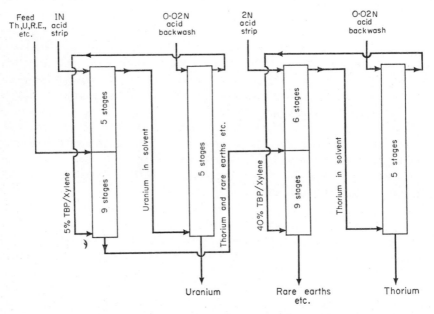

Fig. 4.31. U.K. thorium solvent extraction process.

The U.K. process has been tested by Fareedudin *et al.*[77] in India and a similar degree of purification obtained. It was found possible to use kerosene as the diluent in place of xylene and the formation of a third phase was avoided by maintaining the thorium concentration in the solvent below 70–80 g ThO_2/l.

It is considered that the process could be modified without difficulty to a system based upon a single solvent, e.g. 30 per cent TBP/xylene, with appropriate changes in volumetric flow rates. Alternatively, it might be possible to extract both the uranium and the thorium together in the first extractor and then to backwash first the thorium in extractor 2, and then the uranium in a third extractor. This would save one extractor but it would be necessary to include a solvent stripping section in extractor 2 to prevent undue contamination of the thorium product with uranium. These variants require careful costing before being accepted since the major costs of the process are due to nitric acid and the small solvent losses.

It is envisaged that this process could be operated with the simple type of mechanically stirred mixer-settler which is satisfactory in the Springfields uranium purification process. The Fernald type of sieve-plate pulse column is another alternative.

U.S. processes

A U.S. process[78, 79] for thorium purification is based upon sulphuric acid breakdown, selective ammonia precipitation of thorium phosphate with a rare earth to thorium ratio of 1 : 1, dissolution in nitric acid and solvent extraction with 80 per cent TBP and 20 per cent diluent. The first extractor contains six extraction stages and nine stripping stages, stripping being with 0·5N nitric acid. It is followed by a second extractor for back-washing the thorium with water. With this very high TBP concentration in the solvent, a high proportion of the rare earth nitrates extract into it; hence the need for a fairly large impurity stripping section. Although much of the uranium is eliminated by the first phosphate precipitation, a proportion of it passes with the thorium, through the solvent extraction process, to contaminate the product.

An alternative American process uses a feed produced by oxalate precipitation of thorium and rare earths. This precipitate is calcined to the oxides and dissolved in nitric acid for extraction with undiluted TBP. After stripping with 8N nitric acid, a high proportion of cerium extracts with the thorium, but the other rare earths are eliminated. The cerium is then back-washed in a separate extractor by means of 0·1N sodium nitrite solution, which reduces it to the solvent-insoluble cerous condition. Thorium is then backwashed in the last extractor with either water or 2 per cent sulphuric acid. In order to make this process economic it was necessary to devise an efficient system of oxalic acid recovery, This was based upon treatment of the thorium and rare earth oxalates with sodium hydroxide and recycling the resulting sodium oxalate to the precipitation stage.

The American Battelle Memorial Institute TBP extraction process resembles the U.K. process a little more closely. In this, a feed solution made by the alkali breakdown route is extracted into a solvent mixture of TBP and solvent naphtha. Thorium is selectively backwashed with dilute nitric acid, and the uranium backwashed in a separate extractor with water.

Calkins and Bohlmann describe this route or a similar one, in more detail.[80] They used 50 per cent TBP in pure kerosene, a feed 7·5N in nitric acid and a 6N nitric acid strip, with volume ratios of feed: solvent: strip equal to 1·0 : 1·5 : 0·5. This system extracts thorium and uranium and they are separated by a first backwash of the thorium with 0·5N nitric acid, the system having a solvent stripping section to prevent undue backwash of uranium at this stage. The uranium is finally backwashed with water. Oxalate precipitation of the thorium product solution is employed.

Extraction from sulphate solutions

Attempts have also been made to solvent-extract thorium directly from the sulphate liquor obtained by the acid breakdown of monazite. Tributyl phosphate can be used as the solvent provided a large concentration of nitric acid is added to the liquor before extraction. In order to make the process economic, a high proportion of the nitric acid must then be recovered by distillation of the raffinate liquor. Processes are also being developed which are based upon the use of higher alkyl phosphate or amine solvents to extract from sulphate solutions without the addition of nitric acid, as in the case of uranium, For example bis(1-isobutyl 1–3–5 dimethylhexyl) amine,[81] di-2-ethylhexyl hydrogen phosphate[82] and Primene JM-T[83] have been used.

The latter is a mixture of amines of the type:

$$\text{R}-\overset{\displaystyle \overset{\text{CH}_3}{|}}{\underset{\displaystyle \underset{\text{CH}_3}{|}}{\text{C}}}-\text{NH}_2, \text{ with formulae } C_{18}H_{37}NH_2 \text{ to } C_{22}H_{45}NH_2.$$

It can be used as a $0\cdot1$ M solution in kerosene for the extraction of thorium from the very dilute sulphate liquors remaining after the extraction of uranium by ion-exchange. This applies particularly to the uranium ore from the Blind River area of Canada, where the thorium-to-uranium ratio may be as high as 1 : 4. A completely sulphate system is employed at pH 1 to 2 with a half saturated solution of sulphurous acid as an impurity strip. The thorium is backwashed into nitric acid or another nitrate solution.

Di (tridecyl) amine can also be used for the extraction of thorium from the very dilute liquor left after either ion-exchange or solvent extraction of Blind River ores. For example, in a two cycle process, tri-iso-octylamine first extracts the uranium[49] and the di (tridecyl) amine cycle is then adjusted to remove the thorium with the minimum iron contamination. The thorium is backwashed with 1M sodium chloride–$0\cdot05$M sulphuric acid solution and precipitated with ammonia.

PURIFICATION OF ZIRCONIUM BY SOLVENT EXTRACTION

Hafnium is usually present in zircon to the extent of 2–3 per cent, and its chemical properties are so similar to those of zirconium that the two elements remain together through the ore breakdown and preliminary chemical stages. The resulting metal would, in fact, be an alloy of zirconium and hafnium unless special measures were taken to remove the latter.

Other metallic impurities, including iron and titanium, are fairly readily removed in normal processing, as is most of the silicon.

Two principal solvent-extraction methods are used for the production of high-grade zirconium, based upon the solvents hexone (methyl-isobutyl-ketone) and tributyl phosphate. In both cases, the aim is to purify the zirconium from its chemical homologue, hafnium, but in some variants of the process the other metallic impurities are also removed. It is also possible to obtain the hafnium in a pure condition if required, and to obtain fairly good yields of both zirconium and hafnium.

Hexone–thiocyanate process

The hexone–thiocyanate route has been used commercially for a number of years in both the United Kingdom and the U.S.A. and is based upon a method of hafnium extraction developed by Fischer.[84] In the U.K. process (see Fig. 4.32) operated by the Magnesium Electron Company for the U.K Atomic Energy Authority, the feed solution is made either by the dissolution of zirconium tetrachloride in water or can be obtained from a cheaper ore breakdown stage, e.g. by fusion with alkali. In either case, it contains 100 g/l. of zirconium or more, as zirconyl chloride, and is made about 1N with regard to both free hydrochloric acid and ammonium thiocyanate. This feed is extracted in nine stages with hexone, about 2·7M in thiocyanate, to take up the hafnium, and the solvent is then stripped with dilute hydrochloric acid in three stages, to wash back some of the zirconium which has been extracted. The net result is that about 90 per cent of the zirconium remains in the aqueous phase with a hafnium-to-zirconium ratio of 0·01 per cent or less. Hafnium, together with about four times its weight of zirconium, leaves in the solvent phase.

The hafnium is obtained as an aqueous solution by washing back from the solvent with 5M sulphuric acid in a two-stage extractor, and the solvent is recycled.

Thiocyanic acid is recovered from the zirconium solution by extraction with a secondary stream of hexone in two stages. The hexone is then treated with ammonia solution in a single stage and the resulting ammonium thiocyanate passes back to the primary feed. The secondary hexone is recycled for further thiocyanic acid extraction.

The main feed: solvent: strip flow ratios are 1 : 2·5 : 0·25, but the extraction and stripping sections are separate extractors and the aqueous strip solution is returned to the feed vessel rather than to the point of entry of the feed. This means in practice that the strip volume is already included in the main feed volume, to bring the zirconium feed concentration to 100 g/l. The zirconium product concentration is about 75 g/l. and it still contains an excess of hydrochloric acid, with only a trace of thiocyanic acid.

The hafnium product solution concentration depends upon the flow rate of sulphuric acid. When this is reduced to a low figure, the hafnium con-

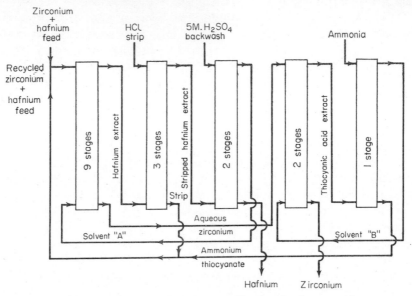

FIG. 4.32. U.K. process for zirconium purification by hexone–thiocyanate route. Solvent A, hexone 2·7M in thiocyanic acid initially; solvent B, hexone initially.

centration is about 10 g/l., with about 40 g/l. of zirconium. It also is about 0·05M in thiocyanic acid.

In the U.K. process, the purified zirconium is precipitated from solution as the sulphite, which is then treated with ammonia and calcined to the oxide, for conversion to pure chloride and finally to metal.

In view of the highly corrosive nature of the process liquors to most metals, the mixer-settlers are fabricated of polythene. They are also of a rather unique design[85] as shown in Fig. 4.33, each stage being a separate entity. Settling chambers are annular-shaped, around the mixing vessels, and the two phases are lifted into them by means of the pumping action of the stirrers. The liquors are then able to flow in counter-current manner from settlers to adjacent mixers, falling freely from outlet pipes into inlet cups. This contact of the process liquors with the air results in atmospheric contamination by thiocyanic acid, hydrochloric acid and ammonia, which makes it necessary to provide good ventilation and probably causes reagent losses to be greater than necessary.

The thiocyanic acid used in this process tends to polymerize and form an adhesive solid, which tends to cause blockages in the mixer-settlers besides representing a waste of a fairly valuable reagent. Polymerization is due to oxidizing materials,[86] is catalysed by metals, and is therefore minimized by the use of polythene equipment, but a small proportion of thioglycollic acid is also added as a stabilizer.

The loss of hexone in the process is fairly high since its solubility in water is about 1·5 per cent and therefore losses of this order occur into all the aqueous streams leaving the process, in addition to any other losses due to its volatility, or to entrainment.

A similar hexone–thiocyanate process has been operated in the U.S.A., firstly by the Northwest Electrodevelopment Laboratories at Albany since 1952 and the Carborundum Metals Corporation plant near Akron, New York, since 1953.[87, 88] They use packed and unpacked columns and the difficulties associated with polymerization of thiocyanic acid were alleviated by using a solvent consisting of 80 per cent hexone and 20 per cent butyl acetate instead of solely hexone.[89, 90] The zirconium product is precipitated as the acid sulphate, phthalate or salicylate, and a certain additional degree of purification is obtained at this stage. A typical analysis of pure zirconium oxide after hexone–thiocyanate extraction and salicylate precipitation is as follows:[89]

Impurity	ppm	Impurity	ppm
Carbon	20,000–30,000	Lithium	0·2
Hafnium	75	Magnesium	10
Aluminium	20	Manganese	1
Boron	0·3	Molybdenum	< 10
Barium	< 10	Sodium	< 20
Beryllium	< 0·02	Nickel	4
Calcium	40	Phosphorus	200
Cadmium	0·4	Lead	< 10
Cobalt	< 10	Silicon	60
Chromium	4	Tin	60
Caesium	< 20	Titanium	20
Copper	1	Vanadium	< 10
Iron	100	Zinc	10
Potassium	15		

Although the solvent purification process is adequate for the production of say reactor-grade zirconium, it is possible to modify it so that pure hafnium may also be obtained. Distribution data are available for various solutions containing thiocyanate, sulphate and chloride[91] from which it is possible, for example, to deduce that both hafnium and zirconium will extract into hexone provided the aqueous phase has a high thiocyanate concentration and a low chloride concentration. The zirconium may then be selectively backwashed in a second extractor using say an aqueous phase of high thiocyanate concentration and moderate sulphate concentration, where the separation factor of the system is high. The hafnium can then be backwashed in a third extractor using 5M sulphuric acid in the normal manner.

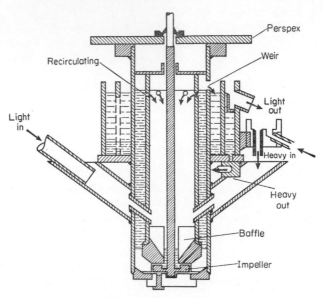

FIG. 4.33. Mixer-settler used for hexone–thiocyanate purification of zirconium (Roberts, F. and Bell, B. T. Ref. 85).

TBP process

Tributyl phosphate is also used for the purification of zirconium from hafnium and other metallic impurities. Several variants of the process exist. One of them depends firstly upon the high distribution coefficient of zirconium between 50 per cent TBP in xylene and an aqueous phase of fairly concentrated nitric acid. Xylene is chosen rather than kerosene in view of the higher solubility of the zirconium–TBP complexes and a concentration as high as 50 per cent is selected for similar reasons. Since a nitrate feed solution is necessary, it is uneconomic to use a chlorination breakdown procedure; the resulting tetrachloride would require hydrolysis with water, precipitation with alkali and re-solution in nitric acid. Instead, the zircon–sodium hydroxide fusion process is employed. The resulting hydroxide paste is freed from silica by a suitable procedure and dissolved in nitric acid. It may, for example, be dissolved in sulphuric acid first and re-precipitated with ammonia.[92, 93] The presence of too high a residual silica content leads to poor phase separation after extraction with TBP, This may in fact be so severe that it prevents the use of a conventional mixer-settler system and continuous extraction into the solvent. The zirconium distribution coefficient is, however, sufficiently high, with a nitric acid concentration above about 8N, for a simple one- or two-stage batch extraction to be used instead, with a settling time of up to several hours if necessary. In one such process, using a feed containing 126 g/l. zirconium/hafnium and an acidity as high as 13·5N, both the zirconium and hafnium can be extracted into 5 volumes of 50 per cent TBP xylene. The loaded solvent is then passed to a ten-stage continuous separation extractor in which 0·8 volumes of 5N nitric acid backwashes out the hafnium and 0·4 volumes of 50 per cent TBP/xylene strips the resulting aqueous hafnium stream to minimize the loss of zirconium. The solvent, containing pure zirconium, then passes to a final extractor of one or more stages, to backwash the zirconium into water. The pure zirconium can then be precipitated as sulphite or in other suitable form for conversion to oxide.

An alternative continuous process[94] extracts only the zirconium into 2·5 volumes of solvent from an 8N nitric acid feed, using four extraction stages. This has associated six stages of stripping with 0·5 volumes of 5N nitric acid. The extraction section aqueous acidity is about 5·2N. The zirconium is recovered by backwashing the loaded solvent with an equal volume of water, in a single stage.

A similar process developed by the French Commissariat a L'Energie Atomique[95, 96, 97] uses 60 per cent TBP in white spirit and a feed solution containing 30 g/l. of zirconium, 3N in nitric acid and 3·5M in sodium nitrate. The strip solution is similarly 3N in nitric acid and 3·5M in sodium nitrate. Flow ratios for feed: solvent: strip are approximately 2 : 1 : 1, and six extraction stages with three stripping stages are employed in practice, each with about 75 per cent stage efficiency. Backwashing is with water and difficulty is experienced owing to retention of zirconium in the solvent.

Any of these processes can be adjusted to a zirconium product containing 0·01 per cent of hafnium or less, although the normal French product is accepted at about 0·02 per cent to 0·03 per cent.[97]

PURIFICATION OF NIOBIUM BY SOLVENT EXTRACTION

Niobium and tantalum have similar chemical properties and the normal methods of niobium extraction do not remove the tantalum. Separation of these two elements is necessary, for example, when the niobium is required for nuclear purposes, and several solvent extraction processes are suitable.[98] Hexone[99, 100] (methyl isobutyl ketone) and tributyl phosphate[101] are the two principal solvents which are used, although processes have also been developed using methyl dioctylamine[102] and di-isopropyl ketone.[103]

Hexone process

Hexone extraction is best carried out with an aqueous feed solution containing hydrofluoric and hydrochloric acids, since separation factors of several hundred are possible.[99] The alternative hydrofluoric acid/sulphuric acid system is less efficient in this respect. In the U.K. Atomic Energy

Authority's process the feed is made by first dissolving ferroniobium (with a niobium to tantalum ratio of 7 : 1) in 50 per cent potassium hydroxide solution, filtering, washing and precipitating the insoluble sodium niobate ($NaNbO_3$) and tantalate ($NaTaO_3$) by the addition of solid sodium chloride crystals. Iron is prevented from being co-precipitated by the presence of a suitable complexing agent at this stage. The white precipitate is treated first with moderately concentrated hydrochloric acid and then with ammonia liquor, to convert to the mixed niobium and tantalum oxides (Nb_2O_5 and Ta_2O_5). This is washed with water to remove a proportion of the chloride ion, and dissolved in hydrofluoric acid. The resulting feed solution has the following composition:

Niobium	140 g/l.
Tantalum	20 g/l.
Hydrofluoric acid	8·3N
Hydrochloric acid	0·2N

The tantalum can then be extracted into an equal volume of hexone in a compound extractor with the minimum volume of a strip solution composed of 2N hydrofluoric acid. Four extraction stages and two stripping stages give a recovery efficiency for niobium of 99·9 per cent and a niobium-to-tantalum ratio of only 0·01 per cent. The niobium remains unextracted in the raffinate, from which it is precipitated as the double fluoride K_2NbF_6 by the addition of potassium carbonate and hydrofluoric acid. The tantalum is removed from the extractor, by backwashing with 5 per cent sodium carbonate solution, as a precipitate of sodium tantalate. This process is designed for operation in mixer-settlers but a similar process has been operated[99] in 12 ft high sieve-plate pulse columns. In both cases the major part of the plant in contact with hydrofluoric and hydrochloric acid is constructed of, or lined with, polythene. Hastelloy C can be used for pumps, but some corrosion takes place.

TBP process

Tributyl phosphate extracts both niobium and tantalum from nitric acid/hydrofluoric acid or sulphuric acid/hydrofluoric acid solutions.[104, 105] The solvent is best used undiluted to avoid the formation of a third phase.

The highest niobium distribution coefficients are obtained in the sulphate/fluoride process and presumably because of these high values, the opinion has been expressed that such a process is best operated batchwise.[101] Using trace quantities of niobium 95, figures as high as 400 have been quoted for the distribution coefficient when the sulphuric acid concentration is 12N. Under a more practicable acidity condition of 6N, the distribution coefficient is 80. Somewhat lower figures would no doubt apply to plant concentrations of niobium however. Under similar conditions, with, for example, 10N hydrofluoric acid and 4N nitric acid, the distribution co-efficient is only 1·85, and this is reduced to 0·8 at higher niobium concentrations (0·5M).

With a sulphate/fluoride system, a continuous process can be employed having four extraction stages and two stripping stages; 12N hydrofluoric acid being used as the stripping agent. A niobium extraction efficiency of about 99 per cent is then obtained. Backwashing with water requires two stages and gives a product with a ratio of tantalum to niobium of 0·4 per cent. The feed solution for such a process can be obtained by the dissolution of ferroniobium in a mixture of sulphuric and hydrofluoric acids to which a trace of nitric acid has been added.[104]

A continuous nitrate/fluoride process has been proposed[105] to take advantage of the ready solubility of columbite ore in a mixture of nitric and hydrofluoric acids, and thus allow the feed solution to be prepared in a cheap and simple manner. The feed contains 45 g/l. of niobium, about 25 g/l. of tantalum and is 8N in hydrofluoric acid and 3N in nitric acid. It is extracted in six stages with three volumes of solvent, together with an additional stage for "acid equilibration". A half volume aqueous strip solution is also 8N in hydrofluoric acid and 3N in nitric acid. About 99 per cent of the niobium is extracted into the solvent and is then backwashed in a second extractor with three volumes of 0·5N hydrofluoric acid. The solvent finally passes to a single-stage backwash extractor for removal of tantalum by sodium carbonate solution.

In general, satisfactory separation is obtained from iron, manganese, titanium and tin impurities in the TBP processes. Mixer-settler plant can be used, but is best constructed of, or lined with, polythene, because of the high concentrations of hydrofluoric acid which are necessary.

REFERENCES

1. McKay, H. A. C. and Mathieson, A. R. The partition of uranyl nitrate between water and organic solvents. *Trans. Faraday Soc.* **47**, 428 (1951).
2. McKay, H. A. C. The physical chemistry of uranyl nitrate solutions, with particular reference to solvent extraction. *Chemistry and Industry*, p. 1549 (1954).
3. Fletcher, J. M. Purification by solvent Extraction. I.M.M. Symposium on Extraction and Refining of the Rarer Metals, London (1957).
4. Jamrack, W. D., Logsdail, D. H., and Short, G. D. C. Laboratory mixer-settlers. *Progress in Nuclear Energy*, Ser. III, vol. 2, *Process Chemistry*. Pergamon Press.
5. Sherwood, T. K. and Pigford, R. L. *Absorption and Extraction*. McGraw-Hill (1952).
6. Kremser, A. *Nat. Petr. News* **22**, No. 21, 43 (21/5/30).
7. Klinkenberg, A. *et al.* Calculation of the efficiency of counter-current stage-wise mass transfer processes. *Chem. Engng. Science* **1**, No. 2, 86 (1951).
8. McCabe, W. C. and Thiele, E. W. Graphical design of fractionating columns. *Ind. Eng. Chem.* **17**, 605 (1925).
9. Varteressian, K. A. and Fenske, M. R. Liquid–liquid extraction. *Ind. Eng. Chem.* **28**, No. 11, 1353 (Nov. 1936).

10. WOOD, J. T. and WILLIAMS, J. A. A multicomponents solvent extraction system *Trans. Inst. Chem. Eng.* **36**, No. 5, 382 (1958).
11. CHILTON, T. H. and COLBURN, A. P. Distillation and absorption in packed columns. *Ind. Eng. Chem.* **27**, 255 (1935).
12. COHEN, R. M. and BEYER, G. H. Performance of a pulse extraction column. *Chem. Engng. Prog.* **49**, No. 6, 279 (June, 1953).
13. WHITMAN, W. G. The two-film theory of gas absorption. *Chem. Metall. Engng.* **29**, No. 4, 146 (July 1923).
14. PRATT, H. R. C. *et al.* Liquid–liquid extraction. (a) Part I. *Trans. Inst. Chem. Eng.* **29**, 89 (1951). (b) Part II. *Ibid.* **29**, 110 (1951). (c) Part III. *Ibid.* **29**, 126 (1951). (d) Part IV. *Ibid.* **31**, 57 (1953). (e) Part V. *Ibid.* **31**, 69 (1953). (f) Part VI. *Ibid.* **31**, 78 (1953). (g) Part VII. *Ibid.* **31**, 289 (1953).
15. PRATT, H. R. C. Liquid–liquid extraction in theory and practice, Part III. *Industr. Chemist* **31**, 63 (Feb. 1955).
16. VON BERG, R. L. and WIEGANDT, H. F. Liquid-liquid extraction. *Chem. Engng.* **59**, 189 (June 1952).
17. TREYBAL, R. E. Liquid extraction. *Ind. Eng. Chem.* **47**, No. 3, 536 (1955).
18. LEIBSON, I. and BECHMANN, R. B. The effect of packing size and column diameter on mass transfer in liquid–liquid extraction. *Chem. Eng. Progr.* **49**, No. 8, 405 (Aug. 1953).
19. PRATT, H. R. C. Liquid-liquid extraction in theory and practice, Part IV. *Industr. Chemist* **31**, 505 and 552 (Oct. and Nov. 1955).
20. FIFE, J. G. and Shell Development Company. Improvements in Methods of Contacting Fluids One with Another. U.K. Patent 615,425 (Jan. 1949, application July 1945).
21. CHANTRY, W. A. *et al.* Application of pulsation to liquid-liquid extraction *Ind. Eng. Chem.* **47**, No. 6, 1153 (June 1955).
22. SCHEIBEL, E. G. and KARR, A. E. Semicommercial multistage extraction column. *Ind. Eng. Chem.* **42**, No. 6, 1048 (June 1950).
23. VAN DIJCK, W. J. D. U.S. Patent 2,011,186 (Aug. 1935).
24. SEGE, G. and WOODFIELD, F. W. Pulse column variables. *Chem. Eng. Progr.* **50**, No. 8, 396 (1954).
25. CRICO, A. L'Extraction par solvant au moyen de colonnes pulsantes. *Génie Chimique* **73**, No. 3, 57 (Mar. 1955).
26. COWARD, L. D. G. Column Sieve Plate Gland. British Patent Application 19047/55.
27. LOGSDAIL, D. H. Conical Sieve Plate for Pulse Column. British Patent 818, 272 (application 1955).
28. STEPHENSON, R. Pulse columns. *Chem. Engng. Progr.* **49**, No. 7, 340 (July 1953).
29. THORNTON, J. D. Recent Developments in Pulsed Column Techniques. A.E.R.E. Report, CE/M.95, and Chemical Engineering Progress Symposium, Series No. 13, *Nuclear Engineering*, Part III, p. 39 (1954).
30. BURNS, W. A. and JOHNSON, W. F. Plate Design for Pulse Columns. U.S. Patent 2,662,001 (1953).
31. BURGER, L. L. Solvent Extraction Equipment. U.S. Patent 2,743,170 (Apr. 1956).
32. WAINWRIGHT, L. Extraction Apparatus. U.S. Patent 2,682,452 (29/6/54).
33. VAN DIJCK, W. J. D. Countercurrent Contact Apparatus. U.S. Patent 2,266,521 (Dec. 1941, filed Dec. 1939).
34. LOWES, L. and TANNER, M. C. "In Line" Mixer-Settler Having Light Phase Transfer Channels. U.K. Patent 835,912 (Application 1957).
35. TANNER, M. C. In-line Mixer-Settler having Double Mixed Phase Ports. U.K. Patent Specification 835,282 (application 1957).
36. GRAEF, E. R. and FOSTER, S. P. Design of box-type countercurrent mixer-settler units. *Chem. Eng. Progr.* **52**, No. 7, 293 (July 1956).
37. HOLT, R. J. W. Improvements in or relating to Liquid-Liquid Contacting Apparatus. U.K. Prov. Patent 57975/57.
38. JAMRACK, W. D. and WALKER, H. A. Improvements in or relating to Airlift Type Mixer-Settler Apparatus. U.K. Patent Specification 774,554 (application 1954).

39. COPLAN, B. V. and ZEBROSKI, E. L. Multistage Mixer-Settler Apparatus. U.S. Patent 2,646,346.
40. COPLAN, B. V., DAVIDSON, J. K. and ZEBROSKI, E. L. The "pump-mix" mixer-settler Chem. Eng. Progr. 50, No. 8, 403 (1954).
41. HOLMES, J. H. and SCHAFER, A. C. Some operating characteristics of the pump-mix mixer-settler. Chem. Eng. Progr. 52, No. 5, 201 (May 1956).
42. HOLLEY, A. E. and MOTT, O. E. Process and Apparatus for the Treatment of a Liquid, More Especially a Petroleum Distillate, with another Immiscible Liquid. U.S. Patent 1,953,651 (April 1934).
43. DAVIS, M. W., HICKS, T. E. and VERMEULEN, T. Mixer-settler extraction equipment. Chem. Eng. Progr. 50, No. 4, 188 (April 1954).
44. PAGE, H., SHORTIS, L. P. and DUKES, J. A. The processing of uranium ore concentrates and recycle residues to purified uranyl nitrate solution at Springfields. Trans. Inst. Chem. Eng. 38, No. 4, 184 (1960).
45. WILLIAMS, J. A., LOWES, L. and TANNER, M. C. The design of a simple mixer-settler. Trans. Inst. Chem. Eng. 36, 464 (1958).
46. THORNTON, J. D. Mechanical contactors for liquid–liquid extraction. Nuclear Engng. 1, 156 (July 1956), and 204 (Aug. 1956).
47. EISENLOHR, H. A. New centrifugal solvent extractor. Industr. Chemist 27, 271 (June 1951).
48. FOOS, R. A. Hydrometallurgy of uranium. Mining Engng. 8, 893 (Sept. 1956).
49. BROWN, K. B. et al. Solvent extraction processing of uranium and thorium ores. Proc. 2nd Int. Conf. on the Peaceful Uses of Atomic Energy, 1958, Paper 509.
50. MOORE, J. G. et al. Further Studies of Amines as Extractants for Uranium from Acid Sulphate Solutions. U.S.A.E.C. Report, AECD–4145 (1955).
51. AUDSLEY, A. A. et al. The Extraction of Uranium from Ore Leach Solutions by Trinonylamine. D.S.I.R. Report, N.C.L./A.E. 177 (1959).
52. COLEMAN, C. F. Amine salts as solvent extraction reagents for uranium and other metals. Proc. 2nd Int. Conf. on the Peaceful Uses of Atomic Energy, 1958, Paper 510.
53. BROWN, K. B. et al. The Use of Amines as Extractants for Uranium from Acidic Sulphate Liquors. U.S.A.E.C. Report, AECD–4142 (1954).
54. DABORN, G. R. Solvent Extraction of Uranium from Sulphate Solution, Part III, D.S.I.R. Report, N.C.L./A.E. 168 (1958).
55. SIMARD, R. Solvent Extraction for the Recovery of Uranium and Thorium from Leach Solutions of a Uranium Ore from the Bancroft Area, Ontario. Canadian Department of Mines, Report, IR 58–4 (1958).
56. BLACK, K. M. et al. Design and operation of a uranium processing mill using liquid ion-exchange (solvent extraction). Proc. 2nd Int. Conf. on the Peaceful uses of 1955, Atomic Energy, Geneva, 1958, Paper 511.
57. ROSENBAUM, J. B. CLEMMER, J. B. and LENNEMANN, W. L. Innovations in Processing Uranium Ores. U.S.A.E.C. Report, AECU–3367 (1956).
58. ELLIS, D. A. et al. Entrainment studies on solvent extraction of uranium from heavy slurries. Proc 2nd. Int. Conf. on the Peaceful Uses of Atomic Energy, Geneva, 1958. Paper 497.
59. GRINSTEAD, R. R. et al. Solvent extraction of uranium from acid leach slurries and solutions. Proc. 1st Int. Conf. on the Peaceful Uses of Atomic Energy, Geneva, 1955, Paper 523.
60. MAGNER, J. E. and BAILES, R. H. Recovery of uranium from ores by direct leaching with organic solvents. Proc. 2nd Int. Conf. on the Peaceful Uses of Atomic Energy, Geneva, 1958, Paper 496.
61. HAZEN, W. C. and HENRICKSON, A. V. Solvent extraction of uranium at shiprock, N.M. Mining Engng. 9, 994 (1957).
62. HINTON, C. The manufacture of uranium metal from ore . Trans. Inst. Chem. Eng. 33, 45 (1955).
63. GRAINGER, L. Uranium and Thorium. George Newnes, London (1958).
64. HARRINGTON, C. D. et al. Uranium Oxide Refinery, Ether Process. U.S.A.E.C. Report, TID–5295 (Jan. 1956).

65. Ryle, B. G. *et al*. T.B.P. Extraction Process, Fernald Refinery. U.S.A.E.C. Report, TID–5295 (Jan. 1956).
66. Harrington, C. D. and Ruehle, A. E. *Uranium Production Technology*, p. 126. D. van Nostrand (1959).
67. Arnold, D. S. and Ryle, B. G. Reactor grade uranium by extraction of slurries. *Chem. Eng. Progr.* **53**, No. 2, 63F (Feb. 1957).
68. Fariss, R. H. *et al*. Uranium Oxide Refinery, T.B.P. Hexane Process. U.S.A.E.C. Report, TID–5295 (Jan. 1956).
69. Thayer, H. E. The newest United States uranium processing plant. *Proc. 2nd Int. Conf. on the Peaceful Uses of Atomic Energy, Geneva*, 1958. Paper 602.
70. Philoon, W. C. Development of the T.B.P.—Hexane Process for Uranium Purification. Mallinckrodt Chemical Works Report, MCW–1441 (Feb. 1960).
71. Goldschmidt, B. and Vertes, P. La Preparation de L'Uranium Metal Pur. French CEA Report 425 (1955).
72. Fletcher, J. M. and Ashworth, G. J. The Production of Pure Thoria by Solvent Extraction. U.K. Patent 783,195 (18/9/57).
73. Audsley, A., Lind, R. and England, P. G. The Extraction of Thorium from Monazite. I.M.M. Symposium on the Extraction Metallurgy of Some of the Less Common Metals, London (March, 1956).
74. Buddery, J. H., Jamrack, W. D. and Wells, R. A. The extraction of thorium. *Chemistry and Industry*, p. 235 (21/2/59).
75. Audsley, A., Jamrack, W. D., Oldbury, A. E. and Wells, R. A. Recently developed processes for the extraction and purification of thorium. *Proc. 2nd Int. Conf. on the Peaceful Uses of Atomic Energy, Geneva*, 1958. Paper 1526.
76. Bridger, G. L. *et al*. Separation Process for Thorium Salts. U.S. Patent 2,815, 262 (Dec. 1957, filed June 1952).
77. Fareeduddin, S. *et al*. Production of nuclear grade thorium nitrate. *Proc. 2nd Int. Conf. on the Peaceful Uses of Atomic Energy, Geneva*, 1958. Paper 1670.
78. Whatley, M. E. Smutz, M. and Bridger, G. L. Purification of Thorium by Solvent Extraction. U.S.A.E.C. Report, ISC–415 (1953).
79. Barghusen, J. J. and Smutz, M. Processing of Monazite Sands. U.S.A.E.C. Report, ISC–947 (1957).
80. Calkins, G. D. and Bohlmann, E. G. Processing of Monazite Sand. U.S. Patent 2,815,264 (1957).
81. Crouse, D. J. *et al*. Progress Report on Separation and Recovery of Uranium and Thorium from Sulphate Liquors by the Amex Process. U.S.A.E.C. Report, ORNL–2173 (1956).
82. Ryan, W. D.S.I.R. Chemical Research Laboratory Report, CRL/AE 153.
83. Ryan, W. The Solvent Extraction of Low Concentrations of Thorium from Sulphate Liquors by means of an Alkylamine Extractant. D.S.I.R. Chemical Research Laboratory Report, CRLAE 162.
84. Fischer, Von, W. *et al*. *Z. Anorg. Chem.* **255**, 79 (1947) and 277 (1948).
85. Roberts, F. and Bell, B. T. Horizontal mixer-settler equipment for liquid-liquid extraction. *Trans. Inst. Chem. Engineers* **35**, 6 (1957).
86. Leaders, W. M. Summary of Progress on the Separation of Zirconium and Hafnium. U.S.A.E.C. Report, Y–449 (1949).
87. Shelton, S. M. *et al*. Zirconium metal production. *Proc. 1st Int. Conf. on the Peaceful Uses of Atomic Energy, Geneva*, 1955. Paper 533.
88. Waldrop, F. B. Zirconium–Hafnium Separation: Mixer-Settler Studies. Final Report. U.S.A.E.C. Report, Y–612 (1950).
89. Leaders, W. M. *et al*. Preparation of Pure Zirconium Oxide. Progress Report. U.S.A.E.C. Report, Y–559 (1950).
90. Grimes, W. R. Preparation of Pure Zirconium Oxide: Laboratory Studies. U.S.A.E.C. Report, Y–560 (1950).
91. Barton, C. J. Preferential Extraction of Zirconium and Hafnium Thiocyanates. Preparation of Pure Hafnium. U.S.A.E.C. Report, Y–611 (1950).

92. PETERSON, H. C. Separation of hafnium and zirconium by liquid–liquid extraction. *Iowa St. Coll. J. Sci.* **31**, No. 3, 498 (1957).
93. COX, R. P., PETERSON, H. C. and BEYER, G. H. Separating hafnium from zirconium. *Ind. Eng. Chem.* **50**, No. 2, 141 (Feb. 1958).
94. HUDSWELL, F. and HUTCHEON, J. M. The Manufacture of Hafnium—free Zirconium. I.M.M. Symposium on the Extraction and Refining of the Rarer Metals, London, 1957. Paper 22.
95. HURE, J. and SAINT-JAMES, R. Procede de Separation du Zirconium et du Hafnium. C.E.A. Report, 427 (1955).
96. HURE, J. *et al.* Method for Separating and Purifying Zirconium and Hafnium. U.S. Patent 2,757, 081 (1955).
97. HURE, J. and SAINT-JAMES, R. Process for separation of zirconium and hafnium. *Proc. 1st Int. Conf. on the Peacefiul Uses of Atomic Energy*, Geneva, 1955. Paper 347.
98. MILLER, G. L. *Tantalum and Niobium*. Butterworths Scientific Publications, London (1959).
99. WERNING, J. R. *et al.* Separation of tantalum and niobium by liquid–liquid Extraction. *Industr. Engng. Chem.* **46**, No. 4, 644 (1954).
100. TEWS, J. L. and Sherman, L. M. Recent Developments in Separating Tantalum and Niobium by Solvent Extraction. Symposium on Columbium (niobium) of the Electrothermics and Metallurgy Division of the Electrochemical Society, Washington, D.C. 16 and 17 May 1957.
101. FLETCHER, J. M., MORRIS, D. F. C. and WAIN, A. G. Improvements in or Relating to Extraction of Niobium. U.K. Patent Specification 767038 (1957).
102. LEDDICOTTE, G. W. and MOORE, F. L. *J. Amer. Chem. Soc.* **74**, 1618 (1952).
103. STEVENSON, P. C. and HICKS, H. G. *Anal. Chem.* **25**, 1517 (1953).
104. DICKSON, G. K. and DUKES, J. A. The Selection of a Process for Development for the Production of Pure Niobium. Institution of Mining and Metallurgy Symposium on the Extraction and Refining of the Rarer Metals, London (1957). Paper 14.
105. MORRIS, D. F. C., and WAIN, A. G. Outline of a solvent extraction process for the purification of niobium from ores or from ferroniobium. *Trans. Instn. Min. Metall. (London)* **65**, 487 (1956).

CHAPTER 5

DRYWAY CONVERSION PROCESSES

THE process of calcination of oxides, hydrogen reduction of oxides to lower oxides, hydrofluorination and hydrochlorination of oxides, etc., can often be carried out by conventional chemical engineering methods. However, the high standards of purity usually required for rare metal extraction at least necessitate novel materials of construction. In addition, a considerable development and pioneering effort has been devoted to the improvement of these techniques, particularly applied to the intermediates in the production of uranium metal, uranium trioxide, dioxide and tetrafluoride. It is possible, therefore, that the resulting processes can be more widely employed in the rare metal extraction field in the future.

STATIC BED REACTORS

The early processes for interconversion of pure rare metal oxides and fluorides, etc., involved simple batch methods with static beds and in some cases these are still adequate. Usually the solid reactants, in powder form, are placed in suitable trays a few inches deep, and inserted into a furnace (Fig. 5.1). The furnace may contain a number of trays in horizontal line or as a vertical stack, with the feed of gaseous reagent to one end and any gaseous product offtake at the other. The tray material and its lid, or possibly the furnace lining, are made of materials which are compatible with the solid and gaseous reactants and products, and should not introduce undue amounts of impurities into the rare metal products. Stainless-steel trays are usually satisfactory if oxides only are involved, but nickel, "Inconel" or "Monel" are necessary for fluoride systems. Graphite trays have been used with success, particularly where a little carbon can be tolerated in the oxide or fluoride product. Alternatively, the surface of the graphite can be flame-sprayed with calcium fluoride or alumina to give a fairly adherent coating which creates a barrier between the graphite and the powder contained in it. Even massive calcium fluoride or alumina, etc., have been used, these materials usually being bonded into hard ceramic ware by high-temperature sintering.

In exceptional cases platinum has been used. This is an expensive material of construction, but the cost is mitigated by the high resale value of the scrap platinum at the end of the plant life.

The kinetics of reactions between solids and gases in static beds have been fairly widely studied. Reaction rates are dependent upon particle size or surface area of the powders, which may not be directly related in the case of particles with a porous or indented structure. Rates of diffusion of the gaseous reagents and products are also important, both through the bed and through the solid itself to the reaction boundary. This inevitably introduces a variability in reaction rate from beginning to end of any reaction.

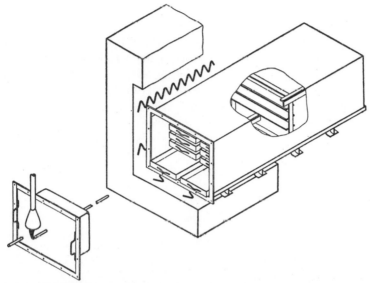

FIG. 5.1. Static bed reactor (From C. D. Harrington and A. E. Ruehle, *Uranium Production Technology*, copyright 1959, D. Van Nostrand, Princeton, New Jersey).

The course of a reaction itself may influence some of these physical characteristics. For example, heating of a crystalline oxalate may produce an oxide with a very porous structure and therefore a very much greater surface area, particularly if there is a tendency to retain the contours of the original crystals. Alternatively, a highly exothermic reaction between solid particles and a gas might sinter the surface of the solid to such an extent as to decrease its surface area markedly and make its interior both much less reactive and less accessible, The upper surface of a static bed of solid particles may become "bridged over" as a result of such sintering action, to produce a relatively impervious layer which obstructs further reaction with particles underneath. It is clear, therefore, that a reaction taking place in a static bed is rarely carried out under uniform conditions and a uniform product does not usually result.

Remedies for these various defects of a static bed system are fairly obvious in principle. They usually involve some type of agitation of the solid to provide better heat transfer conditions and more uniform contacting conditions for the solid and gaseous reactants. An inelegant method of agitation of the bed which is occasionally employed is to open the furnace and rake the tray contents at intervals. Because of its intermittent nature, this accomplishes little more than a breaking up of any impervious layer which might have formed over a whole bed, and has little or no effect upon individual particles.

If the bed is agitated continuously, it can modify the nature of the reaction considerably. Several types of reactor are available for this purpose.

STIRRED BED REACTORS

The stirred bed reactor is one method which has been employed on a fairly large scale for agitating a solid reacting with a gas. At the same time it allows the solid to flow from one end of the reactor to the other, and a counter-current system can be used if required.

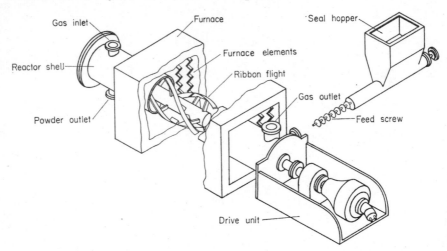

FIG. 5.2. Stirred bed reactor (From C. D. Harrington and A. E. Ruehle, *Uranium Production Technology*, copyright 1959, D. Van Nostrand, Princeton, New Jersey).

The reactor consists simply of a horizontal tube, usually heated externally by means of a suitable furnace.[1] Inside the tube is a screw agitator and conveyor, which is rotated slowly. A typical example is shown in Fig. 5.2. The agitator conveyor can take several forms; the one illustrated consists of four long flights twisted with an even pitch about the shaft in a similar manner to the rotor of a lawn mowing machine. In other models two flights have been used instead of four. The flights are attached firmly to the shaft by means of struts, or studs in the case of a small model, in a direction such that the flat sides follow the contour of the cylinder in which they rotate.

In a large model, the "shaft" usually consists of a stout tube with a diameter perhaps one-third of that of the outer shell of the reactor. It is best supported on bearings at each end so that it leaves a small gap between the flights and the shell. In earlier models, the support was at one end only, the other being allowed to trail in contact with the shell. This, however, tends to wear the surfaces of both flights and shell and introduce impurities into the product. Having fixed the direction of rotation of the agitator conveyor, the powder is fed at the end where a small forward thrust is exerted upon it to convey it to the other end of the tube. The feed can be introduced by means of a small hopper and screw feeder or star feeder so that it acts as its own gas seal. The product outlet takes the form of a branch from the base of the reactor shell which leads to a similar delivery device. The product, being in powder form, is again able to act as its own seal to prevent loss of gas. The gas inlet is near the product outlet and the gas outlet is at the powder feed inlet end, in a counter-current system. The reactor runs with only a proportion, sometimes a small proportion, of its cross-section full of powder. Consequently, ample opportunity is available for by-passing of gas, and a rather inefficient counter-current effect is obtained.

If a high gas utilization efficiency is required, it is advisable to run a set of reactors in series, regarding each one as a single stage in a counter-current system. Unlike a solvent-extraction system, there is not usually a position of equilibrium to be achieved in each stage, i.e. the reaction would proceed to virtual completion in a single stage if the residence time of the reactants was adequate. The degree of reaction is, however, dependent upon the effectiveness of the contact between gas and solid, and the rates of diffusion of reactant gas and product gas within the solid. This can be improved by counter-current flow since this avoids the very slow reaction between a dilute reactant gas and an almost converted solid. Instead, the dilute gas is in contact with virtually unconverted solid, and the fresh feed gas with almost converted solid, and the overall rate of reaction can thus be improved.

ROTATING KILN REACTORS

An alternative method of agitation of a tubular reactor is the rotation of the reactor itself. Flow of solids is caused by mounting it in a position slightly inclined to the horizontal, and caking upon the sides is sometimes prevented by the presence of, for example, a loose H section beam or similar heavy article along the length of the tube. The powder feed can enter the end of the reactor via the hollow shaft upon which the reactor rotates. Similarly it can leave via a lower hollow shaft, gas being passed in the reverse direction.

This type of reactor is commonly used in industry, e.g. for the manufacture of cement or of hydrofluoric acid. It is, however, less suitable for reactions involving the pure intermediates in the extraction of rare metals, since the action of the stirrer is to break down the adherent protective layer from the surface of the reactor and thus allow corrosion to take place. Although the life of the reactor can be guaranteed by using walls sufficiently thick, the contamination of the product by the reactor metal, or its compounds removed from the wall, might be disastrous. In addition, it is less convenient to heat a rotating reactor evenly than a static one. Gas or oil heating is usually employed, with relatively coarse temperature control.

VIBRATING TRAY REACTORS

Another reactor which has been used for a few specific purposes is based upon a horizontal, or almost horizontal, vibrating tray,[2] as shown in Fig. 5.3. A single large tray in the form of a muffle tube is installed in an electric furnace, with a robust vibrating mechanism underneath capable of imparting a horizontal reciprocating motion. The vibrating mechanism is driven by a fairly powerful electric motor operating an eccentric. The powder feed enters via a flexible inlet port at one end, and gradually progresses along the tray when it is vibrated, until it reaches a similar flexible outlet. Gas is passed into and out of the reactor in a similar manner, either co-currently or counter-currently. Less satisfactory contacting of solid and gas is probably achieved than in the stirred bed reactor.

The vibrating mechanism usually operates intermittently for only a few per cent of the time cycle, a few times per hour. The frequency is measured in hundreds of cycles per minute and preferably matches the resonant frequency of the system, to minimize wear on the driving mechanism and supports. The mechanical maintenance of this type of system can be a serious disadvantage, particularly with large reactors involving relatively high forces.

MOVING BED REACTORS

A moving bed reactor consists of a vertical heated tube down which the solid reactant is allowed to fall slowly against a counter-current flow of reactant gas.[3] The solid fills the whole of the cross-section of the reactor and in order to allow free passage of gas it is essential to have large particles with correspondingly large voids. Pieces of $\frac{1}{4}$ in. size or larger are in fact preferred, with a fairly small deviation from the mean size. This is often best achieved by the formation of pellets from a much finer powder. The pellets must however remain stable on reaction to form a new chemical material, since serious channelling of the reactant gas can take place if some of the pellets fall to a powder which is able to fill the voids.

The solid reactant is fed from a self-sealing hopper at the top of the reactor and the flow is restricted by means of a suitable outlet hopper, star feeder, or valve, at the base of the column. A distribution plate with holes

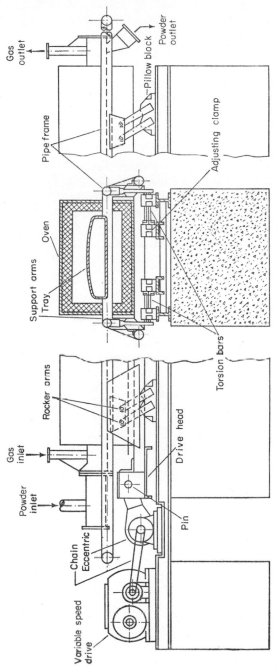

FIG. 5.3. Vibrating-tray reactor (Smiley, S. H., and Brater, D. C. Ref. 3).

of a suitable size is also placed near the bottom, usually just above the gas inlet. This evens out the flows of ascending gas and descending solids but also acts as a restriction to the flow of the latter. Secondary gas inlets are sometimes fitted at various points up the column of solid, and these should also have distributors associated with them.

Moving bed reactors tend to be more compact than the other types of reactor discussed, i.e. to have a high throughput for a given size, and this makes for low capital costs. Also, contacting of solid and gas is good and the consumption of the gaseous reagent tends to be less. However, their smaller size and the piston-type flow of the solids often leads to difficulties in temperature regulation with exothermic reactions. A gradation of temperature is present from top to bottom and the rate of reaction may require control by means of adjustment of the gas flow rate, to avoid overheating of the hot zone. In order to allow a faster reaction, cooling may be applied both by means of a jacket around the reactor and by a series of vertical pipes distributed across the area of the bed. The cooling medium at the normal reaction temperatures can usually be air or steam.

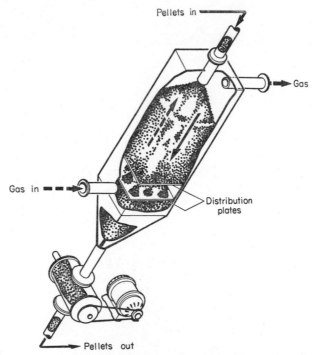

FIG. 5.4. Schematic illustration of moving bed mechanism (Smiley, S. H. and Brater, D. C. Ref. 3).

A schematic diagram of a moving bed reactor is shown in Fig. 5.4 which, in this case, has a square cross-section.

FLUIDIZED BED REACTORS

For fairly large-scale reactions between solids and gases it is becoming recognized that fluidized systems have some advantages. These are discussed in detail by Zeny and Othmer.[4] In a system of this type, the bed of particles of solid is made to flow and generally behave like a liquid. This is accomplished by passing an upward flow of gas through the solid particles at a suitable velocity so that the particles no longer remain in intimate contact with one another. The fluidizing gas is generally the gaseous reactant.

When gas is passed through a bed of solid particles at low flow rates, a relatively low pressure-drop is first experienced. With increasing flow rate, the pressure drop per unit length of bed gradually increases, and the relationship has been expressed by Carman[5] in the form of the equation:

$$\frac{\Delta p}{L} = \frac{2G^2 f}{D_p \rho_f g_c} \frac{(1-\epsilon)^2}{\epsilon^3} \beta \tag{1}$$

Where

$\Delta p/L$ = pressure drop per unit length of bed;
G = mass flow rate per unit area of bed cross-section;
f = a friction factor which is a function of Reynolds number;
β = a shape factor to account for the deviation of the particles from spherical;
ϵ = voidage fraction of the bed;
g_c = gravitational constant;
D_p = mean diameter of particles;
ρ_f = density of fluid.

Eventually a point is reached where the pressure drop is also equal to the weight of the particles,[5] i.e.

$$\frac{\Delta p}{L} = (1-\epsilon)(\rho_s - \rho_f) \tag{2}$$

At this point each individual particle is surrounded by a film[6] of gas and acquires a certain degree of freedom to move. The solid and gas thus behave like a single liquid phase and the system is described as "fluidized". The gas leaving the bed entrains only a small amount of the more finely divided solid. The minimum gas velocity at the point where fluidization just begins is referred to as the "critical mass velocity". This value of the flow rate G signified as G_0, can be evaluated from equations 1 and 2 by elimination of $\Delta p/L$. When the mass-velocity slightly exceeds G_0 the system is said to be in the quiescent region of fluidization, but as the gas rate increases still further the pressure drop per unit length begins to fall, as the bed expands.

Then some of the gas passes through the bed in the form of bubbles and gives the appearance of "boiling". Considerable agitation is produced by the rising bubbles. These bubbles increase in size as the gas velocity is increased, to a maximum diameter of perhaps several inches. If the diameter of the bed is less than this, slugging occurs, i.e. alternate slugs of gas and agitated solids rise up the bed in a similar manner to the passage of gas through a tube full of liquid.

As the gas rate is increased above G_0, more solids are entrained in the gas leaving the bed, until at very high flow rates the whole of the particles are in suspension in the dilute phase.[7] The flow of fluids through packed and fluidized beds is discussed in more detail by Leva et al.[8] and Van Heerden.[9]

The fluidized condition only, with its fairly high density, is of interest for carrying out an efficient reaction between the solid particles and the gas. This is usually encountered at gas velocities between $2G_0$ and $10G_0$. The lower flows are adequate when the particle size of the solid can be controlled. The optimum size, however, depends upon the nature of the solid. Higher flows are necessary where a wide range of particle size must be accepted. In practice, sizes from about 10 mesh to 300 mesh have been fluidized in various systems. The selection of the value of G is usually based upon practical trials with the particular system, the figure being the lowest which is compatible with the desired degree of agitation and the absence of any tendency to segregation.

In the fluidized condition, the solid particles are thoroughly mixed throughout the bed in a similar manner to that seen in aerated liquid. This allows very good temperature control of a reacting system and prevents local overheating. In addition, a very high heat transfer coefficient exists between the solid particles and any heating or cooling surface in contact with the bed.[10] In experimental work by Mickley and Trilling,[11] the heat transfer coefficients were from 3 to 70 times greater than those between the surface and the gas in the absence of the solid particles. The effect is presumably due to the effect of the particles in disturbing the boundary layer and reducing its thickness.

Even in a large fluid bed reactor, the average residence time of the gas is quite short, i.e. a few seconds or tens of seconds. The distribution of gas residence times has been studied by Danckwerts et al.,[12] who concluded that it corresponds much more closely to piston flow than to complete mixing. It is possible to pulse the air supply in order to compress the range of gas residence times and to increase the average residence time. This technique also allows a wider range of particle sizes to be accepted than would otherwise be possible in a fluid-bed process.

Fluidization reactions are generally carried out in fairly tall cylindrical vessels, although this shape is not essential. Provision is usually required for the supply or extraction of heat. The location of the heating or cooling system is of much less importance than in, for example, a moving bed, in view of the rapid and complete mixing which occurs. The reactor may in fact have a cooling or heating jacket, or electric tubular immersion heaters, or cooling pipes may run down the length of the bed. Some of the heat may also be supplied in the reactants. The gas feed may be passed through any suitable type of heater before entering the reactor. It is, however, more difficult to heat the solids supplied to the bed since the high temperature may interfere with the feeding mechanism.

The points of entry and discharge of solids are also relatively unimportant, but usually the former is at the top and the latter near the bottom of the bed. Various types of feeding mechanism are employed, e.g. the solids can flow as a moving bed from a hopper, through a suitable valve, star feeder or screw conveyor, etc., directly into the bed. An alternative arrangement is to fluidize the particles from such a delivery device with a portion of the gas feed, through an inlet pipe and into the bed. The addition of solids to the main supply of fluidizing air before it enters the reactor is not recommended and in some cases is clearly impossible, since the particles must pass through the gas distributing device.

The discharge of solids from the bed is sometimes via a downcomer or vertical pipe immersed in the bed near the base and through to a conveyor of a similar type to that used at the solids inlet point. Another method is to allow the solids to flow over a weir at the top of the bed and pass down a pipe passing through the reactor wall. In certain cases, it is possible to entrain enough of the solids continually in the effluent gas stream and then to disentrain them again away from the bed.

The location of the gas supply is important since it has the dual role of reactant and fluidizing medium. It is normally fed in a vertically upward direction through a distributor plate at the base of the bed, which also acts as a support for the solid particles. The distributor may take the form of a porous plate of sintered metal, or a solid plate perforated with a number of holes as in Fig. 5.5. It is important to obtain even gas distribution over the whole of the cross-sectional area of the bed, and for this purpose a simple wire mesh is often not satisfactory. The irregular distribution and "channelling" of gas which would occur in this case can be avoided, when using a perforated plate, by correct design of holes. A relatively thick plate, as illustrated, with conical holes, relatively few in number, appears to be most satisfactory. The holes are usually larger than the particle size of the solid. To prevent the solids from falling through under shut-down conditions, each hole may be backed by a small plate underneath it, sufficiently close to prevent the solids overflowing it when they take up their angle of repose. Alternatively, the distributor may take the form of a small bed of irregularly shaped granular material which is too coarse to fluidize and is inert to the reactant gas and solids. The voids must then be sufficiently small to retain the solid reactant particles.

Some fluid bed reactors are operated without a distributor plate. The base of the reactor is simply constructed in the shape of an inverted cone. The high linear velocity at the base of the cone prevents blocking of the gas inlet by particles of the solid being fluidized.

The gas phase leaving the bed has solid particles, particularly fines, entrained in it. Cyclones are sometimes used to cause disentrainment, from which the solid feeds back to the reactor through a pipe dipping beneath the surface of the bed. Difficulties are sometimes encountered owing to unsatisfactory flow of the solids back to the bed in these circumstances. Porous sintered metal filters, or porous ceramic ones, are also used for disentrainment of solids, either in addition to, or instead of, a cyclone. It is necessary to have a large filter area and to "blowback" fairly frequently, i.e. to reverse the flow of gas to the filters in order to remove solids which are adhering to their surface. Usually a number of filters are installed and at any time one or more of them is being cleaned whilst the remainder are performing their normal filtration duty. The displaced cakes of solid from the filters are allowed to fall back into the bed, where they become broken up by the fluidization action.

The physical shape of the filters can vary, but a hollow bayonet shape is fairly common and relatively easy to manufacture from sintered stainless-steel, nickel, or nickel alloy.

In a single fluidized bed in which normal good mixing prevails, a long average residence time of the solids is often necessary to achieve efficient conversion. The proportion of relatively unreacted solids which "by-passes" can be considerably reduced by using several fluidized beds in series, the flow of solids and gas being counter-current. The beds can be arranged in a vertical cascade, one above another. Gas passes upwards from one bed to another via distributor plates as shown in Fig. 5.6. Solids pass in the reverse direction, overflowing into a downcomer pipe in each bed, which traverses the distributor plate beneath and ends in the next lower bed. The primary feed of solids is to the top bed only, where the filters and gas exit are located. The final discharge of reacted solids is from the bottom bed alongside the initial gas feed. Control of a continuous multi-stage system of this type is not always easily achieved and depends upon the type of material being processed.[13] For example, the heat evolution or absorption varies from one bed to another depending upon differences of reaction rate under the various conditions. Thermocouples are fitted to each bed and temperatures are controlled by regulating the degree of heating or cooling applied to each separate bed.

Also, it is necessary to design the downcomers and gas distributor plates carefully.[14] The latter require a reasonably high pressure drop across them for good gas distribution. This necessitates reasonably long downcomers to balance the pressure drop, but their height-to-diameter ratio must be kept to a minimum to avoid "slugging" of the solids.

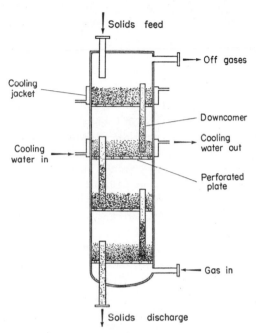

FIG. 5.6. Multi-stage fluidized bed reactor (Jonke, A. A., Levitz, N. M. and Petkus, E. J. Ref. 25).

PRODUCTION OF URANIUM TETRAFLUORIDE
BY THE STATIC BED METHOD

The static bed "dryway process" for the production of uranium tetrafluoride involves less advanced chemical engineering techniques than, for example, fluidization. With careful design and correctly optimized operating conditions, it has been difficult to supplant, however, on purely economic grounds. Many thousands of tons of uranium tetrafluoride have been produced by this method since the Second World War in the United Kingdom and the United States alone.

A process of this type can now only be regarded as competitive for uranium compounds if the scale of production is less than a few hundred to one thousand tons per annum. Although tending to be regarded as obsolete for uranium compounds, therefore, there are other rare metals which are unlikely to be produced in plants with outputs as great as this for many years. Consequently, experience with uranium will be of value in these other fields.

The United Kingdom's process operated at the Springfields factory until recent years[15] used a feed solution of uranyl nitrate in dilute nitric acid, from the solvent-extraction process. This contains about 130 g U/l. and is first treated batchwise with 28 per cent w/w aqueous ammonia solution to precipitate "ammonium di-uranate", at a pH of about 9·5.

$$2UO_2(NO_3)_2 + 6NH_4OH \rightarrow (NH_4)_2U_2O_7 + 4NH_4NO_3 + 3H_2O.$$

The reaction is accomplished in a simple stirred vessel and the slurry run off into a Nutsch type of filter. This is a straightforward stainless-steel rectangular vacuum filter using a twill cloth supported upon a grid. Washing is carried out batchwise on the filter but need not be very efficient since the uranium feed is at its highest state of purity from other metal ions and the ammonium nitrate contaminant is completely removed by the subsequent calcination treatment. The semi-dry cake is then loaded manually into circular graphite trays (Fig. 5.7) which fit one above another to form a nest inside a cylindrical inconel reactor. Ports are arranged in the trays to allow reactant gases to pass upwards from one to another and across the surface of each.

The reactor is lowered into an electric furnace with its top near ground level, a seal is made at the top, and calcination begun. Ammonia, excess ammonium nitrate and water are removed as the temperature rises to 350°C.[16]

$$(NH_4)_2U_2O_7 \rightarrow 2UO_3 + 2NH_3 + H_2O.$$

The next step is to pass hydrogen through the reactor at a temperature of 700°C, to reduce the trioxide to dioxide, i.e.

$$UO_3 + H_2 \rightarrow UO_2 + H_2O.$$

The reaction proceeds fairly rapidly and is complete after a few hours. Uranium dioxide has a higher true density than the trioxide or the ammonium di-urante from which it came. Consequently, the particle size is much reduced and the product is very reactive. It is not generally removed from the reactor at this stage but remains behind to be converted to uranium tetrafluoride. Batches which have been removed have been found to absorb oxygen at normal temperatures, to form an interstitial oxide having a composition between $UO_{2\cdot0}$ and about $UO_{2\cdot2}$. This is an exothermic reaction and if the temperature increases unduly it can sometimes cause reactive oxide of this type to burn spontaneously in air to U_3O_8. This high reactivity of the oxide is similarly exhibited towards hydrogen fluoride at the subsequent stage.

Anhydrous hydrogen fluoride gas replaces hydrogen through the reactor for the hydrofluorination stage, at a temperature of about 450°C, the

FIG. 5.5. Fluidized bed support plate and downcomer-pipe. Conical holes improve distribution of fluidizing gas (Jonke, A. A. *et al* Ref. 21).

FIG. 5.7. "Dryway" plant, ammonium diuranate paste is loaded into trays.

reaction being:

$$UO_2 + 4HF \rightarrow UF_4 + 2H_2O.$$

The high reactivity of the oxide makes control of hydrofluorination a little difficult, since the reaction is fairly highly exothermic. If the rate of supply of hydrogen fluoride is not restricted or the gas diluted, e.g. with nitrogen, the temperature of the bed can rise to the point where sintering of both oxide and fluoride occurs. This considerably reduces the specific surface area of any remaining oxide, and hence its reactivity, with the result that conversion of the last few per cent of oxide to fluoride is very slow. Thus an anomalous situation arises whereby a high initial reaction rate often gives a very low average rate. The resulting fluoride product is also sintered and less reactive than desired towards calcium or magnesium in the final uranium metal production stage.

If this high reactivity of the oxide is unduly embarrassing, it can be lowered by carrying out the hydrogen reduction stage at a little higher temperature. 800°C is generally employed when an oxide product is required instead of a fluoride and it is necessary to expose the oxide to air without undue oxidation. This "stable" oxide absorbs oxygen slowly at normal temperature to a composition of about $UO_{2.04}$. If the hydrogen reduction stage is carried out at too high a temperature, however, and undue sintering or "thermal damage"[17] of the oxide takes place, it may be difficult to complete the subsequent hydrofluorination reaction.

The hydrofluorination reaction is not very efficient, as measured by the usage of hydrogen fluoride, when carried out in a single furnace. This is because a large excess of the gas is required for the conversion of the last few per cent of oxide to fluoride. A method of improving the efficiency is to hydrofluorinate in a number of reactors in series, the first being removed from the line at intervals, and replaced by a new one at the end of the line. This then becomes a counter-current process. The excess hydrogen fluoride is absorbed in potassium hydroxide solution in a suitable scrubber.

The uranium tetrafluoride is cooled in a hydrogen atmosphere before opening the furnace, to prevent atmospheric oxidation. The product has a packing density of 2·2 g/cm³ and contains less than 2 per cent of uranyl fluoride (UO_2F_2) or uranium dioxide impurities.

Since a single furnace is used for three dryway operations, calcination, hydrogen reduction and hydrofluorination, the transfer of solids is minimized. The initial charging of trays and loading these into the furnace is relatively free from dust hazard since the "ammonium di uranate" feed material is damp. Special precautions are needed, however, for removal of the final uranium tetrafluoride product from the trays, since it is a dry dusty powder and tends to adhere to the trays to some extent. This operation is therefore carried out in a small "glove box", i.e. in a sealed and vented cabinet, using rubber gauntlet gloves. Trays are tipped individually through a grid into drums and then brushed clean ready for re-use.

Materials of construction for the dryway plant are selected to be resistant to corrosion by hydrogen fluoride at the last stage, since these conditions

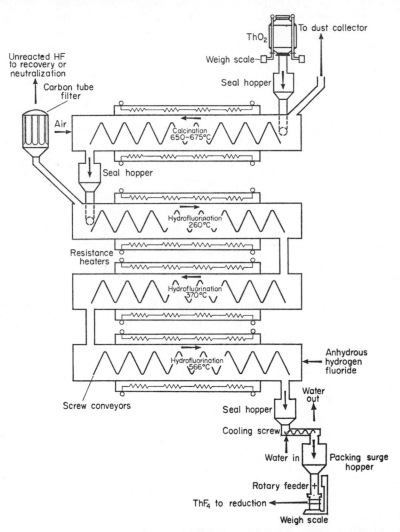

FIG. 5.8. Stirred bed plant for the production of thorium tetrafluoride (From F. L. Cuthbert, *Thorium Production Technology*, 1958, Addison-Wesley, Reading, Mass.).

are the most severe. The maintenace record of the inconel furnace and graphite trays has been generally fairly good.

PRODUCTION OF THORIUM FLUORIDE
BY THE STIRRED BED PROCESS

Thorium oxide is converted to fluoride by the action of hydrogen fluoride in the U.S. process carried out at the National Lead Company of Ohio,[18] i.e.

$$ThO_2 + 4HF \rightarrow ThF_4 + 2H_2O.$$

A bank of four horizontal stirred beds is used, one above another, of the screw conveyor type. The top one is for calcination in air to remove traces of nitric acid, water and carbonaceous products, the middle two for hydrofluorination and the lower one mainly for partial sintering and densification of the product in hydrogen fluoride. Each stirred bed reactor is 20 ft long and 16 in. internal diameter, the lower ones made of inconel and the upper one of stainless-steel. The powder flows from a hopper at the top, via a seal hopper between the calcination and hydrofluorination sections, to another hopper and feeding system at the bottom, as shown in Fig. 5.8. Air and anhydrous hydrogen fluoride pass in counter-current flow to the solids in the appropriate reactors, the effluent gases being conducted to suitable filters and dust collectors.

Each reactor is heated by means of external electric elements, calcination being at a temperature of 650–75°C, hydrofluorination between 260°C and 370°C, and densification at 566°C, as shown in the figure.

TABLE 4

TYPICAL IMPURITIES IN THORIUM OXIDE AND TETRAFLUORIDE

Impurity	ppm in ThO_2	ppm in ThF_4
Uranium	2·5	16·3
Aluminium	<10	<10
Boron	0·4	1·2
Barium	—	<20
Beryllium	<1	<1
Bismuth	<2	<2
Calcium	<200	—
Cadmium	<0·2	<0·2
Cobalt	<1	—
Chromium	8·1	38
Copper	46	81
Iron	46	161
Magnesium	8	24
Manganese	2	6
Molybdenum	<1	5
Nickel	15·6	338
Phosphorus	<40	<40
Lead	27	24
Silica	207	33
Tin	6	—
Vanadium	<10	—
Zinc	<10	29
(Thorium	86%	75·4%)

An excess of hydrogen fluoride is preferably employed, the effluent gas usually containing 70 per cent hydrogen fluoride and 30 per cent water. This is condensed and provides a by-product for other purposes.

Corrosion is a fairly serious problem in this plant, being caused mainly by attack of sulphur-containing gases on the nickel alloy. It is minimized by maintaining the sulphate content of the thorium oxide feed as low as possible, and by avoiding cold spots in the system where aqueous hydrofluoric acid containing hydrogen sulphide or sulphur dioxide might condense.

Typical impurity analyses of thorium oxide feed and thorium tetrafluoride product are shown in Table 4.

PRODUCTION OF URANIUM TETRAFLUORIDE
BY THE FLUIDIZED BED PROCESS

Fluidized bed processes have been devised which convert uranyl nitrate solution to uranium trioxide, by thermal denitration, reduce to the dioxide with hydrogen and finally hydrofluorinate to uranium tetrafluoride. Three separate fluidization systems are needed, with solids transfer throughout. In addition, nitric acid can be recovered from the denitration process and the excess of hydrogen fluoride can be recovered from the hydrofluorination process.

Full-scale processes of this type are operating in the United Kingdom and the United States. Full descriptions of these plants have not been published, but details of the American large-scale pilot plant are available[14, 19, 20, 21, 22, 23] and some information has been published regarding the operation of a production prototype plant in the United Kingdom.[24]

United States process

Uranyl nitrate solution, containing a minimum of free nitric acid, is evaporated to about 70 per cent uranyl nitrate (about 800 g U/l.) to provide a feed solution. This is supplied at a temperature of about 70°C (to prevent crystallization) and under a pressure of up to 4 atm, to four spray nozzles in the side of the denitration reactor, distributed around the circumference. The reactor takes the form of a short column, 6 in. diameter, in the Argonne National Laboratory's pilot plant,[10] but 10 in. diameter[22] in that operated by the Mallinckrodt Chemical Works as shown in Fig. 5.9. The latter is several feet high and holds a bed of uranium trioxide which is 2 or 3 ft deep. Heat is supplied by 18 tubular electric heaters immersed in the bed through the reactor base, together with another 42 electric heaters disposed about the circumference. The fluidizing air is pre-heated and passes through a sintered stainless-steel distributor plate in the base. This is assisted by the smaller flow of "atomizing air" used for spraying the uranyl nitrate, and also by the gases evolved as a result of the denitration reaction. The total air usage may be as much as 2 tons per ton of uranyl nitrate processed, the fluidizing velocity being about $1·5$ ft/sec, which is perhaps as much as 6 times G_0.

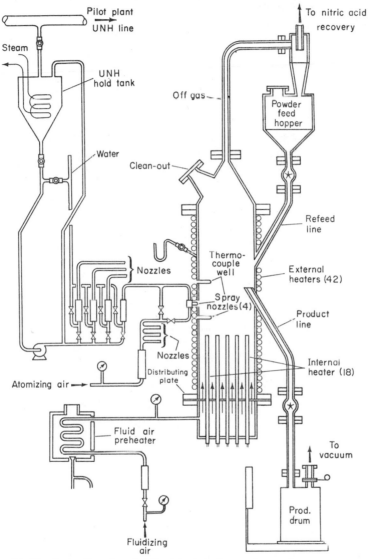

FIG. 5.9. Ten-inch pilot-plant fluidized bed denitrator (From C. D. Harrington and A. E. Ruehle, *Uranium Production Technology*, copyright 1959, D. Van Nostrand, Princeton, New Jersey).

The reaction is carried out at a temperature of 300°C to 350°C and can be represented as:

$$UO_2(NO_3)_2 6H_2O \rightarrow UO_3 + 2NO_2 + \tfrac{1}{2}O_2 + 6H_2O.$$

It is an endothermic reaction, the heat of formation of UO_3 being 570 kcal/g of uranium. The additional solution water is of course also evaporated and in all about $2\cdot5 \times 10^6$ Btu must be supplied per ton of uranium processed.

The gases are fed to a cyclone in this case for disentrainment of solids, although sintered stainless-steel filters are usually preferred. The cleaned gases then pass to absorption towers for conversion to nitric acid. The filters are blown back with pre-heated air after the pressure drop has increased from the normal 2 psig to about 8 psig.

Provision is made for addition of an intitial charge of UO_3 powder by means of a hopper and star feeder which also collects the disentrained powder from the cyclone. The product is similarly discharged as required via a downcomer and star feeder, into a partially evacuated product drum. The particles are almost spherical in shape as shown in Fig. 5.10 and of size about 150 to 200 μ. The packing density (tap density) is about $4\cdot3$ g/cm^3. The form of the product can however be altered by adjusting the conditions of spraying and the bed temperature. For example, "caking" occurs if the spray nozzles are mounted above the bed with the spray directed downwards, or below the bed with the spray directed upwards. Horizontal mounting with the spray directed into the bed at a distance from the base gives the best form of product and also minimizes blockages of the nozzles.[10] The flow rate of uranyl nitrate to the nozzles requires reasonable control. Metering pumps, together with Rotameter type flowmeters, have been used.

The effect of increased bed temperature is to increase the particle size, but this also reduces the nitrate and water content of the product. A reasonable optimum is obtained at the operating temperature of 300–50°C.

The particle size also tends to grow with increasing residence time in the bed, and this is particularly the case with uranyl nitrate concentrations above 70 per cent. This can be counteracted by recycling a proportion of the product continuously, after grinding. The finely ground particles act as nuclei for the deposition of further oxide and a satisfactory average particle size can be achieved. In practice, it is more convenient to employ a uranly nitrate concentration of about 70 per cent.

The UO_3 product from a fluid bed thermal denitration process tends to be less reactive than that produced by ammonium di-uranate precipitation and calcination. It can be considerably improved by the addition of a little sulphuric acid to the feed solution, corresponding to about $0\cdot1$ per cent of the uranium content.[23] The product is then very suitable for the subsequent hydrogen reduction and hydrofluorination stages.

Information has been published in the U.S.A. on the hydrogen reduction of uranium trioxide to the dioxide on a production scale[23] of up to about 10 tons/day. The reaction is: $UO_3 + H_2 \rightarrow UO_2 + H_2O$, and $\triangle H = -24$

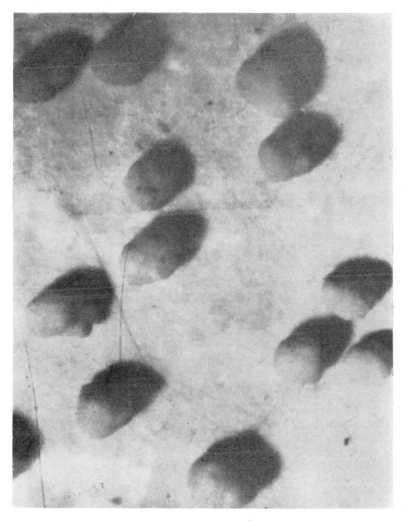

FIG. 5.10. Particles of uranium trioxide produced by fluidized bed calcination of uranyl nitrate solution (magnified 75 times). (Jonke, A. A. *et al* Ref. 19).

kcal/mole. A two-stage reactor system is employed, the cylindrical stainless-steel reactors being about 7 ft in depth by 14 in. diamater as shown in Fig. 5.11. They are heated electrically by externally wound elements when necessary and also cooled by steam coils similarly located. The temperature is controlled in practice at about 600°C, but can be less.

Uranium trioxide is fed into the first reactor about half-way down by means of a hopper and screw feeder, and forms a fluid-bed about 4 ft 6 in. deep. It leaves this bed via a 3-in. diameter pipe at a fairly steep angle and enters the second reactor fairly low down. The resulting dioxide similarly flows from near the top of the second bed into a screw conveyor and thence to a product hopper. The reducing gas consists of three volumes of hydrogen and one of nitrogen from dissociated ammonia to which extra nitrogen is added. This dilutes the hydrogen to a suitable concentration for reduction, in practice as low as 38 per cent. The gas is fed to both reactors in parallel and passes through porous metal plates for distribution. The velocity is about 1 ft/sec. The two effluent gas streams join and pass along with the oxide product to the screw conveyor. At the end of the latter, above the product hopper, the gases leave the solids, and are conducted first to a cyclone and then to burners. Oxide from the cyclone passes to the uranium dioxide product hopper. The excess hydrogen is burned, thus giving only nitrogen and water in which is entrained a quantity of fine oxide. The fine oxide dust is disentrained by means of large bag filters and can be recycled to the uranium trioxide feed hopper.

Stainless-steel is regarded as a suitable material of construction for the reduction reactor. There may, however, be a little doubt about its life in the presence of the trace of hydrogen sulphide which is formed by the action of hydrogen on the sulphate introduced to increase the oxide reactivity.

The uranium dioxide product from this fluid bed reactor does not have the highest possible reactivity towards hydrogen fluoride for the final stage of conversion to uranium tetrafluoride. The reactivity can however be increased simply be reoxidizing to the extent of about 3 per cent. This is carried out in a small fluid bed, the shell of which is made of stainless-steel, about $2\frac{1}{2}$ft deep by 8 in. diameter, coned down to 6 in. at the base. The uranium dioxide is fed in near the top of the bed by means of a screw feeder, and the slightly oxidized product taken off at the same level from the other side of the reactor. A vertical baffle prevents undue by-passing between inlet and exit points. The fluidizing and oxidizing gas consists of a mixture of nitrogen and air containing about 4 per cent oxygen. It is fed through a perforated plate near the reactor base and passes out of the reactor with the solids. In this particular plant, it feeds directly into a stirred-bed type of hydrofluorination reactor, counter-current to the flow of hydrogen fluoride. The nitrogen and oxygen mixture therefore becomes mixed with water and excess hydrogen fluoride and is passed to filters.

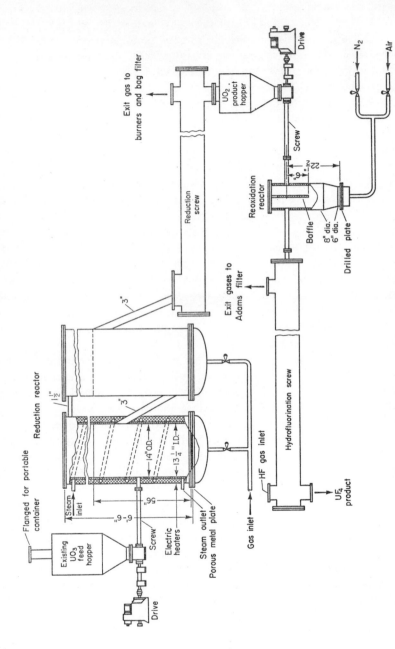

Fig. 5.11. Fluidized bed reduction reactors (Brater, D. C. *et al.* Ref. 23).

A three-stage fluid bed process is also being developed[10] for reduction of uranium trioxide to dioxide at the Argonne National Laboratory. All three stages are located one above the other in a single reactor with downcomers for the flow of solids from one bed to another. This process uses a gaseous reductant of 75 per cent hydrogen and 25 per cent nitrogen and is specifically designed to operate with a feed of uranium trioxide which has been produced by thermal denitration in a fluid-bed rather than with other types of trioxide.

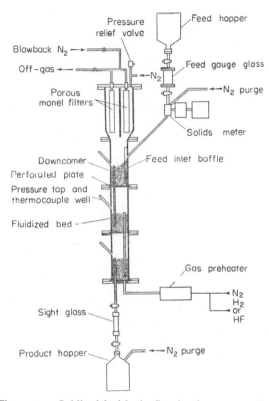

Fig. 5.12. Three-stage fluidized bed hydrofluorination reactor (Jonke, A. A., Levitz, N. M. and Petkus, E. J. Ref. 25).

Several U.S. pilot plants have been described for the hydrofluorination of uranium dioxide to uranium tetrafluoride.[10, 13]

The reaction is simply: $UO_2 + 4HF \rightarrow UF_4 + 2H_2O$, and it is carried out at a temperature of about 500°C. For this reaction, $\triangle H = 43$ kcal/mole approximately.

A fairly long residence time is required for the hydrofluorination reaction to approach completion and this can only be achieved in a continuous process by the use of several fluid-beds in series. Figure 5.12 shows a 3 in.

diameter, three-stage unit, made of monel, which has been used by the U.S. Argonne National Laboratory.[25] It resembles their small three-stage reduction reactor in that the solid flows from one bed to another via vertical downcomers and hydrogen fluoride passes upwards in a counter-current manner through perforated plates at the base of each bed. In the example shown, the oxide flows in from a sealed hopper under gravity to a baffled entry point in the top bed. The fluoride is removed under gravity from the bottom bed to a nitrogen purged product hopper. Special mention should be made of the effluent gas cleaning system, since a high proportion of fluoride fines are produced, and this material is carried away from the beds with the excess hydrogen fluoride and steam. The gas is filtered through fairly large sintered monel filters located at the top of the reactor. These are blown-back in turn with dry nitrogen as required, when they become blinded.

A residence time of 4–8 hr in the reactor leaves only about 1 to 2 per cent of the uranium dioxide unconverted.[10] A temperature gradient in the top, middle and lower beds of 400°C, 500°C, and 600°C respectively gives the best results. The overall excess of hydrogen fluoride is of the order of 100 per cent, and this is recovered as a concentrated solution. The tetrafluoride product has a packing density of about 3·6 from dioxide feed material having a packing density of 4·4.

A larger pilot plant has also operated at the Argonne National Laboratory based upon reduction in a four-stage, 5 in. diameter, stainless-steel reactor, followed by hydrofluorination in a five-stage, 6 in. diameter, monel reactor. This is shown in Fig. 5.13 and is based upon principles similar to those employed in the smaller plant.

An alternative type reactor has been developed which is stated to overcome the tendency to caking and formation of uranium tetrafluoride dust.[1] This is a monel fluid bed reactor with an internal agitator to stir the bed strongly (Fig. 5.14). Two reactors are used in series to obtain a reasonably high conversion efficiency.

United Kingdom process

A production-scale prototype fluidization process has operated at the U.K. Atomic Energy Authority's Springfields Works. It consists of three batch type reactors for denitration, hydrogen reduction and hydrofluorination, with pneumatic solids transfer between.

The feed solution of uranyl nitrate hexahydrate, at 1120 g U/l. is provided by evaporation of the 80 to 90 g/l. solvent extraction product solution. This is carried out in a four-effect natural circulation multi-tube evaporator, shown diagramatically in Fig. 5.15. A little sulphuric acid is added to the feed, to increase the reactivity of the oxide during the later hydrofluorination reaction.

The denitration plant is shown diagramatically in Fig. 5.16. It is fabricated entirely of stainless-steel, most of the bed being contained in the lower
portion of smaller diameter than the remainder. Fluidizing gas distribution

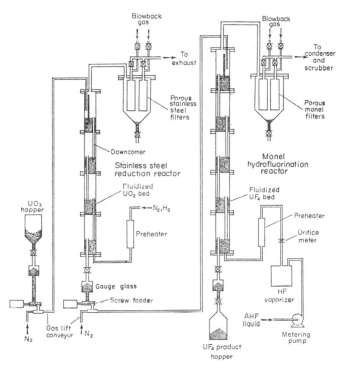

FIG. 5.13. Multi-stage reduction and Hydrofluorination reactors (Lawroski, S.,
*et al. Proc. 2nd U.N. Conf. on the Peaceful Uses of Atomic Energy, United
Nations, New York*, col. 4, p. 48).

is by means of a simple sintered cone at the base, hot air being used. Heating
is by means of vertical tubular electric elements, protected by stainless-steel
cases, in the lower part of the bed. They have sufficient capacity to allow the
endothermic denitration reaction to proceed at 350°C. It is now believed,
however, that temperatures of 300°C or even less are satisfactory, and consequently a less expensive source of heat might be employed, using an organic
heating fluid of the terphenyl type, or possibly an organic silicate.

The evaporator product is fed hot via a metering pump to a set of six
spray guns or atomizers which are positioned around the circumference of
the denitration reactor about 1 ft from the top of the bed. These are made
of stainless steel and have nozzles which can be withdrawn and replaced
when necessary. They are of the two-fluid type, the second fluid being hot
air. This is metered individually to each nozzle by means of a Rotameter
type of flowmeter.

An initial charge of several hundred kilograms of uranium trioxide is fed into the reactor from a storage hopper, the first charge having been produced in a small pilot plant. The uranium trioxide product is withdrawn

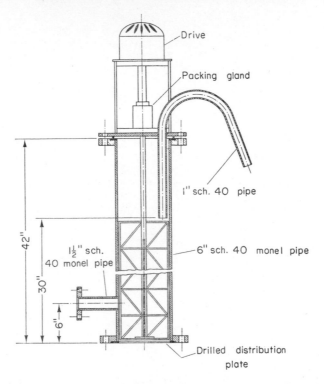

Fig. 5.14. Agitated fluid bed hydrofluorination reactor (Smiley, S. H. and Brater, D. C. Ref. 3).

to a cooler and lift-pot and then sieved and transferred pneumatically to storage hoppers above. One of these feeds to the subsequent reduction reactor and the other back to the denitration reactor.

The hot exhaust gases first pass through sintered stainless-steel filters of a conventional type, which can be blown back with hot air at intervals. They then transfer part of their heat to incoming air, in a heat exchanger, and are finally fed to a nitric acid recovery system which is common to other plants.

The reduction reactor system, shown in Fig. 5.17, resembles the denitration reactor, being made also of stainless-steel. In batchwide operation it is necessary to supply some heat at the beginning of a reaction, and this is by external electrical heating jackets. Channels between the electrical windings allow cooling air to be blown over the external surface of the reactor during the remainder of the run when it is necessary to remove heat.

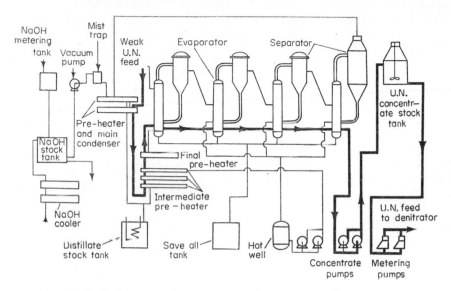

FIG. 5.15. Springfields uranyl nitrate evaporation plant (Hawthorn, E., Shortis, L. P. and Lloyd, J. E. Ref. 24).

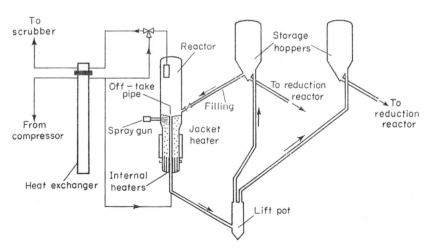

FIG. 5.16. Springfields denitration plant (Hawthorn, E., Shortis, L. P., and Lloyd, J. E. Ref. 24).

The temperature is controlled between about 450°C and 650°C, the lower part of the range being most suitable for the formation of a highly reactive dioxide which hydrofluorinates rapidly.

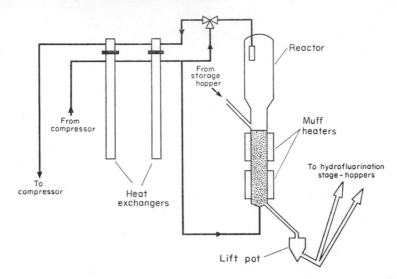

FIG. 5.17. Springfields reduction plant (Hawthorn, E., Shortis, L. P. and Lloyd, J. E. Ref. 24).

The uranium trioxide feed passes to the reduction reactor by means of a reciprocating feeder. The dioxide product is metered in a suitable vessel after withdrawal from the reactor. A special type of poppet valve is used on these lines conveying solids.

The off-gases are filtered by conventional means and heat exchanged between them and the ingoing gases, before recompression and make up with additional hydrogen. The water produced in the reaction is allowed to condense and join the water or dilute sodium hydroxide solution used as the pump seal liquid. When sodium hydroxide solution is present, it tends to scrub out the small proportion of hydrogen sulphide arising from the sulphate addition to the uranyl nitrate feed, and so minimize corrosion.

Two reactors are used in parallel for hydrofluorination, so as to allow a longer residence time, in view of the hydrofluorination reaction being slower than reduction. Each reactor, as shown in Fig. 5.18, although based upon design principles similar to those used for the reduction reactor, is constructed of Inconel throughout, and is also much longer, to provide a greater residence time.

The solids and gas feeding system is similar to the previous reactor. External electrical heaters are needed to initiate the batch reaction. Much more heat has to be removed when the reaction is proceeding than applies to reduction, but a larger wall area is available for this. The operating temperature is about 450°C.

A fairly elaborate hydrofluoric acid recovery system is installed, adapted to batch operation. The concentration of hydrogen fluoride gas fed to the reactor is progressively increased as the reaction tends to slow down. The

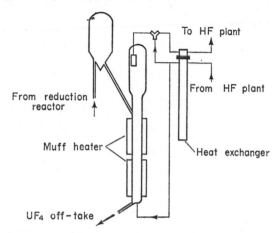

FIG. 5.18. Springfields hydrofluorination plant (Hawthorn, E., Shortis, L. P. and Lloyd, J. E. Ref. 24).

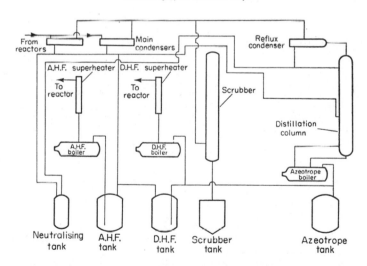

FIG. 5.19. Springfields hydrogen fluoride recovery plant (Hawthorn, E., Shortis, L. P., and Lloyd, J. E. Ref. 24).

off-gases simultaneously increase in hydrogen fluoride and decrease in water content. The gas leaving the reactor initially can be neutralized and the effluent sent to the drain. Later in the run it is fed to a distillation column operating on the weak side of the azeotrope. The resulting azeotrope passes to a dilute hydrofluoric acid stock tank and the water to drain. When the off-gases composition is above the azeotrope composition, it can join the dilute hydrofluoric acid directly. Finally, when the anhydrous hydrogen fluoride passes through the reactor virtually unchanged, it can be re-used as anhydrous acid. The system is shown in Fig. 5.19.

REFERENCES

1. HARRINGTON, C. D. and RUEHLE, A. E. *Uranium Production Technology*. D. Van Nostrand, Princeton, New Jersey (1959).
2. SMILEY, S. H. and BRATER, D. C. Conversion of Uranium Trioxide to Uranium Tetrafluoride in vibrating tray reactors. Current Commission Methods for Producing UO₃, UF₄ and UF₆. U.S.A.E.C. Report, TID–5295 (1956).
3. SMILEY, S. and BRATER, D. C. Conversion of Uranium Trioxide to Uranium Tetrafluoride. *Progress in Nuclear Energy*, Ser. III, *Process Chemistry*, vol. 2, Pergamon Press (1958).
4. ZENZ, F. A. and OTHMER, D. F. *Fluidization and Fluid Particle Systems*. Reinhold, New York (1960).
5. CARMAN, P. C. Fluid flow through granular beds. *Trans. Inst. Chem. Engrs.* **15**, 150 (1937).
6. LEWIS, W. K. *et al.* Characteristics of fluidized particles. *Industr. Engng. Chem.* **41**, No. 6, 1104 (June, 1949).
7. MATHESON, G. L. *et al.* Characteristics of fluid solid systems. *Industr. Engng. Chem.* **41**, No. 6, 1099 (June 1949).
8. LEVA, M. *et al.* Fluid flow through packed and fluidized systems. *Bull. U.S. Bur. Min.* **504** (1951).
9. VAN HEERDEN, C. The fluidized state. *J. Appl. Chem.* **2**, Supplementary Issue No. 1, 57 (1952).
10. JONKE, A. A. and LEVITZ, N. M. Development of a Fluidized Bed Process for the Production of Uranium Tetrafluoride. *Progress in Nuclear Energy*, Ser. III, *Process Chemistry*, vol. 2, p. 122. Pergamon Press (1958).
11. MICKLEY, H. S. and TRILLING, C. A. Heat transfer characteristics of fluidized beds. *Industr. Engng. Chem.* **41**, No. 6, 1135 (June 1949).
12. DANCKWERTS, P. V. *et al.* The distribution of residence times in an industrial fluidized reactor. *Chem. Engng. Science* **3**, 26 (1954).
13. LAWROSKI, S. *et al.* Fluidization techniques as applied to reactor fuel processing. *Proc. 2nd Int. Conf. on the Peaceful Uses of Atomic Energy*, Geneva, 1958. Paper 542.
14. LEVITZ, N. M. A fluidized bed process for the production of uranium tetrafluoride. *Chem. Engng. Progr.* **53**, No. 4, 199 (April 1957).
15. GRAINGER, L. Production of uranium metal. *Proc. 1st Int. Conf. on the Peaceful Uses of Atomic Energy*, Geneva, 1955. Paper 407.
16. GRAINGER, L. *Uranium and Thorium*. George Newnes, London (1958).
17. KUHLMAN, C. W. and SWINEHART, B. A. Production of uranium tetrafluoride, thermal damage effect. *Industr. Engng. Chem.* **50**, No. 12, 1774 (Dec. 1958).
18. CUTHBERT, F. L. *Thorium Production Technology*, chap. 6, Addison–Wesley, Massachusetts (1958).
19. JONKE, A. A. *et al.* The use of fluidized beds for the continuous drying and calcination of dissolved nitrate salts. *Nuclear Science Engng.* **2**, No. 3, 303 (May 1957).
20. THAYER, H. E. The newest United States uranium processing plant. *Proc. 2nd Int. Conf. on the Peaceful Uses of Atomic Energy*, Geneva, 1958. Paper 602.
21. JONKE, A. A. *et al.* Fluidization techniques in producing refined uranium from ore concentrates. *Industr. Engng. Chem.* **50**, No. 12, 1739 (Dec. 1958).

22. SANDERS, E. F. and ROBINSON, S. N. Fluid bed Denitration. U.S.A.E.C. Report, MCW–1409.
23. BRATER, D. C. *et al.* Preparation of High Productivity Uranium Dioxide by Fluid-Bed Reduction. U.S.A.E.C. Report, K–1329 (1957).
24. HAWTHORN, E., SHORTIS, L. P. and LLOYD, J. E. The fluidized solids dryway process for the production of uranium tetrafluoride at Springfields. *Trans. Inst. Chem. Engineers* **38**, No. 4, 197 (1960).
25. JONKE, A. A., LEVITZ, N. M. and PETKUS, E. J. Fluidized Bed Process for the Production of Uranium Tetrafluoride from Uranyl Nitrate Solution. U.S.A.E.C. Report, TID–7501 (Pt. 1), p. 53 (1956).

CHAPTER 6

METAL PRODUCTION BY HIGH-TEMPERATURE REDUCTION TECHNIQUES

THEORY

The most widely used general method of producing the rare metals in a pure condition is by reduction of the oxides or halides. Potentially suitable reducing agents can be selected from thermodynamical considerations.

Reduction of oxides

Figure 6.1 shows ΔG, the free energy change involved in the formation of various rare metal oxides, plotted against temperature. Similarly the

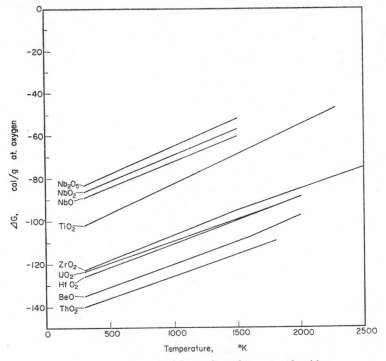

FIG. 6.1. Free energy of formation of rare metal oxides.

oxides of potential reducing agents, e.g. hydrogen, carbon, sodium, calcium, magnesium and aluminium, etc. are shown in Fig. 6.2. The slopes of these graphs $\partial(\Delta G)/\partial T$, are equal to $-\Delta S$, the entropy change. The fact that the slopes are almost all in the same direction, and similar in magnitude, is characteristic of reactions all involving combination of a solid metal with gaseous oxygen to produce a solid oxide. The "condensation" of the oxygen is predominantly responsible for the entropy decrease in each case. As might be expected, above the boiling point of the metal the entropy decrease is greater, and the slope of the ΔG against temperature graph becomes steeper, Similarly, a decrease, or even a reversal of gradient, is observed at the temperature where the oxide becomes volatile, e.g. for the reaction:

$$2C + O_2 \rightarrow 2CO.$$

In Figs. 6.1 and 6.2 the oxides which are most stable are those which lie in the lower part of the figure, i.e. where the greatest loss of free energy is involved in their formation. Consequently, as a general rule, the elements near the top of these figures can be produced by reduction of their oxides with elements in the lower parts of the figures, provided the temperature of

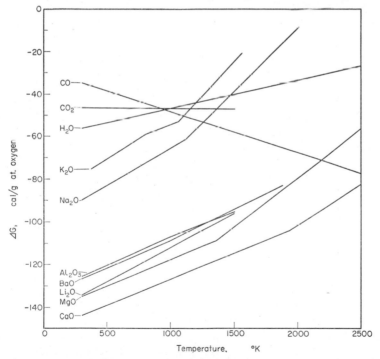

FIG. 6.2. Free energy of formation of reductant oxides.

each system is sufficiently high for an adequate rate of reaction; e.g. calcium will reduce thorium dioxide to thorium metal, with the production of the relatively stable calcium oxide.

Carbon occupies a unique position as a reducing agent; it is more effective at higher temperatures than low temperatures whether carbon monoxide or dioxide is the product. The negative slope of the carbon monoxide curve makes this the more usual product at the highest temperatures.

The figures are based upon the reactants and products being in their standard states, i.e. pure solids or liquids, or gas or vapour at 1 atm pressure, according to the temperature and the individual elements concerned. In practice, therefore, the results of possible reduction reactions are not always those which might be predicted simply by examination of these graphs. For example the reactants or products might enter into solid solution in one another, as is the case with calcium and calcium oxide, Alternatively the pressure might vary widely when the temperature is above the boiling-point of one of the reactants or products. These factors have an effect upon the energy evolved in a particular reaction and may even decide whether or not the reaction will take place at all.

Reduction of halides
Similar considerations apply to the various halides. Graphs of the free energy changes involved in the formation of fluorides and chlorides are shown in Figs. 6.3, 6.4 and 6.5. Again, the rare metal halides are shown, together with those of potential reducing agents. Halides are sometimes preferred to oxides because of the desire to maintain the oxygen contents of the metals at low levels, for metallurgical reasons. Similarly, in these cases, air is usually excluded from the reduction reactions, since oxygen and nitrogen form solid solutions of oxides and nitrides in the metals, making them hard and brittle. An evacuated system or an inert atmosphere such as argon or helium is then employed. Of the halides, chlorides or fluorides are usually preferred to iodides or bromides on economic grounds.

Type of product
The form of the metal and slag products after a reduction reaction depends upon the amount of heat available from the reaction. If this is sufficient to melt both metal and slag, it may be possible to separate them cleanly. The metal falls through the slag and collects at the base, whence it can be removed on cooling as a solid ingot.

When insufficient heat of reaction is available to melt the slag, as is often the case when oxides are reduced with calcium or magnesium, the metal is present as a powder in a matrix of slag. The metal and slag are usually sintered together somewhat, particularly if the original reactants had been pressed together before initiation. The precise form of the discrete particles of metal depends upon whether or not the metal becomes molten or whether sufficient time is available at high temperature for particles to coalesce appreciably. If a flux is used, e.g. of calcium chloride for a calcium oxide slag, and the products are "soaked" at high temperature after reaction, it may be possible to recover the metal in the form of nearly spherical beads of reasonably large size. Without a flux, large coky agglomerates tend to

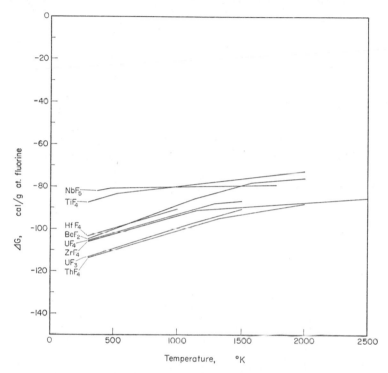

FIG. 6.3. Free energy of formation of rare metal fluorides.

be obtained. At the other extreme, where the melting-point of the meta product is not reached, and the temperature is not even sufficiently high for appreciable sintering together of individual metal particles, the metal powder is often so finely divided that it is pyrophoric on exposure to air.

When the temperature achieved in a reduction reaction is sufficient to melt the slag but not the metal, as in the reduction of certain chlorides by magnesium (or sodium), the metal product is obtained in the form of a "sponge" or as a dendritic powder. This sintering of the metal into a sponge type of structure is assisted by the rare metal chloride having a relatively low boiling-point. In effect, therefore, the metal product forms by contact of the chloride vapour with a pool of molten magnesium (or sodium) and is probably present initially in a very finely divided condition, so aiding sintering. The interstices are filled with magnesium chloride, which requires removal by leaching or distillation before the structure of the metal becomes apparent.

Reaction conditions

An adiabatic reaction is usually preferred, as far as practicable, so that the highest possible temperature is obtained. This is achieved by a rapid

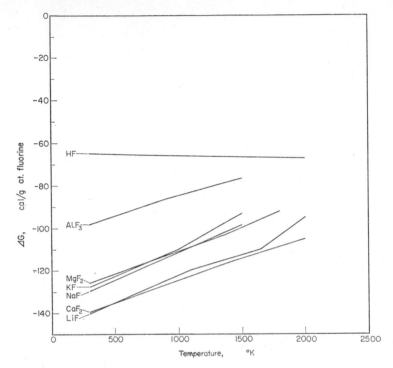

Fig. 6.4. Free energy of formation of reductant fluorides.

reaction and good thermal insulation of the system. In addition, the reaction vessel and reactants are often allowed to "soak" at a temperature just below that required for initiation. This gives the charge a uniformly high temperature and so increases the total heat available when the reaction eventually takes place. This practice might, however, in some circumstances lead to a premature slow reaction, or to slow side-reactions, which could actually create the opposite effect to the one desired, i.e. the heat of reaction could be "frittered away" before the main temperature peak was reached.

Additional heat is sometimes introduced into the system by the addition of a "booster" to the reactants. This may take the form of, for example, iodine or sulphur, which combines with a suitable excess of the reducing agent (say calcium) at the same time as the reaction takes place.

In some cases, it is necessary to prevent the reaction temperature becoming too high, e.g. because of rapid vapourization of one of the reactants or products, with the possibility of explosions. Sodium, for example, boils at

880°C and it may sometimes with advantage be replaced by magnesium for this reason.

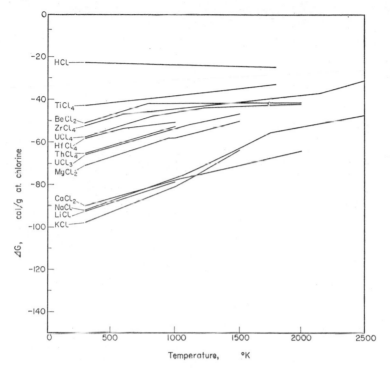

FIG. 6.5. Free energy of formation of rare metal and reductant chlorides.

Excessive reaction between the container material and the products or reactants must be avoided, and this may impose a limit upon the peak temperature which is allowable, or upon the materials of reactor construction. Reactors take different forms and are made from or lined with a variety of refractory materials. Lime, magnesia, electrically fused dolomite, calcium fluoride, nickel, stainless-steel, molybdenum, tantalum, niobium or graphite have all been used, for different purposes.

INGOT PRODUCTION PROCESSES

The production of ingots of various rare metals, is carried out commercially on the kilogram to the ton scale. This technique is particularly valuable for uranium[1] and beryllium,[2] but smaller quantities of, for example, zirconium,[3] vanadium and thorium have also been manufactured. The fluorides are generally preferred to the chlorides since they are less volatile. Oxides do not result in molten slags unless large quantities of other materials, e.g. arising from the use of "boosters", are present. Sodium is not generally used as the reducing agent owing to its rather low boiling-point (880°C), and potassium is too expensive. Magnesium and calcium are favoured, therefore, magnesium being the cheaper of the two although reactions with calcium are usually more exothermic.

Form of reactants

Methods of reacting a halide with calcium or magnesium involve mixing the two reagents fairly intimately, packing the mixture in a reactor of suit-able shape and size, and initiating the reaction.

It may be important for the halide to be free from oxide or oxyhalide, either of which might cause side reactions, reduce the amount of heat available for melting the metal and slag, or interfere with rapid phase separation. The physical form of both halide and reducing metal may also be critical, since it is necessary to have a fairly homogeneous mixture of the two, The calcium or magnesium metal is usually present as small chips, flakes, or nodules rather than a powder, since the latter might become unduly oxidized before use, owing to its high surface area. During use, its excessive reactivity might lead to explosive reactions. For any particular reaction carried out in different plant or on different scales, widely differing methods of packing the charge have been used. These vary from a loose-packed mixed powder to pelleted blocks of mixture, either random packed or arranged in a particular geometric pattern. Differences in technique might, to some extent, be caused by different insulation conditions or methods of initiation, and each individual set of conditions is usually selected on an empirical basis.

Reduction plant

Reactors can be of mild steel for an ingot production process, since a refractory lining is necessary in any case to protect it from the molten metal. Graphite is a satisfactory lining material for use in, for example, a magnesium reduction process, but when calcium is used as a reductant the graphite tends to react with it and introduce carbon into the rare metal product. The disadvantages of its high thermal conductivity and specific heat may be minimized by using only a thin graphite lining, separated from the reactor by a gas space or a loose-packed insulating powder.[4] Linings may be built up from blocks, plates or annuli, or a small lining may be machined from a single block.

Calcium or magnesium fluoride can be used as linings provided the wall thickness is sufficient to prevent collapse through melting when in contact with molten slag of the same composition. Lime, magnesia, or fused dolo-mite, have also been used for reactions where they do not introduce oxygen into the metal. This might occur by virtue of the presence of a little water, which in effect acts as a catalyst as the reactants are being taken up to temperature. The water first hydrolyses a quantity of metal fluoride in the charge, liberating hydrogen fluoride, i.e.

$$MF_4 + 2H_2O \rightarrow MO_2 + 4HF.$$

The hydrogen fluoride diffuses to the lining and fluorinates a portion of it, yielding at the same time a little water, i.e.

$$M_gO + 2HF \rightarrow M_gF_2 + H_2O.$$

The original amount of water is thus available to diffuse back into the charge and cause further hydrolysis, until a proportion of oxide has been built up in the charge which is much greater than the stoichiometric equivalent of the water content of the system. If the oxide is not reduced, it may tend to enter the metal ingot, either in solution or as a separate phase.

The refractory linings may be jolted or vibrated into position between the inner wall of the reactor and a wooden or metal former, which is inserted specially for this purpose. The surface may be sintered by heating from inside and in any case a drying-out operation is required before use. Fairly small linings of calcium fluoride have been made as separate entities away from their reactors by slip-casting and sintering. A similar technique is applicable to the other materials provided a small quantity of a binding agent is present. About 1 per cent of sodium fluoride has been used effectively with a calcium oxide refractory.

After inserting the charge into the reactor lining in a suitable manner, loose packed, tamped into position, or pelleted, it is covered with refractory powder or a solid refractory lid. It is finally sealed tightly by means of a steel lid, if the intention is to use a closed "bomb" technique. The lid may have connections for evacuation and inlet of argon when it is necessary for the reaction to be carried out in complete absence of air.

The usual method if initiating the reaction is to heat externally by means of a furnace, which can be gas or oil fired, or heated electrically. The furnace and reactor are sometimes heated together from cold, but where a more rapid initiation is desired, the reactor can be charged to a furnace which is already at temperature. Initiation is accompanied by a rapid and pronounced rise in temperature, and often an increase in pressure. The latter can be excessive and lead to explosions if water or other volatile material has been allowed to remain inside the reactor. Internal temperatures are not generally recorded routinely since peak temperatures may be too high to be measured by means of thermocouples. Thermocouples may be located in the lining, however, in such positions that an indication of reaction initiation may be given with relatively little time lag. These recorded temperatures may be several hundred degrees below the true temperatures of the molten metal and slag. Pressures may be recorded by means of a

16

pressure gauge.provided it has a virtually instantaneous response, since the pressure peak may only be present for a fraction of a second, and might easily pass undetected. A contact microphone inserted inside a deep well passing from the reactor lid is a sensitive means of determining the time of initiation, since the rise in pressure and the movement of material give a good response.

Reactions are sometimes initiated from cold by means of a small coil of molybdenum or tungsten through which an electric current is passed. One end of the coil can conveniently be connected to the metal reactor casing or lid, while the other may pass to a sparking plug connected in the lid. This allows a good insulating seal to be provided.

When an open reaction is used, as in the well-known "thermit" process, initiation is usually from the cold condition and is carried out by igniting a piece of magnesium in the top of the charge, or by dropping in a lighted ignitor pellet, e.g. of sugar and potassium chlorate mixture.

The reactor is removed from the furnace and allowed to cool, cooling perhaps being assisted by means of a water spray in the case of a closed bomb. Breakdown of the reactor contents is then carried out. A clean ingot should be present underneath a solidified pool of slag, which has separated from the molten condition. Unless graphite has been used as the reactor lining, it is usually necessary to break the lining when recovering the ingot. The ingot is picked out and brushed clean, or possibly the surface requires "pickling" in, for example, a dilute acid, to remove slag inclusions.

Residue recovery

The slag usually contains a few per cent of the rare element, either as metal globules which have failed to agglomerate with the ingot, as unreacted halide, or possibly as a secondary product such as an oxyhalide or a solid solution of halide in the slag phase. The intrinsic value of this residue material may be sufficiently high to warrant recovery, since the rare element might have undergone a considerable degree of expensive purification before reduction. Methods of recovery vary according to individual circumstances, but processes upon which they might be based include acid leaching, complete dissolution of the slag, and chlorination to a volatile halide.

Some of the impurities might pass into the reactor lining. Also, parts of the lining inevitably become mixed with the slag, and vice versa, when separating them and recovery processes must be able to tolerate this. For this reason, it is convenient to use a common recovery process for slag and lining, where possible. Sometimes the lining can be crushed and re-formed for another reaction. Where the slag is of the same composition as the lining, it may even be possible to treat the two as one, crushing together and avoiding separation. It is, however, not usually satisfactory to re-form the lining from crushed slag which has been in the molten condition, without elaborate powder preparation techniques to make the slag satisfactory for ceramic fabrication.

Graphite components can be re-used a number of times, possibly with a simple brushing, scraping or machining operation between each occasion. If the residual rare element content of the graphite warrants recovery, an acid leach operation is at least partially effective, in most cases. Leaching may be after every reaction or after a series of reactions, possibly when the graphite is ready for discarding.

Calcium reduction of uranium tetrafluoride

Large tonnages of uranium metal have since about 1947 been produced at the U.K. Atomic Energy Authority's Springfields factory by the calcium reduction process, i.e. [5]

$$2Ca + UF_4 \rightarrow U + 2CaF_2.$$

This process is entirely satisfactory in operation and in the quality of the metal produced from it; a high proportion of the early uranium fuel for experimental and power reactors in the U.K. was of this type. It has, however, now been rendered obsolete by the magnesium reduction process which gives an equally satisfactory product at a lower cost.

The reaction is highly exothermic and can therefore tolerate a fairly large range of conditions with regard to scale, physical form of the reactants, oxide or oxyfluoride content of the fluoride, or temperature of initiation. The reaction as carried out on the 100 kg scale involved calcium in the form of small nodules, produced by crushing a condensed product from a distillation purification process. The uranium tetrafluoride was in the form of a fairly coarse powder with a combined oxide and oxyfluoride content of about 2 per cent. The reactants were mixed by tumbling in a rotating vessel and poured into a mild steel reactor, lined with calcium fluoride. An open-top reactor was used, in the form of an inverted truncated cone supported on a bogie. The lining was made from powder vibrated in position using a wooden former, and baked before use by passing the bogie through a heated oven. The charge was added to the cooled reactor soon after baking, and transferred to a well-protected firing bay. Here, an incendiary pellet of burning sugar and potassium chlorate mixture was dropped on to the top of the charge, remotely, to cause the reaction to initiate. This occurred with considerable vigour but was only occasionally accompanied by violent consequences such as the spilling of portions of the reacting charge. An ingot or "billet" was quickly formed, containing about 97 per cent of the uranium content of the charge, and of density about 18·9 g/cm^3. The bogie was then passed first to a cooling bay and next to a breakdown area. The breakdown operation involved the complete emptying of the reactor from billet, slag and lining. The cylindrical billet was removed, brushed and some-times "pickled" in ammonium nitrate solution before weighing and passing for casting. An attempt was made to achieve a rough separation of the slag and lining, the former being sent to a uranium recovery process and the latter being washed and recycled to form a new lining for another reaction. About once every five cycles, the lining material was leached with dilute acid to remove the accumulated silicon and iron contamination. Although this leach was originally introduced to remove impurities, the liquor con-tained sufficient uranium to warrant recovery, and for this purpose an alkali precipitation step was applied before discarding.

The reaction slag, having been fused, was harder than the lining and required both crushing and grinding before being leached with nitric acid for uranium recovery. The uranium was never completely leached out, but a high proportion of it entered the nitric acid solution and was subsequently extracted by means of an organic solvent.

Calcium reduction processes have also been carried out in France[6] and Belgium.[7]

Magnesium reduction of uranium tetrafluoride

The present United States A.E.C. technique for magnesium reduction of uranium tetrafluoride, on a scale of about 100 kg, has been fully described.[8] This is a considerable improvement on their early process which used booster reactions involving, for example, potassium chlorate, to provide additional heat.[9] The process uses a uranium tetrafluoride which is specified to be about 55 per cent less than 325 mesh and the remainder less than 60 mesh. The uranyl fluoride (UO_2F_2) content and uranium dioxide (UO_2) content combined, should preferably not exceed 2 per cent, although yields are reasonably satisfactory up to 4 per cent. The packing density should also preferably exceed $3\cdot0$ g/cm^3. The magnesium is reduced to pieces of about 10 to 60 mesh by an elaborate process involving coarse and fine comminuting mills and several magnetic separation stages to remove "tramp" iron picked up from the machines.

The reactants are weighed out, mixed in a double cone blender and tamped into cylindrical reactors made from 13 in. nominal bore piping, lined with either lime or electrically-fused dolomite. The lining is jolted into position in the 1 in. annular space between the inner wall of the reactor and a slightly tapered mandril, before charging. The charge comes to within 3 in. of the top of the lined reactor. A graphite disc is forced into the reactor to the top of the charge and the space on top of the disc filled with powdered refractory before bolting on the lid.

The reaction is initiated in a gas-fired furnace at 365°C after about 3 hr. A contact microphone inside a small thermocouple well indicates the point of initiation. The molten uranium settles beneath the magnesium fluoride slag, the former remaining in the molten condition for a few minutes.

The reactor is finally raised from the furnace, cooled in air and then sprayed with water for additional cooling, before breakdown of the reactor contents and extraction of the "biscuit" of metal.

The U.K. Atomic Energy Authority's magnesium reduction process[4] differs from its U.S. counterpart in that the charge is in pellet form and the reactor lining is of graphite. The lining is made from a series of annuli which are stacked one above another inside the stainless-steel reactor. The lower end of the bottom annulus is closed and forms a well or catchpot for the molten ingot. The top of the graphite assembly consists of a graphite plate and the stainless steel reactor lid fits above this. The lid carries inlet and out-let pipes for purging with argon and evacuation.

The charge is fabricated into pellets about 4 in. diameter by 4 in. deep. which are stacked in a regular manner inside the graphite.

The initiation temperature is achieved as rapidly as possible by lowering the reactor into a gas-heated furnace which is already at a temperature of about 1000°C. This minimizes "pre-reaction", i.e. a series of slow local reactions which would dissipate some of the available heat before the point of rapid initiation. Thus the maximum temperature peak is achieved for the maximum duration, so allowing good settling and agglomeration of the uranium metal.

After reaction, the reactor is lifted out of the furnace whilst still hot, and then cooled in air. Breakdown of the reactor contents is relatively easy, the ingot, slag and graphite separating fairly cleanly.

A yield of up to 98 per cent and density of about 18·8 g/cm³ are generally obtained.

Most of the graphite assembly is re-used, annuli being trued on a lathe or rejected as necessary.

The magnesium reduction slag is recovered by nitric acid leaching and solvent extraction in a manner exactly analogous to the recovery of calcium fluoride slag.

Magnesium reduction of beryllium fluoride

Anhydrous beryllium fluoride is first manufactured, one method being to use ammonium bifluoride as a fluorinating agent. Processes of this type are operated by the U.S. Brush Beryllium Company[10] and the Imperial Smelting Corporation at Avonmouth.[11] In the Imperial Smelting Corporation's process, pure beryllium hydroxide is first dissolved in ammonium bifluoride solution of 25 per cent concentration by weight, to give ammonium fluoberyllate solution, i.e.

$$Be(OH)_2 + 2NH_4HF_2 \rightarrow (NH_4)_2BeF_4 + 2H_2O.$$

This salt is isolated by evaporation and crystallization from a 50 per cent solution. Rubber-lined, Keebush or polythene plant is employed for these stages. The crystals are then dried to remove their 1 per cent to 3 per cent of water, in a steam-heated trough-type dryer. Finally, the dry free-flowing crystals are decomposed by heating in a gas-heated furnace of special design (Fig. 6.6) at a temperature of 800–50°C.:

$$(NH_4)_2BeF_4 \rightarrow BeF_2 + 2NH_4F.$$

This decomposition will, if necessary, take place relatively slowly at quite low temperatures, with the production of the beryllium fluoride in a finely divided form. The furnace used, however, is designed specifically to allow decomposition primarily above the melting-point (797°C) so that the coarse product resulting can be handled more easily and is less subject to hydrolysis. The furnace hearth is constructed of graphite, over which the decomposing ammonium fluorberyllate is fed continuously at a rate of about 35 lb/hr. The fused beryllium fluoride is tapped off in 60 to 80 lb batches at a temperature of 900°C. The ammonium fluoride and decomposition products (ammonia and hydrofluoric acid) are led away from the furnace to condensers and scrubbers for recovery.

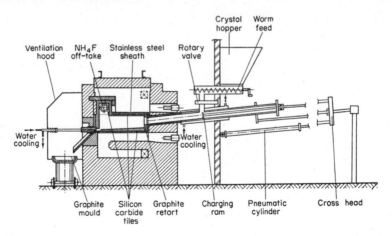

Fig. 6.6. Gas heated furnace used for the decomposition of ammonium fluoberyllate (Derham, L. J., and Temple, D. A. Ref. 11).

After cooling, the glassy solid beryllium fluoride has an ammonia content of only 0·001 per cent and a beryllium content of about 0·2 to 0·6 per cent. It is crushed to pass a ¼ in. screen, ready for reaction with magnesium. The magnesium is provided in the form of small "raspings".

$$BeF_2 + Mg \rightarrow Be + MgF_2.$$

The reactor used for the magnesium reduction of the fluoride by the Imperial Smelting Corporation[10] is shown in Fig. 6.7. It consists of a mono-lithic graphite crucible 11 in. internal diameter at the top and 9 in. at the base, fitted with a graphite lid containing a charging hole. The crucible is heated in a gas-fired furnace, but surrounded by clay-bonded silicon carbide or plumbago to protect it from oxidation by the hot gases. The fur-nace is lined with aluminous firebrick, but a portion of this is cut away at the bottom to allow the crucible to be tapped by means of a water-cooled graphite valve.

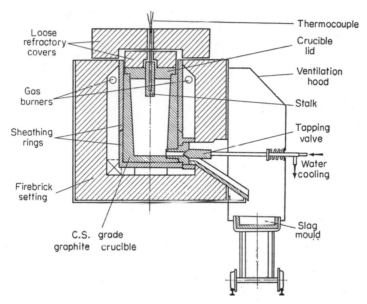

FIG. 6.7. Beryllium reduction furnace showing the arrangement for bottom tapping of the crucible (Derham, L. J. and Temple, D. A. Ref. 11).

This reaction was originally carried out at a high temperature,[12] but the present reduction technique consists of charging stoichiometric quantities of the mixed reactants to the crucible containing fused calcium chloride at 1000 to 1100°C. The reaction takes place rapidly, since its initiation tem-perature is about 650°C. The products are heated to above the melting-point of beryllium metal (1283°C) and held for about 2 hr, whilst the beryllium floats to the surface and aggregates into small ingots or 'beads" of about 1 in. in size. The calcium chloride acts as a flux, and reduces the melting-point of the slag below that of magnesium fluoride (1263°C).

The reaction products are finally cooled in the crucible to 1050–1100°C, the lid removed, and the beryllium beads skimmed from immediately below the surface of the molten flux, the magnesium fluoride having settled as a crystalline deposit on the base of the crucible. The beads are quickly placed in an argon-filled vessel where they can be cooled to room temperature. The slag can then be run from the crucible through the graphite valve at the base.

Beads or ingots larger than about 1 in. lead to the formation of cavities owing to the high (3 per cent) shrinkage of beryllium upon solidification. These entrap flux and slag inclusions which would be difficult to remove later.

The almost spherical beads are washed with hot water in a rubber-lined tumbler vessel to leach out calcium chloride and remove any adhering magnesium fluoride crystals. They are next rinsed in cold water and dried in a steam-heated oven. The beads are then vacuum-melted in beryllia crucibles, and the metal cast into large ingots, with simultaneous removal of traces of magnesium and halides.

In the Brush process[10] a rather larger graphite crucible is used, which is heated electrically by a high-frequency induction furnace and takes a charge of 260 lb of beryllium fluoride and 96 lb of magnesium, the latter being in the form of 1 in. lumps. The large excess of beryllium fluoride is needed to act as a flux. 31 lb of metal are recovered at an efficiency of only 62 per cent. Most of the beryllium fluoride loss is recovered later by leaching and re-cycling to the chemical purification stage of the process.[13]

The beryllium metal and slag is wet milled to leach out the soluble salts and liberate the insoluble magnesium fluoride as fine crystals. The latter are taken away from the coarse beryllium "pebbles" as a fine slurry. The pebbles pass through a sink-float process using a mixture of ethylene dibromide and light mineral oil to remove remaining pieces of slag. The pebbles are dried, after washing away the ethylene dibromide with isopropyl alcohol, and then given a water wash. The few per cent of impurities in the beryllium metal product (particularly magnesium) are finally removed by a vacuum melting operation, at 300 to 500 μ pressure. The magnesium con-tent is then 0·03 to 0·05 per cent, total impurities being about 0·5 per cent.

An alternative method of reducing beryllium fluoride with magnesium has been described by Kawecki[14] in which the reaction takes place at a rela-tively low temperature. Approximately equal quantities of beryllium fluoride and calcium fluoride are first melted together in an induction-heated graphite crucible, open to atmosphere. The melting-point of the mixture is about 700°C, but the temperature is actually raised to 800°C. Massive magnesium metal is then added, in about 10 per cent stoichiometric excess, to carry out the reduction. The magnesium is held below the surface of the fused fluoride until it melts and floats to the top. The beryllium metal forms as a powder, and the fusion mixture is stirred sufficiently to prevent this from settling out at the top of the fluoride and forming an interface layer between it and the molten magnesium. The reaction is fairly rapid but is moderated somewhat by the diluting effect of the molten calcium fluoride upon the beryllium fluoride. The heat of reaction raises the temperature to 1000°C which is sufficient to prevent solidification of the melt when its final composition becomes magnesium fluoride–calcium fluoride instead of beryllium fluoride–calcium fluoride.

After complete reduction, the melt is maintained unstirred at a temperature just below 1100°C to allow the beryllium powder to collect near the surface and sinter together. It is important that the boiling-point of magnesium (1107°C) is not reached, for above this temperature the reduction reaction tends to reverse and re-form beryllium fluoride and magnesium metal.

The semi-sintered, porous, metallic mass is removed from the fluorides by decanting away the latter and the beryllium is melted quickly at about 1300°C (m.p. 1283°C) and finally cooled rapidly, since it is important to prevent the reverse reduction reaction taking place at the high temperature. Both the magnesium vapour and the molten fluorides play a useful part in preventing atmospheric oxidation of the beryllium metal during the melting stage. The beryllium ingot resulting from this melting operation can be separated cleanly from the small amount of associated slag. It is then melted again, for a longer period, to distil out the magnesium completely. This operation is performed in an elongated chamber, designed in such a manner that the distilling magnesium vapour protects the beryllium from atmospheric oxidation. By this technique beryllium metal can be obtained without much difficulty with a total impurity content of 0·2 per cent.

Calcium reduction of vanadium oxides

Insufficient heat is available from the calcium reduction of vanadium pentoxide or trioxide alone to melt the metal and slag. This has been overcome[15] by the use of a "booster" of iodine or sulphur, which is allowed to react with a large excess of calcium. Iodine is less effective than sulphur on a comparative weight basis, and is in any case much more expensive. Quantities of sulphur and iodine up to about 0·9 and 0·35 moles/mole of vanadium have been used.

A small-scale technique only has been described,[15] but the equipment was reasonably representative of a possible industrial process. Graphite, fused dolomite, pure magnesia or pure calcium fluoride have been used as reactor linings, inside a cylindrical steel casing, 18 in. deep by 8 in. diameter. Reactor lids consisted of either screw caps or bolted flanges and provision was made for argon purging and evacuation prior to initiation.

Initiation was either by heating the base of the "bomb" in a furnace or by means of an electrically heated molybdenum wire buried in the charge.

Ingots were obtained by this technique in about 75 per cent yield using either the pentoxide or trioxide. In both cases they were usually rough and contained either porosity or slag inclusions.

The ductility varied greatly from one ingot to another and a uniform product always capable of rolling, extrusion or drawing cannot be guaranteed. The nature of the impurity which causes embrittlement is not known. Impurity levels are very approximately as follows:

	%
Oxygen	0·05 to 0·3
Nitrogen	0·004 to 0·08
Hydrogen	0·002 to 0·03
Carbon	0·06 to 0·2
Sulphur	0·025 or less
Iron	0·01 to 0·2
Silicon	0·03 to 0·6
Calcium	0·04 to 0·2

Calcium reduction of thorium tetrafluoride

Thorium tetrafluoride is produced fairly readily by reacting the pure oxide with anhydrous hydrogen fluoride by a typical "dryway" technique. A simple tunnel furnace made of inconel may be used, with inconel trays. A 98 per cent yield can be obtained in about 10 hr at 550°C, using an excess of the fluorinating agent.

Reduction of the fluoride is carried out on a small scale in a manner analogous to the production of vanadium metal ingots from vanadium oxides and, as in that case, using sulphur as a booster, with a large excess of calcium.[16] A bomb type reactor 12 in. deep by 6 in. internal diameter is lined preferably with graphite, filled with the mixed reactants, covered with a graphite lid, and a metal lid fitted by means of a screw thread. The calcium, thorium fluoride and sulphur are compacted together to form four pellets and another calcium–sulphur pellet may be used at the base of the reactor. Initiation is preferably by means of an electrically-heated molybdenum coil placed inside a few grammes of a loose mixture of calcium and sulphur. The yield of metal ingot is not high, usually below 91 per cent, but well-formed billets can be obtained if the quantity of sulphur exceeds about 1 gramme atom per gramme atom of thorium. Typical billets produced in the U.K.A.E.A.'s Culcheth Laboratories are shown in Fig. 6.8 .

Average impurity contents of billets produced at Culcheth were as follows:

	%
Oxygen	0·26
Nitrogen	0·038
Carbon	0·24
Sulphur	1·0
Fluorine	0·33
Calcium	0·21

FIG. 6.8. Typical thorium billet from thorium tetrafluoride (Audsely, A., Lind, R. and England, P. G. Ref. 16).

In a comparable American process, operated on a semi-production scale by the U.S.A.E.C. Ames Laboratory, zinc chloride is found to be the most satisfactory booster, as a 10 per cent admixture with the thorium tetra-fluoride. A 25 per cent excess of calcium is used over the stoichiometric requirements of the thorium tetrafluoride.

The reaction takes place in a closed steel vessel, 45 in. long by 12 in. internal diameter, which is lined with electrically fused dolomite or lime, as in the American uranium metal production process. Initiation is carried out in a gas-fired furnace at a temperature of 640°C. A thorium/zinc alloy is formed, from which the zinc is removed by distillation under vacuum, between 1000°C and 1100°C in graphite pots. About 85 per cent of the zinc can be recovered for re-use.

METAL POWDER PRODUCTION PROCESSES

Some high-melting metals are produced with relative ease in the form of powder, resulting from, say, an oxide reduction with, for example, sodium, calcium, or magnesium. Difficulties may arise, however, in the later stages of the process when separating from slag owing to the tendency of metal powders to be oxidized in air or aqueous solutions.

Reductions in absence of metal vapour

The technique can be applied in several different ways. In one of these, the reactants (say an oxide with calcium) are pressed together to form pellets of perhaps several inches diameter by a similar height. A pressure of several tons per square inch is necessary, and it is advisable for the calcium to be in the form of small "shreds", i.e. with one dimension larger than the other two, to bind the components together. When the reduction is carried out on a scale of only a few kilograms, it may be possible to avoid the use of a refractory lining to the reactor. A single pellet, or possibly several stacked one on top of another, may be placed inside a simple mild steel reactor of adequate diameter. They rest perhaps upon a refractory material, e.g. a plate of sintered alumina or a thin layer of powdered lime. The reactor is usually purged with argon and evacuated, to maintain moisture-free and oxygen-free conditions. It is then lowered carefully into a furnace without dislodging the pellets and causing them to touch the reactor wall. An electrically heated nichrome-wound furnace operating at a temperature of 1000°C should be satisfactory. The pellets may become plastic at tempera-ture during initiation, but they retain their rigidity sufficiently to avoid touching the wall. After cooling, preferably by lowering the furnace tem-perature, the cake of rare metal powder and lime can be taken out as a single piece, pellets usually having fused together somewhat. Very little or no iron impurity is introduced into the reaction cake if the technique is applied carefully. On a larger scale, say equal to 100 kg of rare metal, pellets may still be used but the reactor is lined with a refractory. For a calcium reduction, a vibrated lime lining is suitable Pellets are best stacked in a regular manner to allow uniform heat transfer conditions from the furnace to the charge before initiation. After reaction and cooling, the pellets and lining are emptied out of the reactor together, the former being then picked out by hand.

In all cases where the reactants are pressed together into pellets, it is necessary to crush the product before separating the metal powder from the oxide slag.

An alternative method of reacting a rare metal oxide with calcium is to mix the loose components together and pass in trays through the hot zone of the furnace in a semi-continuous manner. The furnace temperature is maintained at 1000°C and the reaction takes place in an inert gas, e.g. argon. The throughput of this type of process is limited by the rate at which the furnace can raise the reactants to the initiation temperature. This is similar in practice whether a slow stream of large batches or a faster stream of small batches is employed, and the latter is usually most convenient. A batch size of only a few kilograms is used, therefore, but under these conditions it is possible to process about one ton of rare metal per week in quite a small furnace. The mixed metal powder and slag product from this type of process remains as a powder and does not require crushing before separation of the components.

A third technique of carrying out metal powder reductions is exemplified by the obsolete German process for the production of a relatively impure zirconium during the 1939–45 war.[17] In this process, potassium zirconium fluoride (K_2ZrF_6) was reacted with a small excess of sodium in a molten mixture of sodium and potassium chlorides. In this case the cake required crushing and grinding before leaching away the salts from the metal powder.

Magnesium reduction of oxides can be carried out in a similar manner to calcium reduction, but in general the reactions are less exothermic. Consequently a very finely divided rare metal powder results, which tends to be pyrophoric, and therefore unsafe to handle, on exposure to air. Pyrophoric powders are sometimes obtained in calcium reductions and in the case of metals whose melting-point is not too high, it may be possible to soak after reduction, for a period, at a temperature at or approaching the melting-point. This sinters the surfaces of particles and causes neighbouring ones to aggregate, so reducing the reactivity towards aerial oxidation.

Reactions in presence of metal vapour

Sodium reduction of fluorides has also been used to produce metal powders. The reductions can be performed in simple mild steel or stainless-steel unlined reactors, without introducing large quantities of iron into the product. Since the sodium will easily melt and to a large extent be present as a vapour in the reaction, there is little need for homogeneous mixing of the reactants. Alternate layers of the fluoride and sodium are simply packed into the cylindrical reactor, the sodium first being cut into pieces of about 1 in. in size or less. An open system has been employed on a scale of a few kilograms, in which the reactants are simply covered with a layer of sodium chloride, and possibly a loose fitting lid. Initiation is then carried out by heating in a small electric or gas-fired furnace. Excess sodium distills into the relatively cold sodium chloride and is condensed.

In the corresponding closed-bomb technique,[18] provision must be made for a high proportion of free space, owing to the relatively high pressures which can develop in reactions involving sodium (see Fig. 6.9). This space is preferably purged with an inert gas and evacuated, to avoid the large volume of air taking any part in the reaction. The reactants are packed in a crucible, which rests inside the reactor coupled to an expansion chamber. Initiation is by means of an electrically heated surface, and after the reaction it may be desirable to continue heating to about 1100°C and distil the excess sodium to a cooler part of the reactor whilst it remains in a closed system.

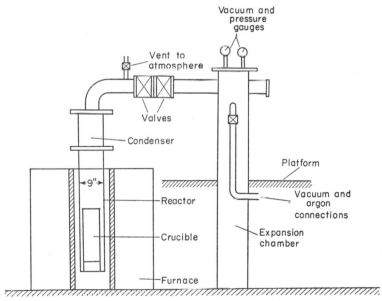

FIG. 6.9. Closed bomb reactor (as used for reacting K_2NbF_7 with sodium) (U.K. Patent 791,121. By permission of the controller of H.M. Stationery Office).

Powder recovery

In all the types of reaction described, it is necessary to recover the rare metal powder from intimate association with a slag, usually by an aqueous leaching operation. This presents certain difficulties, which might be insuperable if for example fluorides were reduced with calcium or magnesium. These would give slags which are insoluble in simple leaching agents, or at least any successful leaching agent would probably also dissolve the metal powder. Sodium fluoride can be leached out with water, hence the preference for this reductant when fluorides are used. Calcium or magnesium oxides are readily soluble in dilute acids and a relatively weak one such as acetic can be chosen if the metal is also attacked.

A common difficulty in all the leaching processes is the surface dissolution or oxidation (or both) of the metal particles. A compromise is sometimes achieved by limiting the time, or temperatures, of exposure of the metal-slag reaction cake, to the aqueous leaching agent.

If leaching is carried out in simple stirred vessels, the high density of most metal powders cause them to remain on the bottom of the leaching vessel. Here, under relatively static conditions, they are liable to entrain particles of the slag which may be dissolving in the acid leaching agent with the liberation of a certain amount of heat. Under conditions such as this, where the heat is not dissipated, the temperature of local portions of the metal powder has been known to rise to the point where it will burn or react explosively with the acid solution. Some care is required therefore in the design of leaching plant. One method which has been used successfully is to leach in a six- or eight-sided vessel which is inclined at an angle of say 45° and rotated. This ensures frequent movement of the densest metal powder. Control of temperature is often necessary, and a rotating vessel of this type can have a static cooling coil fitted, capable of a high heat transfer rate from the vessel contents to a refrigerant liquid inside the coil. A fixed thermometer or other suitable temperature-reading instrument is advisable at a point inside the fixed coil. The batch size is usually restricted to only a few kilograms of metal powder, for safety reasons.

Various continuous leaching processes have also been employed. Usually the powder and leaching acid are fed in a co-current manner into a rotating or stirred vessel and at some point it is necessary to separate the resulting metal powder under conditions where it is not allowed to remain static for long periods. The complexity of a safe continuous system, coupled with the relatively small scale of operation, usually leads to a preference for a batch leaching system.

It is advisable to wash the residual leaching agent away from the metal powder and dry fairly promptly, again to avoid surface oxidation and the possibility of runaway reactions which may reach explosive violence. In order to maintain temperatures and contact times as low as possible in the drying operations, vacuum drying, or rinsing with miscible organic solvents, or both, may be employed.

Vacuum drying of metal powders is best carried out in ovens with large individually heated shelves, upon which the powder can be spread in thin layers. This allows good heat transfer conditions, with the minimum disturbance of the powder by pockets of water vapour being evolved. In practice, particularly if deep beds of powder are dried in narrow vessels, ice quickly forms amongst the powder and the operation becomes one of freeze drying. The much lower vapour pressure of ice than water, near 0°C, together with the worse heat transfer conditions which arise, can then make the drying operation very slow. A vacuum drying operation with an air ballast pump is preferred to the use of a cold trap, i.e. the water vapour is passed through the pump and to atmosphere.

Calcium reduction of uranium dioxide

The specific surface area, and therefore the reactivity, of uranium dioxide varies greatly depending upon its method of preparation. The most highly reactive material, produced by hydrogen reduction of a precipitated uranium compound at a relatively low temperature, is unstable in air and converts rapidly either to a non-stoichiometric oxide between UO_2 and U_4O_9, or to U_3O_8. This type of oxide reacts too vigorously with calcium, whereas a relatively inert type which has been sintered at high temperature during its preparation may react too slowly. An ideal oxide is manufactured from precipitated ammonium di-uranate by calcining at 800°C and reducing slowly in hydrogen at the same temperature. It should have a specific surface area of about $2 \cdot 5$ m² per gramme and on exposure to air would be expected to take up additional oxygen only to the extent of $UO_{2.03}$.

This oxide is commonly reduced with calcium[19] by the technique involving the production of pellets and their reaction in a closed vessel in an atmosphere of argon:

$$UO_2 + 2Ca \rightarrow U + 2CaO.$$

70 to 100 kg batches of natural uranium are produced in this manner by the U.K. Atomic Energy Authority, but the process has been adopted for use on all scales down to less than 1 kg. This flexibility of scale is necessary owing to the "criticality" limitation placed upon batch sizes in processes involving uranium which is enriched to various degrees with respect to the 235 isotope. The smallest scale applies to nearly pure uranium 235.

For a 70 kg-scale reaction, 260 pellets are made, size 2 in. long by 2 in diameter. Each of these contains 265 g of uranium dioxide and 135 g of shredded calcium, i.e. a 25 per cent excess of the latter. These are stacked in a mild steel crucible, 42 in. deep by about 15 in. diameter, in regular staggered layers up to a height of 26 in. The crucible has previously been lined with a layer of lime, $1\frac{1}{2}$ in. thick on the walls and 3 in. thick at the base. A graphite lid is placed over the charge and covered with a 1-in. layer of calcium shreds and lime. The crucible is then placed inside a 9 ft deep by 22 in. diameter reactor, which in turn rests in an electrical resistance furnace of about 150 kW heat output. The reactor is evacuated and purged with argon three times, via a connection at the top, before switching on the furnace. Heating takes place under an argon pressure of 3 psi.

The reaction initiates in about 6 hr when the furnace temperature is at about 820°C. Afterwards, the temperature is taken up to 1000°C and held there for 2 hr before cooling.

On the smaller scale it is common practice to "soak" the reaction products for 2 hr at 1200°C to give a product which has a similar particle size to the 100 kg scale powder, i.e. less than 100 mesh but not sufficiently fine to be pyrophoric.

Although pyrophoric metal is normally absent in the case of uranium, pyrophoricity can be introduced into the product by the presence of uranium hydride. This is formed if traces of moisture are present in the system, e.g. introduced in an imperfectly dried reactor lining.

After first crushing the reaction cake by hand, or with a mechanical stamp, it is passed through a jaw crusher to reduce it to about 10 mesh and it can then be leached in a 15 per cent aqueous solution of acetic acid. This is a relatively safe operation even at normal temperatures, but the product metal powder has a film of oxide on the surface, which makes it unsuitable for subsequent consolidation by sintering or melting. After dissolving the calcium oxide in acetic acid, the uranium oxide film can be removed by a rapid polish in 10 per cent nitric acid solution. More recently, it has been found practicable to carry out the whole leaching and polishing operation in one, using dilute nitric acid and controlling the temperature between 10°C and 15°C. Explosive reactions occur when the upper temperature limit is exceeded, whilst the leaching rate becomes excessively slow below 5°C.

The yield of uranium metal powder is about 93 per cent of the uranium content of the original oxide. The loss is entirely into the leaching solution, from which it is recoverable.

After water-washing and vacuum drying for 40 hr, uranium metal powder is sometimes coated with a thin film of paraffin wax to stabilize it against surface oxidation on storage. The wax is applied in the molten condition at a temperature just above its melting-point. An alternative is to store the powder under an atmosphere of argon in steel containers.

A typical analysis of the product for impurities is as follows:

	ppm
Calcium	40
Iron	250
Silicon	120
Boron	0·1

Fluorine	150
Nitrogen	10
Oxygen	200
Carbon	700
Water	300

The true density is about 18·6, with pour and tap densities of about 10·6 and 11·5 respectively.

Calcium reduction of thorium dioxide

Thorium metal powder was produced on a small production scale for a number of years in a U.K. Atomic Energy Authority factory in Sheffield, managed by Messrs Firth Brown Ltd.[20], but this has now been discontinued. The semi-continuous type of process was employed in which kilogram batches (on a thorium basis) of mixed calcium and thorium oxide are passed through a furnace in nickel boats.

The reagent mixing is carried out in a glove box with a hydrogen atmosphere. 70 per cent excess of shredded calcium is used and the mixture is loaded into the boats as a loose powder. The boats pass through the furnace in a series, the temperature being maintained at 1000°C. A current of argon is fed to the furnace tube but the windings, being of molybdenum, have a separate atmosphere of hydrogen. Thirty-two boats pass through the furnace per day and ignition of each charge takes place with the evolution of a little heat.

The reaction products consist of loosely aggregated cakes of thorium metal powder and calcium oxide. Each cake is individually quenched and immersed in water for 4 hr. They disintegrate to a fine powder as the excess calcium is destroyed and the calcium oxide is converted to the hydroxide. The hydroxide is then dissolved by the addition of nitric acid to the solution until an excess of about 0·3N remains. The time of exposure of the thorium metal powder to the acidic conditions is limited, to prevent its dissolution. It is fairly rapidly filtered by vacuum, rinsed with water, and dried in a vacuum oven. The dry metal powder is about 300 mesh in particle size and has the following typical analysis:[19]

Impurity	ppm
Nitrogen	150
Oxygen	5500
Hydrogen	500
Iron	100
Calcium	250
Aluminium	800
Silicon	100
Manganese	10
Chloride	12

17

A similar process has been operated in the U.S.A.[21] and the U.S.S.R.[22] In the United States process, a steel crucible is used for the reaction, lined with sheet molybdenum. The reaction is carried out under an inert atmosphere and the reactor is heated to 1200°C. One hundred per cent excess of calcium is needed. After cooling, the product is leached with 10 per cent acetic acid, washed successively with water, alcohol and ether, and finally dried *in vacuo*.

The Russian process uses only a 25 per cent excess of calcium but also a quantity of calcium chloride is added to the reactants, equivalent to 40 per cent of the weight of the thorium oxide. Leaching is with hydrochloric acid, but this is followed by a polishing operation with 15 per cent nitric acid before washing and drying.

Sodium reduction of potassium heptafluoniobate

The double fluoride can be produced by wet precipitation methods from a pure solution, after removal of the corresponding tantalum compound, e.g. by solvent extraction. The salt is produced in crystalline form by the addition of potassium fluoride solution to a solution of niobium fluoride containing a free acidity in excess of 4N. The reaction has been carried out successfully on a 20 kg (of niobium) scale. The yield depends upon the concentration and acidity conditions but, for example, can be about 95 per cent if precipitation is carried out at 0°C from a solution 8N in free hydrofluoric acid.

The crystals are easily recovered by decantation and filtration, but their drying involves difficulties owing to the presence of hydrofluoric acid near to the constant boiling mixture concentration. Consequently the problem is essentially one of freeing the crystals from a large quantity of concentrated aqueous hydrofluoric acid. This involves ideally a temperature somewhat above 100°C and materials of construction which are not subject to appreciable corrosion. Nickel, graphite and polythene have all been used. Polythene is restricted to relatively low temperatures to avoid softening and melting, but it has the advantage that it does not contaminate the product. A drying unit has been constructed of this material consisting of a rotating drum about 2 ft in diameter by 2 ft long with a current of warm air passing in through the shaft. Additional heat is provided by means of external electric radiant heaters, but the drying time is as much as 24 hr. It is advisable, therefore, to use a second drum in series with the first containing a coarse polythene filter to recover entrainment losses. Graphite allows the highest drying temperatures and can be used in the form of oven trays, or deep reactors for insertion in a furnace, but a certain amount of contamination with carbon takes place. Nickel or monel are suitable materials for a final drying operation at a rather higher temperature than polythene will withstand. Short drying times have been achieved by spreading the almost dry crystals in layers about 1 in. deep, upon shallow nickel trays which are heated in a nickel lined oven at about 200°C. Nickel contamination is less than 50 ppm on a niobium basis.

The dry double fluoride is best reduced on a 2 kg niobium scale, either the closed bomb or the "open" reactor technique being suitable, i.e.

$$K_2NbF_7 + 5Na \rightarrow Nb + 5NaF + 2KF.$$

In the open reactor technique, 7 kg of the double fluoride is packed into a 3 ft deep by 6 in. diameter reactor, in layers about 2 in. deep, which alternate with similar packed layers of sodium. The sodium is in the form of cubes about $\frac{1}{2}$ in. in size, which have been freshly cut with a knife or guillotine to reduce their surface layer of sodium-oxide to a minimum. 2·9 kg of sodium are used, which constitutes an excess of 10 per cent. The bulk density of the charge is about 1·37 g/cm³. The reactants occupy a depth of about 2 ft, and another 9 in. of sodium chloride are finally added and a heavy lid placed loosely on top of the reactor. The sodium chloride acts as a trap to condense sodium vapour which is evolved in the reaction. A simple gas ring burner, fitting around the reactor, initiates the reaction from the top, within a few minutes. The burner is then gradually lowered, allowing the reaction to penetrate slowly to the base in about 20 min. The initiation temperature is normally about 420°C but can be less if traces of water are present. If an appreciable amount of moisture has remained in the double fluoride, the reaction can be vigorous and eject material from the reactor, but under normal conditions this does not occur. After cooling for several hours, the sodium chloride is removed for re-use, and methylated spirits is added to the reactor to destroy the excess of metallic sodium and potassium. The alcohol vapour and hydrogen liberated usually catch fire, but it does not constitute a hazard on this reduced scale, and if a suitable location is chosen. It is found that this small-batch scale for the reduction is reasonably economic for throughputs up to several tons per annum, since plant capital costs are almost negligible and the principal labour charge is for packing reactors. This is proportional to the total amount packed irrespective of whether the packing is in small or large reactors.

After the sodium reaction has subsided, the alcohol fire is suppressed by by means of the reactor lid. The alcohol is allowed as much as 24 hr to completely penetrate the cake and after decanting the liquid away the solid contents are broken in the reactor by means of a chisel and emptied carefully onto a steel tray. The cake is then cracked by hand on the tray and fed to a roll-crusher. The powdered mixture of niobium metal and alkali metal fluorides is next leached with water. The first leach with several hundred litres of water can be in a rotating inclined vessel, carried out as a simple batch operation, to remove most of the potassium fluoride and a propor- tion of sodium fluoride, relatively quickly. Owing to the fairly low solubility of sodium fluoride in water, the final leaching operation is carried out in a simple elutriator. This consists of a conical stainless-steel vessel about 3 ft deep, with a water feed to the apex at the base, and a stirrer fitted through a gland. The cone runs full of water and also contains the powder being leached, in suspension. A "Porvic", or sintered stainless-steel, filter at the top releases the water and dissolved fluorides but retains the metal powder in the cone. The equipment will run continuously without attention for about 20 hr with a water pressure of 40 psi. An initial water flow rate of 300 l./hr gradually falls by a factor of about 10. The rate recovers considerably if the water pressure is released from time to time during the elutriation period. The progress of elutriation is followed by maintaining a continuous check on the electrical conductivity of the water wash passing through the filter. The process is judged to be complete when the conductivity corresponds to the presence of only 0·1 g of sodium fluoride per litre. The water is then decanted from the settled powder and the latter is removed via the valve at the base of the vessel.

The powder is next given a leach of $\frac{1}{2}$–1 hr duration with 2 to 3N analytical reagent hydrochloric acid, in order to remove iron contamination arising from the reduction and breakdown operations. This operation is carried out in a polythene-lined rotating vessel. After a water rinse, a "polishing" process is given in the same vessel with dilute hydrofluoric acid. This removes the oxide film surrounding the niobium particles. Dilution and removal of the acid is then followed by the final water washes until the powder is virtually acid free.

Drying is in a conventional vacuum drying oven at 40°C for 10 hr, although niobium metal powder produced by this route is sufficiently coarse for it to be oxidized only with difficulty. Drying can therefore, if necessary, be done in an ordinary air oven at 80°C.

The yield of niobium is about 90 per cent from the double fluoride, although the loss is dependent principally upon the care exercised in the handling operations. Clearly, this could be improved if the throughput of the plant was sufficiently high to justify more careful attention to the design of equipment for handling operations.

The particle size of the niobium powder produced by this method is about 5 to 66 μ and a typical analysis is as follows:

	%
Oxygen	0·6
Nitrogen	0·2
Iron	0·06
Silicon	0·05
Carbon	0·06
Tantalum	<0·1

The quality is satisfactory for consolidation into ductile massive metal by sintering at a temperature of 2300°C. It is advisable for the carbon content not to be unduly low, so that carbon and oxygen can be eliminated together as carbon monoxide during sintering. Failing this, an excess of oxygen tends to allow loss of the volatile oxide, NbO, during the sintering operation.

Tantalum metal powder is produced by the sodium reduction of potassium heptafluotantalate (K_2TaF_7) in a similar manner to the niobium reaction.[23] The particular open reaction technique for niobium was in fact based upon that for tantalum in some details.

Hydrogen reduction of niobium trichloride

Niobium metal powder has been produced by the reduction of the relatively inert black solid, niobium trichloride, in a current of hydrogen,[24] i.e.

$$2NbCl_3 + 3H_2 \rightarrow 2Nb + 6HCl.$$

Kilogram batches of the chloride are reduced in molybdenum trays, it being rather important to distribute the powder in thin layers in the trays. A silica tube furnace is used at a temperature of 800°C to 1000°C. A plant consisting of six tubes each 12 ft long by 6 in. diameter, filled with molybdenum trays, has an output of 25 kg of niobium metal powder per week. An 80 per cent yield is then obtained in 60 to 70 hr.

The process has the disadvantage of being dependent upon a slow reaction and also is unfortunately affected by side reactions. Niobium trichloride disproportionates at temperatures near 1000°C, with the production of a mixture of niobium metal and higher chlorides. The latter have been reported as the tetrachloride and pentachloride,[25] with the former preponderating, i.e.

$$4NbCl_3 \rightarrow Nb + 3NbCl_4$$
$$5NbCl_3 \rightarrow 2Nb + 3NbCl_5.$$

The higher chlorides are volatile and reduce directly in hydrogen, depositing both niobium metal and niobium trichloride on the walls of the furnace tube, away from the reaction trays. Besides the inconvenience of this mass transfer effect, the niobium metal powder deposited from reduction of the gaseous higher chlorides tends to be very finely divided and therefore pyrophoric on exposure to air. Nevertheless, the product of the trichloride reduction reaction, has been handled satisfactorily, and has given ductile massive metal on sintering.

Methods of achieving good contact between the niobium trichloride and hydrogen, based upon the use of thicker beds, have been examined with a view to keeping the size of the reduction plant low. The passage of hydrogen through a bed of the trichloride (instead of over it) has led to blockages, caused by the deposition of material resulting from the side-reactions. However, the use of a horizontal rotating bed is more promising for a future large plant, where the design of such equipment, with appropriate rotating glands would be justified. Better results have been obtained by the reduction of niobium trichloride with magnesium.

METAL SPONGE PRODUCTION PROCESSES

In principle, a rare metal is produced in the form of a sponge when one of its volatile compounds reacts with a molten metal reductant at a temperature sufficient to melt the resulting slag but not the rare metal itself. The finely divided condition of the rare metal product is a direct result of one of the reactants being present as a gas. The fluidity of the slag allows the fine particles to come into contact and sinter together loosely as a sponge.

The rare metal chlorides are reacted with magnesium or sodium. Magnesium chloride and sodium chloride are satisfactory slag materials owing to their relatively low melting-points (712°C and 804°C respectively) compared, for example, with fluorides or oxides. Also, their subsequent removal is relatively easy, i.e. they can be leached out of the sponge with cold water, or alternatively distilled away from it. This would not be possible with magnesium fluoride slag, and even sodium fluoride is only soluble in water with difficulty. Furthermore, they would have been made relatively inert as a result of fusion, so that the rate of leaching would be low even if a suitable medium were available. In the case of magnesium, the more commonly used reductant, dilute acid is necessary at some stage of the leaching operation, to dissolve the excess magnesium metal.

The decantation of the molten magnesium chloride and magnesium metal, followed by vacuum distillation, is a more satisfactory technique than leaching, from the viewpoint of avoiding oxidation of the rare metal, since the rare metal can thus remain under completely anhydrous conditions. This type of sponge may, however, be less stable on subsequent exposure to air, since the very fine pyrophoric particles of the rare metal tend to be oxidized or dissolved in an aqueous leaching process.

A titanium sponge production process was originally developed by Kroll[26, 27, 28, 29] using titanium tetrachloride and magnesium. The technique has since been applied to zirconium, [30, 31, 32, 33] vanadium, [34] and niobium.[35]

Purification of reagents

The rare metal chloride is first obtained in a high state of purity, i.e. free from the chlorides of contaminating metals and also from oxychlorides or oxides. Various preliminary methods of purification have been employed, but the final purifications is generally by distillation or sublimation. After this stage, it is most important to prevent access to the pure chloride of air or moisture, which would cause hydrolysis. The oxygen picked up in this way would pass into the metal sponge as oxide and result in a lowering of the ductility of the metal on subsequent consolidation. It is equally important for the magnesium or sodium metal reductant to be free from oxides, which, in both cases, are frequently present as surface layers. The principle of using only freshly cut surfaces, e.g. by means of a guillotine for sodium, or a lathe for magnesium, is of some value, but it results in high reductant costs on account of the discarded scrap. Magnesium is sometimes freed from superficial oxide by a "pickling" process, with a suitable reagent, and one of the advantages of sodium is that it can be purified by filtration of the molten metal, the melting-point being only 97°C whereas that of the oxide is higher.

Reduction plant

The metal chloride reduction stage is always carried out in a closed reactor, in the presence of an inert gas, argon or helium, again, to avoid the introduction of oxygen (or nitrogen). The usual technique involves the prior addition of an excess of magnesium or sodium, melting, and passing in the chloride either as solid (vanadium), liquid (titanium) or gas (zirconium and niobium). In all cases, the majority of the chloride vapourizes before reacting with the magnesium. The reaction is exothermic and it is important to limit the rate of reaction so that the temperature does not reach 1100°C, the boiling-point of magnesium. Above this temperature, the rate of reaction becomes uncontrollably high unless the inlet of chloride is restricted. Also, the rare metal product from a reaction occurring completely in the vapour phase is very finely divided and pyrophoric on subsequent exposure to air. Furthermore, in the case of zirconium and titanium, for example, alloys are formed between the sponge and the steel reactor at about 1000 to 1100°C, resulting in fairly rapid penetration of the reactor or at least contamination of the sponge with iron. Similarly, the temperature must not be allowed to fall too low, i.e. below the melting-point of magnesium chloride (712°C), or a crust of the latter forms and prevents access of the chloride vapour to the magnesium. The temperature range is, in practice, limited to about 712°C to 920°C. One of the limitations of the sponge production process is the very rapid and sudden rate of reaction which takes place initially when the magnesium surface is fresh and a large excess of it is present. This lead originally to batch sizes not exceeding about 200 lb to 300 lb of sponge, which was about the maximum for the reaction to be guaranteed to remain in control.

The reaction vessel is usually constructed of mild steel, 25/20 nickel/chromium steel, or possibly stainless-steel. This does not apply in the case of niobium production, since niobium pentachloride is reduced by metallic iron at quite low temperatures. The vessel is closed by means of suitable seals and has thermocouple wells located at its external surface, near the

reaction zone. Appropriate facilities for introducing the chloride are provided, i.e. an inlet pipe for a gaseous or liquid chloride, or a hopper, sealed
from the atmosphere, when the chloride is added as a solid. In the case of
zirconium, the chloride is introduced as a solid adhering to a cooling coil
on which it has been previously condensed. When this is heated at a controlled rate, the vapour is released inside the reactor itself. Inlet and outlet
pipes are also provided for feeding inert gas, evacuation, and bleeding away
excess inert gas. That part of the reactor containing the magnesium is usually
heated by means of a nichrome-wound electrical resistance furnace, in the
form of an upright cylinder of suitable diameter.

Reactions are carried out over a period which may be as long as 36 hr,
depending upon the particular rare metal being manufactured, the batch
size, and the skill of the operator in controlling the reaction.

After reaction, the reactor is cooled in inert gas, additional gas being
added to make up for contraction and to maintain a slight positive pressure.
The sponge may be exposed to air carefully, without undue oxidation, after
cooling to an appropriate temperature. This temperature varies from one
metal to another and even from batch to batch of the same metal, but about
150°C is usually regarded as safe.

Sponge recovery

When separation of slag from sponge is carried out by means of an
aqueous leaching process, the technique closely resembles that for metal
powders. The mixture of sponge and slag is first broken up by crushing
and milling. It can then be leached with water, in batches, using a rotating
inclined vessel to dissolve the magnesium chloride. A leach with a little
dilute acid in the same equipment, followed by a water rinse, removes excess
magnesium metal and leaves the metal sponge in a suitable condition for
drying. Low-temperature vacuum drying can be used, as for metal powders.

Vacuum distillations of the magnesium chloride and excess magnesium
is usually preferred to aqueous leaching, since products are obtained with
substantially lower oxygen and magnesium contents. Mild steel or stainless-
steels are satisfactory materials of construction for the still, provided the
temperature does not exceed 900°C to 1000°C, where alloy formation tends
to take place between the metal sponge and the steel wall. The first stage
usually involves purging with argon or helium and running off superfluous
magnesium chloride, after which the system is evacuated and distillation
commenced. A fairly high capacity pumping unit is required, operating at a
pressure in the region of 1μ of mercury.

Magnesium reduction of titanium tetrachloride

Pure titanium metal sponge is now manufactured on a scale of thousands
of tons per annum, in a number of countries, by the magnesium reduction

of the tetrachloride. This was the original magnesium metal chloride process developed by Kroll[26] and can be represented as:

$$TiCl_4 + 2Mg \rightarrow Ti + 2MgCl_2.$$

The commercial titanium tetrachloride usually available, is a liquid containing substantial amounts of impurities, e.g. an analysis of typical material is as follows:[28]

	%
Iron	0·05
Vanadium	1·8 –1·9
Sulphur	0·03–0·15
Silicon	0·25
Free chlorine	1·0 –3·5
Non-volatile residue	1·7 –5·9

Numerous purification processes have been used, but distillation with hydrogen sulphide is probably the most effective, the principal object of this reagent being to reduce the vanadium oxytrichloride ($VOCl_3$, b.p. 127°C) to a less volatile compound.[27] At the Boulder City station of the U.S. Bureau of Mines, 4300 lb batches are treated in a mild steel vessel over 4 to 6 hr, at 90°C, hydrogen sulphide gas being introduced at a rate of about 1 lb/hr. The treated titanium tetrachloride is decanted into a mild steel boiler and subjected to fractional distillation using a 20 ft high column packed with Raschig rings. With a reflux ratio of 4 : 1, condensation is in two stages, at 100°C for the titanium tetrachloride (b.p. 136°C) and 40°C for the lower boiling impurities. Liquid transfers are carried out either by gravity or by means of compressed helium, and all operations are carried out under a slight positive pressure of helium after the hydrogen sulphide addition stage, to exclude moist air. The specification of the distilled product is as follows:

	%
Iron	0·03–0·04
Sulphur	0·01–0·08
Vanadium	<0·10
Silicon	<0·10
Free chlorine	<0·10
Distillation residue	Nil

Corrosion of mild steel containers and pick-up of iron is negligible on storage under helium.

In the Boulder City plant, the magnesium reduction reaction is carried out in a mild steel cylindrical vessel about 3 ft deep by 30 in. diameter, fitted with a tall neck containing two inlet pipes. The lid and neck comprise a single piece which is attached to the cylindrical base by means of a weld, the weld being made for each run and ground away to open the vessel. A tapping hole is provided at the base of the reactor. The reactor is heated in a gas-fired furnace, as shown in Fig. 6.10. The neck protrudes through the lid of the furnace, which can be moved away as required.

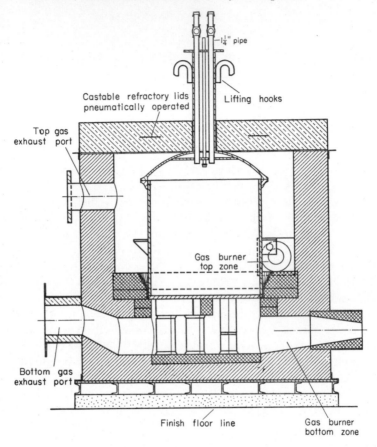

FIG. 6.10. Titanium sponge reactor (O.E.E.C. Ref. 28).

Three hundred and thirty lb of magnesium is first cleaned, pickled in hydrochloric acid and dried, before charging into the reactor in a "dry room" fitted with activated alumina desiccating facilities. The lid is welded on, the air in the vessel replaced by helium, and the reactor placed in the furnace. The magnesium is then melted and held at 850°C by the heat of reaction, whilst 1070 lb of liquid titanium tetrachloride is run in at a controlled rate, over a period of 6 hr. The temperature is allowed to rise to 920°C for the last hour of the reaction. Twice during the reaction, and again at the end, molten magnesium chloride (m.p. 712°C) is run away from the titanium sponge, through the tapping hole and down a steel channel, to a container outside the furnace. The hole is sealed again each time by a plug of magnesium chloride being allowed to solidify, as a result of local cooling by a water jacket. The pressure is maintained a little above atmospheric. Helium is added if it falls too low and the titanium tetrachloride feed rate is restricted if it becomes too high.

The titanium chloride is virtually completely reacted and 80–85 per cent of the magnesium is utilized. If more titanium tetrachloride is added in an attempt to use some of the excess magnesium, it is found that some of it reacts instead with the titanium metal sponge, producing titanium di-chloride and trichloride, i.e.

$$3\,TiCl_4 + Ti \rightarrow 4\,TiCl_3, \text{ and } 2\,TiCl_3 + Ti \rightarrow 3\,TiCl_2.$$

The reactor is removed from the furnace, cooled to room temperature, and stored for 24 hr under a small positive pressure of inert gas, before opening in the "dry room". Here, the mixture of titanium sponge, residual magnesium chloride, and excess magnesium metal is drilled out on a lathe in the form of $\frac{1}{2}$ to 1 in. turnings. A jet of helium is available as a precaution against the finely divided metal catching fire.

The turnings are then placed in a stainless-steel, perforated basket of sufficient size to take the whole batch, i.e. about 36 in. deep by 24 in. dia-meter. The basket is placed inside the vacuum distillation retort shown in Fig. 6.11. This is about 8 ft deep and is divided into a lower, mild-steel portion, heated by a furnace, joined by a cooled neoprene gasket to an upper, stainless steel portion, which acts as a condenser. The furnace is in the form of an evacuated bell with a rating of 50 kW, although only about 20 kW is used in a distillation. The retort is capable of evacuation to a pres-sure of 100 μ mercury equivalent by means of an oil diffusion pump, and the furnace can be evacuated to 1 mm mercury equivalent by a high-capacity mechanical pump, which serves five furnaces.

During a distillation run, the basket rests in the furnace zone of the retort, with a non-perforated lid to prevent distilled magnesium chloride from falling back into the sponge. After evacuation, distillation is carried out for 35 hr at a temperature of 875°C to 920°C. At 900°C the vapour pressure of magnesium and magnesium chloride are respectively equivalent to 90 and 7 mm of mercury. When distillation is complete, the retort is cooled to 815°C under vacuum and then to room temperature under inert gas. Dry air is finally sucked through the retort for 6 hr to remove volatile matter, consisting mainly of titanium subchlorides. The total cycle time is about 50 hr. A compressed-air hammer is used for removal of lumps of sponge from the basket. These are finally broken into smaller pieces and the fines rejected by sieving.

The Boulder City scale of production is based upon batches of about 250 lb of sponge, but reactors of about 5 ft diameter are employed by other producers, such as the Du Pont Company, with a reduction batch size of up to 3000 lb of sponge. Stainless-steel reactors have also been employed, although it is doubtful if these have much advantage over mild steel, since the latter become coated with a layer of ferrotitanium which is fairly resistant to corrosion.

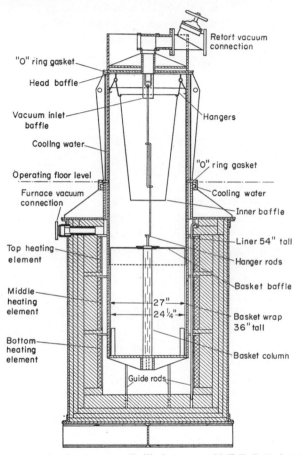

FIG. 6.11. Titanium sponge distillation retort (O.E.E.C. Ref. 28).

An alternative type of distillation unit is used by Imperial Chemical Industries Ltd.[29] at Widnes, in which the reduction reactor itself is held in an inverted position, as shown in Fig. 6.12. The unit is $9\frac{1}{2}$ ft high by $6\frac{1}{2}$ ft diameter, weighs 8 tons, and is suitable for the purification of $\frac{1}{2}$-ton batches of titanium. The reduction reactor is supported on a vertical tube, which also carries a collector bucket for molten magnesium and magnesium chloride. A perforated grid under the reactor prevents titanium sponge from falling into the collector bucket. The lower part of the distillation retort is jacketed and water cooled, a radiation screen being provided between the wall and the hot equipment. An oil diffusion pump, backed by mechanical pumps, is used to evacuate the retort to about 5 mm of mercury equivalent. Mechanical pumps alone are used to evacuate the furnace, as in the U.S. system, to prevent collapse of the wall of the retort. The actual distillation, cooling and conditioning procedure also resembles that used by the U.S. Bureau of Mines, despite the inversion of the reactor.

Yet another technique is used by the Titanium Metals Corporation of America.[36] They tap off as much magnesium chloride as possible during the reduction reaction and then distil *in situ* from the reactor retort. A special design of stout reactor retort is required to withstand both the conditions of magnesium reduction and those of distillation, the latter involving high vacuum.

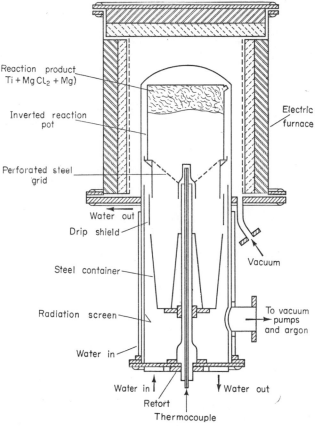

Reaction product
Ti + Mg Cl$_2$ + Mg)

Inverted reaction pot

Electric furnace

Perforated steel grid

Water out

Drip shield

Vacuum

Steel container

Radiation screen

To vacuum pumps and argon

Water in

Water in   Water out

Retort

Thermocouple

Fig. 6.12. I.C.I. process for vacuum purification of titanium sponge (Gray, J. J. and Carter, A. Ref. 29).

The titanium was isolated from early magnesium reductions by leaching out the magnesium and magnesium chloride with dilute acid, and a return to this method has been made by the Titanium Metals Corporation of America.[37] In this case, it is essential to break down the melt into small pieces, but at the same time to avoid prolonged exposure to atmospheric moisture, so avoiding hydrolysis of magnesium chloride, which would result in contamination of the product with oxide. This is done by the use of large boring machines (cf. Fig. 6.13), with multiple cutters, operating at high speed. Reactors containing 1500 lb of titanium are emptied in this way in a "dry room". Leaching is carried out with hydrochloric acid[38] containing an inhibitor to minimize dissolution of the titanium, or dilute nitric acid. The concentration and amount of acid must be sufficient to dissolve the magnesium. Hydrogen liberated in the dissolution reaction tends to be absorbed by the titanium, but this is not a serious disadvantage when the metal is consolidated by vacuum arc melting.

U.S. Government purchasing specifications for titanium sponge produced by magnesium reduction followed by (a) vacuum distillation, or (b) leaching, are as follows (Table 5):

TABLE 5

Impurity	% in vac. distilled titanium	% in leached titanium
Nitrogen	0·03	0·03
Carbon	0·03	0·03
Magnesium	0·20	0·40
Chlorine	0·15	0·15
Iron	0·20	0·15
Manganese	0·20	0·20
Silicon	0·10	0·10
Hydrogen	0·005	0·03
Total of listed elements .	0·70	0·80
Other metals not listed (each) .	0·10	0·10
Other metals not listed (total) .	0·25	0·25
Titanium (+ oxygen) . . .	Balance	Balance

Sodium reduction of titanium tetrachloride

The sodium reduction process is favoured by Imperial Chemical Industries Ltd. for the manufacture of titanium metal sponge. It was first operated commercially by their General Chemicals Division, at Wilton, but similar plants have since been installed in the United States.

The plant is essentially the same as that used for the Kroll process involving magnesium reduction of titanium tetrachloride, but with the substitution of sodium for magnesium as the metal reductant. In the I.C.I. process, a mild steel cylindrical reactor is used, with a welded-on lid, which carries a neck and connections for the introduction of the reactants, the supply of

FIG. 6.13. Boring machine for removal of sodium chloride/titanium mixture from the reactor (Gray, J. J., and Carter, A. Ref. 29).

argon, and evacuation. Heat is applied by means of an oil-fired furnace, from which the reactor can be removed as required.

In operation, the warm reactor is first evacuated and tested for leaks before supplying argon to a small positive pressure. Purified molten sodium is run in at a temperature a little above its melting-point (97°C), and heated to about 700°C in the reactor. Liquid titanium tetrachloride is then fed at a suitable rate to maintain the temperature at about 850°C to 900°C. This temperature is decided by the melting-point of sodium chloride (801°C) and the point at which undue alloying of the reactor walls would take place with titanium. Unlike the magnesium reduction process, it is necessary to avoid an excess of the sodium metal reductant at the end of the reaction, owing to the fire hazard which would be introduced at the subsequent water leaching stage. A small excess of titanium chloride is therefore used. The molten sodium chloride is tapped off at the end of the reaction, through a pipe passing down the interior of the reactor, by application of a pressure of argon to the reactor.

The mechanism of the sodium reduction reaction is principally via the vapour phase, since the sodium tends to be volatile (b.p. 883°C) and to be boiling under reflux during the reaction. This reflux action of the sodium tends to wash the reactor walls free of titanium metal and sodium chloride, so that the disposition of sponge, after completion of a reaction, is different from that in the magnesium process.

The reactor is cooled for a period of several days before opening and removal of the titanium sponge and sodium chloride mixture. The removal operation, as in the magnesium process, is carried out rapidly by means of large horizontal boring machines of the type shown in Fig. 6.13, operated in a "dry room".

Vacuum distillation of sodium chloride is more difficult than that of magnesium chloride because of its higher boiling-point (1465°C against 1412°C at atmospheric pressure). Consequently an aqueous leaching technique is employed, both in the U.K. and the U.S.A. In the I.C.I. process, leaching is carried out in rubber-lined steel vessels which are fitted with stirrers. A plastic filter medium is fitted at the base of each vessel, with a bottom outlet and valve underneath. The leaching reagent consists of a 2 per cent nitric acid solution, which neutralizes any alkalinity present and also functions as an oxidant. If the sodium reduction has been carried out with an excess of titanium tetrachloride, this is usually reduced to dichloride. On dissolution in water, this is converted to the trivalent condition, in the absence of an oxidant, and the hydrogen liberated tends to be absorbed by the titanium metal sponge, e.g.

$$6TiCl_2 + 6H_2O \rightarrow 4TiCl_3 + 2Ti(OH)_3 + 3H_2.$$

The presence of nitric acid inhibits the liberation of hydrogen and also prevents the contamination of the metal sponge by insoluble hydroxides or oxychlorides, provided it maintains the pH below 2. It is not advisable to carry out the sodium reduction reaction under conditions such that an excess of sodium remains behind, since this reacts with the aqueous leaching agent, liberating hydrogen, and in this case the absorption of the hydrogen by titanium metal cannot be prevented by dilute nitric acid or similar oxidants. The sodium hydroxide, however, is neutralized by the dilute acid.

The leaching operation is carried out fairly rapidly in a semi-continuous manner. The vessel is first filled with 2 per cent nitric acid and then further acid and coarsely ground reaction cake are added simultaneously over a period of time. The bottom valve is opened sufficiently to allow the salt solution to drain away at the same rate as fresh acid is added, so maintaining a constant liquor level in the vessel. The titanium metal remains behind on the filter until the conclusion of the run. It is then taken away as a slurry, via an exit pipe just above the filter level. The slurry is finally dewatered in a rubber-lined batch centrifuge and dried in air at a moderate temperature.

The purity of sodium-reduced titanium sponge can be inferred from the U.S. government's purchasing specifications as follows:

Impurity	%
Nitrogen	0·03
Carbon	0·03
Sodium	0·05
Chlorine	0·30
Iron	0·10
Manganese	0·10
Silicon	0·10
Hydrogen	0·0125
Total of listed elements	0·70
Other elements not listed (each)	0·10
Total of elements not listed	0·25
Titanium (+oxygen]	Balance

Attempts have been made to carry out the sodium reduction of titanium tetrachloride in other ways. For example, the reaction of the two vapours at a temperature of about 2000°C to give molten, or massive solid, titanium metal.[29, 39] This reaction can be carried out in a vessel lined with sponge as in the National Smelting Company's patent[39] applicable to titanium or zirconium. Alternatively, the low-temperature fluidization process has been used,[29] in which titanium tetrachloride vapour reacts with a dispersion of 1 to 2 per cent of molten sodium, in a bed of titanium sponge and sodium chloride reaction products, at 200°C to 600°C, fluidized with a flow of pure argon. It is not known that these, or similar processes, have been operated on a commercial scale yet.

The sodium reduction of titanium tetrachloride was actually carried out as early as 1939 in Germany,[17] and about 670 kg was produced by the Deutsche Gold and Silber Scheideanstalt, during the 1939–45 war. The process, now obsolete, involved reduction in a molten bath of 50 per cent sodium chloride and 50 per cent potassium chloride at 800°C in an atmosphere of hydrogen. The reactors consisted of expendable welded sheet-iron cylindrical vessels, 50 cm diameter by 70 cm deep and 2 mm thick. These rested loosely in a stout iron crucible, fitted into a gas-fired furnace. A portable stirrer was used to agitate the reactor contents. Approximately 20 kg batches of titanium were reduced by distilling 85 kg of titanium tetrachloride at a controlled rate into a melt of 15 kg sodium chloride and 15 kg of potassium chloride, covered with a layer of 46 kg of molten sodium. The titanium sank to the bottom of the molten salts, and at the end of the reaction was recovered from the crushed solidified melt by leaching with dilute hydrochloric acid, in a ceramic-lined vessel. It was finally washed in water and dried at a moderate temperature. The same plant was also used for the production of zirconium metal by the sodium reduction of potassium fluorozirconate (K_2ZrF_6].

Magnesium reduction of zirconium tetrachloride

Zirconium tetrachloride is a white solid when pure, and sublimes at 331°C. It is normally coloured orange by traces of iron. Unless special care has been taken in its manufacture and storage, it is also usually contaminated with small amounts of zirconyl chloride ($ZrOCl_2$], which is non-volatile.

Magnesium reduction of the tetrachloride was developed under the direction of W. J. Kroll[30, 31, 32, 33, 40, 41] at the U.S. Bureau of Mines, and a plant has since operated for the production of zirconium sponge on a scale of more than 100 tons per annum. Reactor grade sponge, of low hafnium content, is the principal product, and details were given by Shelton et al.[42] at the First International Conference on the Peaceful uses of Atomic Energy, in 1955. It is necessary to purify the zirconium, free from oxygen-containing materials and iron, immediately before reduction, and this is now done in a combined purification-reduction furnace on the large-scale plant. Before this, separate furnaces, and reactors were required[43] for the two operations, the purification stage being carried out by sublimation of the chloride in a hydrogen atmosphere.

The purification-reduction furnace now used is shown in Fig. 6.14. It includes a $\frac{1}{4}$ in. thick stainless-steel retort of about 6 ft depth and just over 2 ft internal diameter, heated electrically by three independently controlled nichrome resistance windings. The top heating zone, rated at 13 kW, extends about 11 in. down the reactor around an annular trough, which is partially filled with a lead-containing eutectic melting at 247°C.

18

When molten, this acts as a lute, and when frozen, as a seal, for the lid of the retort. Under operating conditions, the internal pressure is such that the lid floats in the lute. A stainless-steel pipe is welded to the base of the lute,

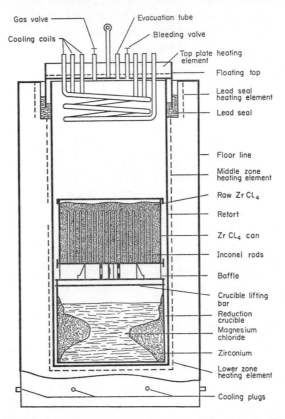

Fig. 6.14. Reduction furnace for $ZrCl_4$ (O.E.E.C. Ref. 28).

so that it can be cooled by air or water when it is necessary to freeze the eutectic. The lid itself carries a 9 in. deep cooling coil of stainless-steel piping, together with branches for evacuation, feeding of inert gas, and "bleeding" of excess gas pressure to atmosphere. Provision is also made for the attachment of a cable to the centre of the lid, which then passes over a pulley and is connected to a counter-weight. The position of the lid is then indicated by the movement of a pointer connected to the pulley.

The middle heating zone, of 46 kW, starts 2 in. below the lower part of the top zone and extends for a depth of 28 in. The chloride container rests in this zone, on a baffle. The container is made of sheet inconel, about 20 in. deep and 24 in. diameter, with a capacity of about 500 lb of zirconium tetrachloride. A number of 16 in. long by 1 in. diameter inconel rods are welded to the base of this container to provide better heat transfer into the zirconium tetrachloride charge.

The lower heating zone is of 46 kW capacity, which includes a 4 kW element in the bottom of the furnace. This zone heats the chrome-steel reduction crucible, which rests on the base of the retort. It is fabricated of $\frac{1}{4}$ in. sheet and is about 20 to 24 in. deep and 24 in. diameter. A lifting bar is fitted to the crucible to allow it to be removed from the retort.

An additional 5 kW heating element is provided in the retort lid and can be moved with it. Furnace tops, comprising lids, cooling coils, connections, etc., are interchangeable.

All heating elements are provided with thermocouples and temperature controllers, since the various operations are controlled by means of time-temperature cycles. The operations originally included an initial purification stage in which the zirconium chloride was sublimed from its container onto the cooling coils in the top half of the furnace, whilst the magnesium remained unheated in the reduction crucible. Oxygen was left behind in the container as zirconium oxide (ZrO_2) or oxychloride ($ZrOCl_2$). If hydrogen was introduced, any contaminating iron would be reduced from the ferric condition to the non-volatile ferrous chloride, and this would also remain in the container. The present technique involves direct evaporation of the zirconium tetrachloride from its container into the hot magnesium, relatively little actually condensing on the cooling coil, which is only being used to control the pressure in the retort while the reaction proceeds.

The present mode of operation is first to add 120 lb of distilled magnesium, in the form of metal blocks, to the reduction crucible and 520 lb of zirconium chloride to the inconel container, excluding that amount of chloride which may already be in the system from the previous run, adhering to the cooling coil. This constitutes a magnesium excess of about 10 to 15 per cent, which prevents the formation of pyrophoric sub-chlorides of zirconium. The molten metal lute is heated at about 550°C. until the furnace top is placed in position, after which it is cooled to solidity and make the seal. The lower and middle retort heating zones, together with that in the lid, are then set at 300°C and the system evacuated by means of a water pump to remove gross amounts of gases in the charge. Three evacuations are made, the reactor being filled with helium or sometimes hydrogen, and "soaked" at temperature for 2 hr, before the second and third evacuation. The reactor is next filled with helium for a third time and the middle zone, lower zone, and lid heaters taken to 350°C, the metal seal at the same time being melted quickly at 550°C. The furnace is "bled" at 10 min intervals to release gas as the seal temperature is raised. After 2 hr at 350°C, the two zone and lid heaters are raised to 450°C at a rate of 10°C every $\frac{1}{2}$ hr, the furnace being bled 100 times during this period, to maintain the furnace top in a suitable floating position.

The above procedure satisfactorily removes volatile impurities from the zirconium charge, but leads to an unduly high ratio of zirconium chloride to inert gas in the vapour phase. The reaction with magnesium, carried out with this ratio, would be difficult to control in the early stages, so air is passed through the cooling coil with the middle zone heater off and a controlled flow of helium is fed to the system. In this way, some of the zirconium chloride is condensed and replaced by helium as the temperature of the reduction crucible, containing the magnesium, is raised to 825°C. The reduction reaction then begins and is controlled by supplying additional heat to the middle zone to vapourize more zirconium chloride, at the same time maintaining the reactor top in the normal floating position. The reaction rate is as high as possible, compatible with the recorded lower temperature not exceeding 875°C. The "bleeding" operation is continued about once every $\frac{1}{2}$ hr at the start of the reaction and several times as frequently when the reduction temperature falls to 850°C. Towards the end of the reaction, external heat is supplied from the lower zone to maintain the temperature above 850°C. As the zirconium tetrachloride supply becomes exhausted (indicated by a marked fall in pressure), the middle zone temperature is raised to 650°C. Helium is added as necessary to maintain the pressure at this stage.

Cooling is carried out under a slight positive pressure of helium and is assisted by blowing a stream of air between the reactor and its heating elements. The furnace is opened at a temperature of 150°C, by removing the top zirconium chloride container and baffles. The reduction crucible itself may then be taken out. Exposed sponge is removed from the surface of the reaction mass and the crucible is then transferred to a distillation retort.

The total reduction time cycle is typically 41·5 hr, of which 18 hr is for the reduction reaction itself. Attempts have been made to increase the throughput[41, 44] by tapping off magnesium chloride from the reduction crucible or using two crucibles, so providing space for an increased amount of sponge in equipment of a similar size to that normally employed. These appear to have been successful in experimental runs.

Distillation of the magnesium chloride and excess magnesium away from the sponge is carried out in the special retort, 10 ft high by 30 in. diameter, shown in Fig. 6.15. The top of the retort, which is heated by a bell type resistance furnace, is made of 0·5 in. thick stainless-steel. The lower part, which is fitted with a water cooling jacket, is of mild steel. The reduction crucible is located at the top of the retort in an inverted position; a small table placed inside the crucible entrance prevents sponge from falling out, although adhesion to the crucible is normally very good. The table extends from the crucible support, which is supported by means of a 4 in. diameter hollow stainless-steel column, extending from a hydraulic ram. A stainless-steel "salt can" is attached to the column in the lower part of the furnace to collect molten magnesium chloride, This is surrounded by a thin stainless-steel shield for condensing the distilled magnesium chloride and magnesium metal. Baffles are attached to the lower part of the column and a vacuum connection is made to the shell of the retort at a low level. The retort base-plate can be detached from the top of the ram and clamped to the retort by means of a lightly greased rubber sealing gasket.

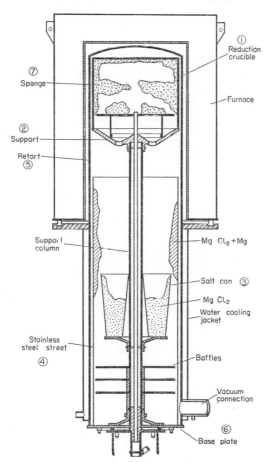

Fig. 6.15. Zirconium sponge distillation furnace (O.E.E.C. Ref. 28).

A pumping system is available, capable of evacuating the retort to a pressure of $0\cdot05\,\mu$ (mercury equivalent). This consists of an oil diffusion pump, backed by a mechanical pump. In order to reduce the maintenance rate of the main pumping system, a small portable vacuum pump is used to achieve a pressure of a few millimetres, before the main pump is started. The furnace bell is also capable of evacuation to balance the pressure and prevent collapse of the hot portion of the retort during operation. A mechanical pump capable of achieving a pressure of 0·1 mm mercury, is used for this purpose.

In operation, the retort pressure is first reduced to 20 μ, whilst cold, over a period of 45 min. The furnace bell is then lowered and a vacuum-tight seal made between it and the retort. The space between the furnace and retort is then evacuated, as the resistance winding temperature is raised to 960°C for distillation. This corresponds to a sponge temperature of 825°C. The retort pressure is gradually reduced to the minimum as distillation and pumping proceeds.

After distillation, the power is turned off and the pressure of the furnace bell is allowed to rise to atmospheric by admitting dry air. The bell can then be removed and the retort top is cooled rapidly be means of a water spray. Helium is admitted to the retort at a temperature of 600°C, as the vacuum pumps are turned off, to allow better heat transfer. When the temperature reaches 37·5°C, the retort is evacuated again and dry air is admitted to "condition" the sponge, i.e. to oxidize any fine sponge under controlled conditions rather than risk a fire on subsequent exposure to air. The conditioning operation is repeated a second time, using room air, for a period of 1 hr.

The overall time cycle of the sponge purification process is 40 to 50 hr, of which about 14 are devoted to distillation. Attemps have been made to increase the throughput of the distillation stage by combining two batches of sponge into one distillation batch. This is accomplished by the use of expendable liners in the reduction crucibles. These can be stripped away from the sponge, so allowing two sponge batches to be placed in one crucible. Experimental trials have apparently been quite successful. Alternatively,[41] two batches can be reduced in one crucible if fused magnesium chloride is tapped off after the first reduction, to leave space for the second.

Each batch of product is unique, but Fig. 6.16 represents the result of a typical reduction. Sponge is first classified on the basis of its appearance and location in the crucible. Removal from the crucible is carried out with the help of pneumatic chisels whilst the crucible is flooded with inert gas. The sponge is then crushed in a crusher to about $\frac{3}{8}$ in. in size, the various types being stored separately pending chemical and spectrographic analysis. It is then blended to meet one of two purity specifications, in batches of about 1 ton. About 10 per cent of the sponge, including the type E shown, is rejected from blending and is recycled to the chlorination stage.

Typical analyses of types A, B and C sponge are shown below, in ppm parts of zirconium (Table 6):

Specification limits for the two grades of blended material are based only upon the elements iron, nitrogen, silicon and aluminium, as follows (Table 7):

FIG. 6.16a. Zirconium sponge.

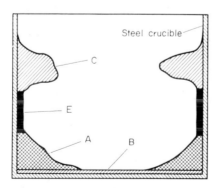

FIG. 6.16b. Reduction crucible with various sponge types indicated (O.E.E.C. Ref. 28).

TABLE 6

Impurity	A	B	C
Iron	500	600	300
Nitrogen	40	70	40
Magnesium . . .	200	200	900
Chlorine	200	150	700
Aluminium . . .	30	90	25
Manganese . . .	35	55	15
Silicon	40	150	35
Titanium	25	25	25
Molybdenum . . .	<20	<20	<20
Chromium . . .	65	85	45
Copper	15	15	20
Nickel	13	12	12
Lead	40	55	25
Tin	10	10	10
Zinc	<50	<50	<50
Boron	0·2	0·2	0·2
Hafnium	67	63	73
Cadmium	<0·5	<0·5	<0·5
Arsenic	<50	<50	<50
Phosphorus . . .	<100	<100	<100
Vanadium . . .	<20	<20	<20
Bismuth	<1	<1	<1
Cobalt	<20	<20	<20
Antimony . . .	<50	<50	<50
Silver	<0·5	<0·5	<0·5
Beryllium	<1	<1	<1

The oxygen content should be below about 0·1 per cent to avoid embrittlement, but this is achieved without difficulty by experienced operators.

TABLE 7

Grade	Iron	Nitrogen	Silicon	Aluminium
P grade . .	<4000 ppm	<150 ppm	<200 ppm	<100 ppm
R grade . .	<4000 ppm	<400 ppm	—	<300 ppm

All C grade sponge, and other material having a magnesium content of more than 1000 ppm, is redistilled a second time.

Hafnium is obtained as a by-product in the manufacture of zirconium.[45] It is converted to the chloride in an analogous manner to zirconium, and can then be purified, reduced by magnesium, and the sponge distilled in the actual plant used for zirconium manufacture. The technique is slightly modified in detail; e.g. the chloride sublimation temperature is a little lower to avoid carry-over of hafnium oxychloride. The preferred initial magnesium reduction temperature is 50°C lower, and the final temperature after magnesium reduction is a little higher.

Both zirconium and hafnium metal sponges are generally converted to massive metal by arc melting processes. A consumable-electrode type of furnace is usually preferred, to avoid contamination by electrode impurities. The massive metal may have a Brinell hardness as low as 192. At figures below 300, it can be cut, machined, forged, swaged and rolled.

Magnesium reduction of vanadium trichloride

Either vanadium trichloride or tetrachloride can be reduced to vanadium metal by magnesium. The tetrachloride (b.p. 152°C) is obtained as a red liquid, contaminated with a high proportion of vanadium oxytrichloride (b.p. 127°C) from which it is not easily separated by distillation, owing to the thermal instability of the tetrachloride. Removal of the oxygen-containing compounds is most important, to avoid oxygen contamination of the metal product, and consequently the trichloride is the preferred starting material.

Vanadium trichloride is a purple solid, made by thermal decomposition or reduction of the tetrachloride, the latter, in turn, being produced by chlorination of ferrovanadium as described in Chapter 2. Before use, the trichloride can be freed from the oxytrichloride, and other low boiling impurities, by simple distillation. The solid is then cooled, crushed and screened ready for use.

Sponge production is carried out by the U.K. Magnesium Electron Company[34] on a 40 to 45 lb batch scale, in a mild-steel reactor heated by means of a gas-fired furnace. This small-scale production plant (described as a "pilot plant") is based upon the smaller laboratory unit shown in Fig. 6.17. It consists of a hopper and screw feeder for adding the vanadium trichloride down a pipe and into the heated mild steel reaction crucible. In the production unit, the crucible is 24 in. deep and fits into the lower end of a $15\frac{3}{4}$ in. diameter reactor, which projects into the furnace. A facility is also provided for the addition of 2 lb blocks of magnesium from a side-arm during the course of the reaction. A water jacket, in between the heated portion of the reactor and the hopper, protects the latter from an excessive rise in temperature. The whole reactor and vanadium trichloride feed system is capable of withstanding a vacuum, and has connections for evacuation and purging with argon. Thermocouples are fitted in pockets penetrating the reaction crucible, to allow adequate control of the reaction.

The reaction procedure involves drying and degassing the reactor and then adding 45 lb of magnesium to the crucible in the form of blocks weighing about 2 lb apiece. Care is taken to remove superficial oxide first, by pickling the blocks in dilute nitric acid, washing with water, then with acetone, and drying at a low temperature. The hopper is then charged with about 140 lb of vanadium trichloride, the reactor is sealed, and the system evacuated at 300°C. A pressure equivalent to less than 20 μ of mercury is reached before admitting argon, up to a few pounds per square inch above atmospheric pressure. The argon is welding-quality gas which has been specially purified before use by passing over heated scrap vanadium sponge.

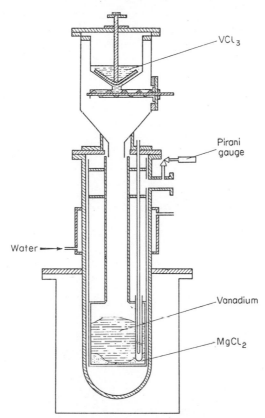

FIG. 6.17. Vanadium trichloride reduction (Foley, E., Ward, M. and Hock, A. L. Ref. 34).

The magnesium is then melted and the temperature raised to between 750°C and 800°C. Vanadium trichloride is next fed to the molten magnesium, under controlled condition, at such a rate as to maintain the temperature between 750°C and 850°C without the use of further external heat. Additional blocks of magnesium are added towards the end of the reaction, to provide an adequate excess for reasonably complete utilization of the vanadium. Reductions require about 7 hr for completion.

After reduction, the reactor and crucible are cooled and the latter transferred quickly to the distillation equipment. This consists essentially of an inverted reactor, the small-scale version of which is shown in Fig. 6.18. The reduction crucible is inverted near the top of the distillation reactor, with the mass of sponge resting upon a stool and a small collecting crucible underneath. The reduction crucible is maintained at 920°C to 950°C for about 8 hr, under continuous evacuation, down to a pressure equivalent to 1 to 5 μ of mercury. In the large-scale unit the heat is supplied by means of an electric furnace, which is surrounded by a movable bell. The latter can be evacuated to a pressure equivalent to 1 mm of mercury when required. During the distillation process, some of the molten slag runs into the collecting crucible and the remainder is distilled away from the sponge, together with the excess magnesium metal.

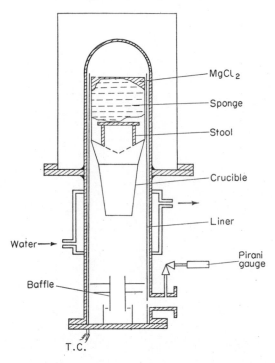

FIG. 6.18. Melting and sublimation of slag from vanadium sponge production (Foley, E., Ward, M. and Hock, A. L. Ref. 34).

After cooling to room temperature, the distillation vessel is opened to atmosphere slowly, and under conditions of careful temperature control to prevent burning of the sponge. A small proportion is always sufficiently finely divided and reactive to oxidize on exposure to air and, if this is allowed to occur too rapidly, local temperatures in excess of the normal ignition temperature can be reached. After this atmosphere conditioning operation, the vanadium can be removed, principally as a single piece of fairly soft sponge, which is subsequently broken into pieces and stored under argon.

Vanadium from near the crucible wall contains a higher iron content and is removed by mechanical means and stored separately.

The overall recovery efficiency, from vanadium trichloride to metal sponge, is 96 to 98 per cent. Typical vanadium and impurity contents are as follows:

V	Fe	Mg	Cl	O	N	H
99·5%	0·06%	0·15%	0·02%	0·2%	0·01%	0·02%

After arc melting, a hardness in the range 150–180 VHN is generally obtained for the massive metal.

Magnesium reduction of niobium and tantalum pentachlorides

Attempts have been made to develop a small-scale process for the magnesium reduction of niobium pentachloride at the Springfields factory of the U.K. Atomic Energy Authority. It appears that this process would have been entirely successful if suitable materials of plant construction had been available at the time. The equipment consisted of a 2 ft long by 9 in. diameter stainless-steel, cylindrical reactor, containing a crucible about 10 in. by 8 in. diameter. The crucible contents were agitated by means of a simple rotating stirrer passing through a gland in the reactor lid. The sealed reactor, with about 0·5 kg of magnesium in the crucible, was heated externally in an electric furnace, to a crucible temperature of 800°C, after purging with argon. Niobium pentachloride was distilled from a glass vessel into the reactor at a rate sufficient to maintain the crucible temperature at 800°C without external heat. A known weight of the chloride (about 3 kg) was fed, sufficient to allow the magnesium to be in excess to the extent of up to 100 per cent. The reactor was then cooled and dismantled. The cake of niobium, magnesium and magnesium chloride was leached in water, dilute acid, and water again, to recover the niobium, in a form resembling a powder more than a sponge.

The product was satisfactory except for a high iron content. This was believed to arise from the reaction of the niobium pentachloride vapour with the metallic iron of the reactor, away from the crucible. A deposit of niobium trichloride was produced on the reactor wall and ferric chloride entered the vapour phase. From here it was fed to the magnesium along with the niobium pentachloride, to take part in the reaction and allow iron to enter the product. A reactor made from nickel-plated steel was partially successful in reducing the iron content, but the nickel was relatively easily separated from the steel at reactor temperatures. It was expected that a reactor made entirely of solid nickel would have given satisfactory results, vapour-phase corrosion of the nickel itself being reasonably low.

Similar and independent results are reported for the magnesium reduction of tantalum pentachloride[55] the process being satisfactory apart from vapour phase corrosion of the steel reactor by tantalum pentachloride.

REFERENCES

1. LEMMON, A. W. *et al.* The Thermodynamics of the Reduction of Uranium Compounds to Uranium Metal. BMI–550 (1952).
2. KROLL, W. J. Extractive Metallurgy of Beryllium. U.S. Bureau of Mines, Information Circular 7326 (June 1945).
3. WALSH, K. A. Preparation of Zirconium Metal. Ames Laboratory, Iowa State College, Ames, Iowa. AECD–3640 (July 1950).
4. HARPER, J. and WILLIAMS, A. E. Factors Influencing the Magnesium Reduction of Uranium Tetrafluoride. I.M.M. Symposium on the Extraction Metallurgy of Some of the Less Common Metals, London (1956).
5. GRAINGER, L. Production of uranium metals. *Proc. 1st Int. Conf. on the Peaceful Uses of Atomic Energy, Geneva,* 1955. Paper 407.
6. GOLDSCHMIDT, B. and VERTES, P. Preparation of pure uranium metal. *Proc. 1st Int. Conf. on the Peaceful Uses of Atomic Energy, Geneva,* 1955. Paper 341.
7. VAN IMPE, J. Uranium and fabrication. *Chem. Engng. Progress.* **50,** No. 5, 230 (May 1954).
8. WILHELM, H. A. The preparation of uranium metal by the reduction of uranium tetrafluoride with magnesium. *Proc. 1st Int. Conf. on the Peaceful Uses of Atomic Energy, Geneva,* 1955. Paper 817.
9. SPEDDING, F. H. *et al.* The Production of Uranium by the Reduction of UF_4 by Mg. U.S.A.E.C. Report, CT–2712 (1945).
10. SCHWENZFEIER, C. W. The sulphate extraction of beryllium from beryl. *The Metal Beryllium.* American Society for Metals, Cleveland, Ohio (1955).
11. DERHAM, L. J. and TEMPLE, D. A. The Preparation of Beryllium Metal by Thermal Reduction of the Fluoride. I.M.M. Symposium on the Extraction Metallurgy of Some of the Less Common Metals, London (1956).
12. KROLL, W. Process for the Production of Metallic Beyllium. U.S. Patent 1,740,857 (1929).
13. KJELLGREN, B. R. F. Process for Producing Beryllium. U.S. Patent 2,381,291 (1945).
14. KAWECKI, H. C. Methods of Producing Metallic Beryllium and Alloys of Beryllium. U.S. Patent 2,486,475 (1949).
15. TYZACK, C. and ENGLAND, P. G. Processes for the Extraction of Vanadium. I.M.M. Symposium on Extraction Metallurgy of Some of the Less Common Metals, London (1956).
16. AUDSLEY, A., LIND, R. and ENGLAND, P. G. The Extraction of Thorium from Monazite. I.M.M. Symposium on Extraction Metallurgy of Some of the Less Common Metals, London (1956).
17. POTVIN, R. and FARNHAM, G. S. Producing zirconium and titanium in Germany. *Trans. Canad. Inst. Min. Metall.* **49,** 516 (1946).
18. WILLIAMS, A. E., EYRE, P. B. and JACKSON, J. Improvements in or relating to the Production of Niobium. British Patent 791,121 (1958).
19. GRAINGER, L. *Uranium and Thorium.* George Newnes (1958).
20. The production of thorium. *Metallurgia* **53,** No. 320, 253 (June 1956).
21. CARLSON, O. N. *et al.* The metallurgy of thorium and its alloys. *Proc. 1st Int. Conf. on the Peaceful Uses of Atomic Energy, Geneva,* 1955. Paper 556.
22. MEERSON, G. A. Powder metallurgy of thorium. *Proc. 1st Int. Conf. on the Peaceful Uses of Atomic Energy, Geneva,* 1955. Paper 635.
23. BERRY, B. E., MILLER, G. L. and WILLIAMS, S. V. Production of Tantalum in Germany. B.I.O.S. Final Report No. 803 (1946).
24. DICKSON, G. K. and DUKES, J. A. The Selection of a Process for Development for the Production of Pure Niobium. I.M.M. Symposium on the Extraction Metallurgy of Some of the Less Common Metals, London (1956).
25. AINSCOUGH, J. B. The Thermal Decomposition of the So-Called Trichloride of Niobium. UKAEA Report IGR–TN/S–731.
26. KROLL, W. J. Method for Manufacturing Titanium and Alloys Thereof. U.S. Patent 2,205,854 (25/6/40).

27. POWELL, R. L. Chemical engineering aspects of titanium metal production. *Chem. Engng. Progress.* **50**, No. 11, 578 (Nov. 1954).
28. Titanium, Zirconium and Some Other Elements of Growing Industrial Importance. Project No. 247, O.E.E.C. (1956).
29. GRAY, J. J. and CARTER, A. *Chemistry and Metallurgy of Titanium Production.* Royal Institute of Chemistry Monograph (1958).
30. KROLL, W. J., SCHLECHTEN, A. W. and YERKES, L. A. Ductile zirconium from zircon sand. *Trans. Electrochem. Soc.* **89**, 263 (1946).
31. KROLL, W. J. *et al.* Recent progress in the metallurgy of malleable zirconium. *Trans. Electrochem. Soc.* **92**, 99 (1947).
32. KROLL, W. J. *et al.* Large scale laboratory production of ductile zirconium. *J. Electrochem. Soc.* **94**, No. 1, 1 (1948).
33. KROLL, W. J., STEPHENS, W. W. and HOLMES, H. P. Production of malleable zirconium on a pilot plant scale. *Trans. A.I.M.E.* **188**, 1445. *J. Metals* (Dec. 1950).
34. FOLEY, E., WARD, M. and HOCK, A. L. The Production of High-Purity Vanadium Metal. I.M.M. Symposium on Extraction Metallurgy of Some of the Less Common Metals, London (1956).
35. McINTOSH, A. B. and BROADLEY, J. S. The Extraction of Pure Niobium by a Chlorination Process. I.M.M. Symposium on Extraction Metallurgy of Some of the Less Common Metals, London (1956).
36. MADDEX, P. J. and KROLL, W. J. Process by the titanium metals corporation at Henderson. *J. Metals* **6**, 734 (1954).
37. KROLL, W. J. Titanium. *Birm. Metall. Soc. J.* **35**, No. 3, 248 (1955).
38. DEAN. *Metals Technol.* **13**, Technical Publication No. 1961 (Feb. 1946).
39. Zirconium (or Titanium) Metal Production. U.K. Patent 762, 519 (Nov. 1956).
40. KROLL, W. J. and STEPHENS, W. W. Production of malleable zirconium. *Ind. Eng. Chem.* **42**, 395 (1950).
41. KROLL, W. J., HERGERT, W. F. and YERKES, L. A. Improvements in methods for the reduction of zirconium chloride with magnesium. *J. Electrochem. Soc.* **97**, 305 (1950).
42. SHELTON, S. M., DILLING, E. D. and McCLAIN, J. H. Zirconium Metal Production. *Proc. 1st Int. Conf. on the Peaceful Uses of Atomic Energy, Geneva,* 1955. Paper 533.
43. BLOCK, F. F. and ABRAHAM, A. D. Recent innovations in the control and operation of zirconium reduction furnaces. *J. Electrochem. Soc.* **102**, No. 6, 311 (June 1955).
44. GILBERT, H. L. and MORRISON, C. Q. Variations and modifications of the Kroll Process for the Production of Zirconium. Paper presented to the Washington D.C. meeting of the A.I.Ch.E (March 1954).
45. SHELTON, S. M., DILLING, E. D. and McCLAIN, J. H. The production of zirconium and hafnium. *Progress in Nuclear Energy,* Ser. V, *Metallurgy and Fuels,* vol. I, p. 305.
46. SHELTON, S. M. *et al.* Zirconium, its production and properties. *Bull. U.S. Bur. Min.* **561**, (1956).
47. MILLER, G. L. *Zirconium.* Butterworths Scientific Publications (1954).
48. WARTMAN, F. S. *et al.* Production of ductile titanium at Boulder City. Rep. Invest. U.S. Bureau of Mines, No. 4519 (1949).
49. COOK, M. A. and WARTMAN, F. S. Removal of magnesium and magnesium chloride from titanium sponge by vacuum distillation. Rep. Invest. U.S. Bureau of Mines, No. 4837 (1952).
50. KROLL, W. J. *Trans. Electrochem. Soc.* **78**, 35 (1940).
51. Peter Spence & Sons Ltd. Report No. X23/24. Issued by T.P.A., Technical Information Bureau, Ministry of Supply (May 1955).
52. SHELTON, S. M. and DILLING, E. D. The manufacture of zirconium sponge. *Zirconium and Zirconium Alloys,* pp. 111–14. A.S.M. (1953).
53. HAYES, E. T. and STEPHENS, W. W. The metallurgy of zirconium *Metal Progress,* pp. 97–110 (May 1953).
54. DE WET, ERASMUS, H. Process and Apparatus for Reducing Metal Chlorides employing Calcium Carbide. U.S. Patent 2,814,561 (Nov. 1957).
55. JOHANSEN, H. A. and MAY, S. L. Ductile tantalum by the Kroll process. *Industr. Engng. Chem. (Industr.)* **46**, No. 12, 2499 (1954).

CHAPTER 7

MOLTEN SALT ELECTROLYTIC PROCESSES

COMPARISON WITH METAL REDUCTION

In principle the use of electric power for the production of a rare metal might be expected to be cheaper than the use of say calcium, magnesium or sodium reducing agents, and it has the additional advantage that the product cannot be contaminated by the reducing agent or any of its associated impurities.

In practice, it is necessary to consider each electrolytic process on its merits and the economic comparison with any competing metal reduction process is sometimes favourable and on other occasions unfavourable. It has not generally been possible to bring the cost of rare metal production by electrolysis within striking distance of the bare cost of the electric power used, since substantial subsidiary materials costs arise and the maintenance and replacement rate of equipment is high.

INERT SALTS

The only electrolytic processes of any commercial importance for rare metal extraction are based upon the use of molten salt baths. Chlorides or fluorides of the rare metal are invariably electrolysed from solutions in similar but inert salts, usually of the alkali or alkaline earth metals.

The decomposition potentials of rare metal chlorides and fluorides are generally lower than the corresponding salts of the alkali or alkaline earth metals. It is necessary that the decomposition potential at unit activity of the salt being electrolysed is substantially less than that of the other "inert" salts present. A large difference in the two potentials at unit activity allows an adequate margin of potential when the activity of the salt being electrolysed falls, e.g. at the end of a batch electrolysis period when the rare metal salt concentration is low.

In order to keep the maintenance cost of the electrolytic equipment low, an inert salt mixture which has a low melting-point is often selected. Since the melting-point is then below that of the rare metal product, the latter is produced in solid form, usually as a powder or a collection of adhering crystals with a dendritic appearance. If a molten metal product is required, it is necessary to use a salt bath with a higher temperature, but this is rarely practicable. Table 8 gives the melting-points of a number of rare metal

274

salts and other salts from which electrolytic salt baths are frequently made. Table 9 shows the melting-points of various salt mixtures, often eutectic mixtures, which have been employed.

TABLE 8

MELTING-POINTS OF PURE SALTS

Salt	Melting-Point (°C)	Salt	Melting-Point (°C)
$BeCl_2$	405	BeF_2	797
$TiCl_2$	675		
$TaCl_5$	207		
$NbCl_5$	212		
$ZrCl_4$	437	ZrF_4	925
$HfCl_4$	432	HfF_4	925
$ThCl_4$	765	ThF_4	1030
$LiCl$	613	LiF	847
$NaCl$	804	NaF	995
KCl	775	KF	857
$CaCl_2$	782	CaF_2	1418
$MgCl_2$	712	MgF_2	1263
$BaCl_2$	960	BaF_2	1353
$AlCl_3$	190 (at 2·5 atm)	AlF_3	> 1272

TABLE 9

MELTING-POINTS OF TYPICAL SALT MIXTURES

Salt mixture	Melting-point (°C)
50% $CaCl_2$ − 50% $NaCl$ . .	625
40·4% $LiCl$ − 53·2% KCl − 6·4% $NaCl$	362
50% (2) + 50% $BeCl_2$ . . .	238
52% $CaCl_2$ − 48% $NaCl$ . .	508
52% $CaCl_2$ − 6% KCl − 42% $NaCl$.	504
34% $SrCl_2$ − 36% $NaCl$ − 30% KCl .	504
24% $BeCl_2$ − 41% KCl − 35% $NaCl$.	522
60% $LiCl$ − 40% KCl . . .	350
$LiCl$ − LiF eutectic . . .	485
$NaCl$ − NaF eutectic . . .	675
KF − LiF − NaF cutectic . .	454
LiF − NaF eutectic . . .	652
KF − NaF eutectic . . .	610
KF − LiF eutectic	492

It is frequently possible to use a relatively inexpensive inert chloride salt mixture to which the rare metal fluoride is added, when for example the latter is less hygroscopic or more easily produced than the corresponding chloride. Uranium tetrafluoride in a bath of potassium chloride/lithium chloride, or potassium fluorozirconate (K_2ZrF_6) in sodium chloride, are examples of this type. Chlorine is evolved at the anode, rather than fluorine, and the decomposition potential is that corresponding to the rare metal chloride, which suggests that the various salts are freely ionized in the melt. In a process of this type, where a rare metal fluoride is electrolysed from a chloride melt, since chlorine is evolved, the fluoride to chloride ratio in the melt will increase. This may have an adverse effect,[1] for instance if calcium chloride were one of the inert salts comprising the original melt, it would be effectively converted to the fluoride with a higher melting-point. This might necessitate carrying out the electrolysis, or at least the later stages, at a relatively high temperature.

CELL ATMOSPHERE

Rare metal electrolytic processes are frequently carried out in an inert atmosphere of argon or helium, particularly when it is essential for the oxygen and nitrogen contents of the rare metal products to be as low as possible. However, this does not always apply and large quantities of uranium, for example, have been produced by the American Westinghouse Electric Corporation[2] in cells from which air was not excluded. In this case it was even possible to produce metal with a low oxygen content directly by electrolysis of uranium oxide added to a melt.

ELECTROLYSIS PLANT

A variety of refractory materials has been used in the construction of cells. Monolithic construction of the cell container is possible if the cell is small; it can sometimes be machined from a single piece of graphite, or an alumina, silica or glass vessel might be employed. On a larger scale it is necessary to construct the cell of brickwork and a range of proprietary materials are available, mostly based upon alumina and relatively free from other metal oxide impurities. A suitable cement must be selected which is preferably as pure, impervious and resistant to the molten salts as the bricks themselves. The practice has sometimes been adopted of facing the internal surface of the brickwork with a high quality aluminous cement of the same type as that used between the bricks. In this way a homogeneous surface is presented to the melt, but care in construction and use is necessary to prevent the lining from flaking away and contaminating the melt.

The cell requires "baking" before use, to harden the cement and to remove moisture and gases from both the cement and the bricks. This operation must be carried out with care and often with a very slow increase of temperature. Cells are usually too large for complete insertion in an oven, but hot air, gas heaters, or suitable sources of radiant heat, can be applied to the internal surface of the cell. A final heat treatment is given by filling the cell with a molten salt mixture of a similar composition to the electrolyte and maintaining in a molten condition for a period of time. Besides expelling traces of moisture and gases, this treatment seals the pores of the refractory surface by filling them with salt. Even if an adherent film of salt is not left behind on the surface after removal of the melt, some of it solidifies in the pores at a distance from the surface according to the temperature gradient through the refractory.

Provision is usually left for removing the melt from the cell via a tapping hole, which can be sealed by means of a refractory bung or a plug of solidified salts, when the cell is full.

In some cases cell containers have been constructed of metal, e.g. nickel or iron, but it is then necessary to make the container the cathode to avoid excessive corrosion and contamination. This results in the rare metal powder product being deposited over the whole of the cell walls, from where it cannot be recovered conveniently. This technique is in fact mainly suitable for cells which are sufficiently small to be completely emptied at the end of each run and the product quickly scraped out.

When a cell container is constructed of graphite, it is usual for this to be made the anode. If a non-conducting refractory container is employed, a special graphite anode, or series of anodes, is inserted through the wall or immersed in the electrolyte from above. The grade of graphite is important since, although it is always resistant to the melt and the gaseous products, a close textured type is preferred which machines well and does not absorb excessive amounts of the melt. It should also be as resistant as possible to thermal shock. Although graphite is useful as an anode, it is of little value as a cathode material owing to its tendency to spalling, with the result that the powdered metal product becomes mechanically contaminated with graphite powder, which is difficult to remove.

Molybdenum is usually a suitable cathode material,[3] or it may be convenient to use some of the rare metal product, compacted into massive form.

Molybdenum can be manufactured in a pure condition, it has a high melting-point, and does not alloy with most other metals. Although it oxidizes rapidly at 800–900°C, it is so resistant to chlorine at this temperature that the chlorine atmosphere in the cell is sufficient to protect the cathode from oxidation by air. Also, any oxide which is formed is volatile, and therefore does not contaminate the electrolyte or the rare metal product.

Heating of large cells from an external source is not usually practicable, since the cell material is often thick and a poor conductor of heat. In addition, since most cell containers are somewhat porous, it is advisable to have a falling temperature gradient from the interior to the exterior so that the absorbed salt may solidify and seal the pores at some point. Graphite resistance immersion heaters have been used, but if the electrolyte is premelted and poured into the cell, the temperature may be maintained by the

19

electrolysis current itself. In the case of a small cell, it may be necessary to superimpose an a.c. current on the d.c. electrolysis current in order to keep the electrolyte in a molten condition. With the largest cells the reverse condition could apply, i.e. the surface area may be too small to dissipate the heat generated by the electrolysis current, and some cooling may be necessary. To a certain extent the correct heat balance may be achieved by careful design, e.g. the selection of an appropriate size and shape of cell to suit the current density, or a degree of external cooling may be applied. The heat is mainly liberated at the electrodes, however, and it is often preferable to remove it directly from this source. Cooling the electrodes must be carried out with care to avoid solidification of melt and, in the case of the cathode, the form of the deposit can be affected, e.g. the adherence may be reduced.

An efficient electrolysis process must run under substantially irreversible conditions, i.e. the gas evolved at the anode must be unable to react again, either directly or indirectly, with the rare metal product. To this end, the gas (usually chlorine) is often led away in a fairly direct manner without contacting the cathode. It is particularly important to avoid processes where the chlorine can effectively dissolve in the melt and subsequently migrate to the cathode. This might occur, for example, in the electrolysis of uranium trichloride, where the liberated chlorine is capable of reacting with excess uranium trichloride to form uranium tetrachloride, which is freely soluble in the melt. If the tetrachloride is allowed to diffuse to the cathode it can attack the uranium metal product to re-form uranium trichloride, i.e.

$$2UCl_3 + Cl_2 \rightarrow 2UCl_4$$

$$3UCl_4 + U \rightarrow 4UCl_3.$$

This may be prevented by avoiding stirring, or, more effectively, by constructing a cell with separate anolyte and catholyte compartments, separated by a diaphragm. It is difficult to obtain suitable disphragms for large molten salt electrolysis cells, although sintered glass has been used on a laboratory scale. In circumstances of this type, a high current density is advisable so that the rate of production of rare metal exceeds the rate of mixing of the anolyte and catholyte.

INTRODUCTION OF RARE METAL SALT

Anhydrous rare metal chlorides are usually hygroscopic and therefore difficult to introduce into a melt without producing deleterious oxychlorides as a result of hydrolysis in moist air. This has been overcome for some metal chlorides by producing them in situ in the melt. A suspension of the rare metal oxide in the inert alkali metal chloride melt is chlorinated directly at a suitable temperature, in the presence of a reducing agent such as sulphur, barium sulphide or carbon. A "chlorine carrier" in the form of a metal ion of variable valency, such as iron, is used to increase the rate of reaction. Sometimes the rare metal ion itself is of variable valency and will perform this function. Reactions of this type have been used, at least on the development scale, to produce molten salt solutions of the chlorides of niobium, tantalum, titanium, zirconium and more particularly, thorium and uranium, directly in alkali metal chloride melts.[4] In the case of beryllium and probably some others, the reaction is slow and incomplete at any temperature. In the case of titanium, the carbide has been chlorinated directly under an inert salt mixture instead of using a mixture of oxide and carbon.[5] With zirconium, a further development has been the use of carbide as an anode material during electrolysis.[6]

ELECTROLYTIC PURIFICATION

The electrolytic technique allows the introduction of a special purification stage before metal production. Purification is accomplished by pre-electrolysis at a lower potential than that used for deposition of the main product. Many of the impurity metals, particularly iron, are deposited in this way over a period of a few hours on to a special cathode. This is then replaced by a clean cathode for deposition of the rare metal itself. The pre-electrolysis period also serves for the removal of moisture and so reduces the oxygen content of the later product.

When an electrolytic product is required of very high purity, a refining cell may be employed instead of a winning cell, i.e. a soluble anode is fabricated of the required metal, in a less pure condition, which may have been produced by a method other than electrolysis, or which may be scrap from later metallurgical processing, In this case chlorine is not liberated in the cell, and gaseous corrosion may be eased. It is of course necessary to reject some or all of the inert salts after each electrolysis batch, in order to obtain the full benefit of the electrolytic purification, since the impurities are of such a nature that they remain undeposited on the cathode.

RECOVERY OF METAL PRODUCT

Removal of adhering salt from the metal power product may be carried out in several ways. When the particle size of the rare metal powder is large, as in the case of "flake" beryllium, the molten salt is at least partly removed by pressing at a temperature above the melting-point. In other cases the salt is removed by leaching with water. Before leaching, however, it is necessary to withdraw the hot electrode, with the adhering powder, from the melt, and cool. If the electrolysis has been carried out in an inert gas, it may be convenient to cool in an upper compartment of the cell, in the same atmosphere, to avoid oxidation by air. When the cell has operated in air, or the anode gas has been allowed to form the atmosphere, protection is sometimes given by "smothering" the electrode and deposit with dry powdered sodium chloride, but the load on the leaching system is then increased. If it can be achieved, removal of the electrode is best accomplished whilst it is still hot and the adhering salt is still fluid. Otherwise, the cold mixture of salt and metal powder sets hard and requires chipping away with hammers, followed by crushing to small pieces, or to powder, ready for leaching.

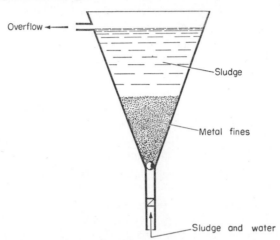

FIG. 7.1. Elutriator (Marden, J. W. *et al* Ref. 19).

The leaching process itself usually resembles that described for rare metal powder produced by calcium or sodium metal reduction processes. Water is employed as the leaching agent and, in view of the high density of the metal powder, it is usual to construct the leaching vessel in the shape of say an eight-sided "tumbling barrel", which can be rotated, rather than attempt to agitate by means of a stirrer. Elutriation may be necessary, as in the simple equipment shown in Fig. 7.1, when the melt contains water-insoluble salts such as calcium fluoride, but in view of the difficulty of removing such components completely it is preferable to select a melt which is, and remains, completely soluble.

Drying of the metal powders is generally carried out by methods which are similar to those used for the powder products of metal reduction reactions. Vacuum drying usually gives an acceptable product.

ELECTROLYSIS OF BERYLLIUM CHLORIDE

A process has been available since about 1936 for the electrolysis of beryllium chloride in an alkali metal chloride melt at relatively low temperatures.[7, 8] A eutectic mixture of lithium, potassium and sodium chlorides in the proportions 40·4, 53·2 and 6·4 per cent is employed.

The eutectic melts at 362°C, and in the presence of an equal proportion of beryllium chloride, the melting-point is depressed to as low as 238°C. This allows electrolysis to be carried out well below the boiling-point of beryllium chloride (500°C), and even below 400°C, where the vapour pressure is still considerable.

The German Degussa process,[9, 10] operated during the Second World War, was essentially of this type, but Degussa tended to operate their cells simply with a sodium chloride–beryllium chloride melt. This necessitates a higher temperature and vapour losses, or alternatively working between two high beryllium chloride concentration limits, so that even at the end of electrolysis about 30 per cent of beryllium chloride is still present in the melt.

Production was carried out on a scale of 5–6 kg/day, in refractory cells with nickel linings, the latter also acting as cathodes. Graphite anodes are used. Heating is by means of resistance wires in the refractory. The hygroscopic $BeCl_2$ is removed from its airtight aluminium storage container and melted with an equal quantity of sodium chloride in the cell. Electrolysis takes place in batteries of five cells run together. Operation is at 350°C or a little higher, and a current of 500 A is passed in runs lasting 24 hr. The melting-point rises as the proportion of beryllium chloride falls throughout the run. Current efficiency is about 50 per cent. At the end of a run, the molten, partially expended electrolyte, is poured into another cell containing fresh $BeCl_2$ and NaCl, to make up a new charge. The flakes of beryllium metal are scraped from the crucible, with adhering chlorides, and placed in a heated nickel vessel. Pressure is then applied by means of a plunger to exude the molten salts through holes in the base of the vessel.

Leaching is first carried out with water, but the temperature is kept low to prevent hydrolysis of the chloride. Finally, washes with sodium hydroxide, nitric acid and water are given to remove adhering hydroxides. The beryllium flakes are then dried in air at normal temperatures to avoid oxidation. This process is now carried out both in the U.K.[11] and the U.S.S.R.[12] virtually unchanged, and a similar process is in operation by Pechiney et Cie, in France.[13] The French product in particular, is stated to be purer than beryllium made by thermal reduction, except for a high chlorine content (0·14 per cent).[13] Attempts have been made to remove the chlorine. The chlorine is present in layers about 10 μ apart, but it does appear to be present simply as beryllium chloride. Ball milling with ammonium carbonate and oxalic acid solutions reduces the chloride content to 0·02 per cent and with the latter reagent particularly, produces a powder which is satisfactory for compacting.

PRODUCTION OF URANIUM METAL BY ELECTROLYSIS

Uranium metal was produced in the early 1930's by the electrolysis of the fluoride in a molten salt bath,[2] at the U.S. Westinghouse Electric

Corporation. Production was later expanded as it became the standard uranium process for the Manhatten Project. The process eventually involved the electrolysis of the double salt KUF_5 mixed with calcium chloride and sodium chloride.[18, 19] An inert atmosphere was not employed.

The feed material, KUF_5, was originally produced in quantity by the photochemical reduction of a uranyl salt with formic acid or sucrose in the presence of potassium and hydrogen fluorides, i.e.

$$UO_2(NO_3)_2 + HCOOH + KF + 4HF \rightarrow KUF_5 + 2HNO_3 + CO_2 + 2H_2O.$$

Since yields were only a few grammes per square foot in artificial light, or 100 to 200 g/ft^2 even in strong sunlight, other aqueous methods were developed such as the reaction of uranium dioxide with a solution of potassium fluoride and hydrofluoric acid, i.e.

$$UO_2 + 4HF + KF = KUF_5 + 2H_2O.$$

The less hygroscopic compound K_2UF_6 could be produced if the reaction were carried out with an excess of potassium fluoride, and this is equally satisfactory for electrolysis.

If the electrolytic route were used on a large scale today, it might be more convenient to manufacture uranium tetrafluoride by a "dryway" process from uranium dioxide, and add this to the melt, together with anhydrous potassium fluoride, i.e.

$$UO_2 + 4HF \rightarrow UF4 + 2H_2O.$$

In this process as operated in the U.S.A., a monolithic graphite cell is used, which also acts as the anode. The cathode material is molybdenum. A typical design of small cell is shown in Fig. 7.2. The graphite crucible (1) is protected from oxidation by coating with a suitable graphite cement (2), which in turn is sometimes surrounded by an iron container (3). Where necessary, a resistance heater (4) is used, insulated from the outer steel shell (5) by the material (6). An insulating cement (7) is used at the top of the cell. The anode connection is as shown at the base of the cell, the component (8) being of graphite and (9) of copper, together with the water cooling coils (10). The molybdenum cathode (11) is supported in a simple manner through an insulating lid.

The size and design of the cathode is of some importance. A large cathode is required to give a high current-carrying capacity, but a smaller one allows better adhesion of the deposit of uranium powder, particularly at the top of the molten salt bath. A large electrode gives localized cooling in this zone, and a thick deposit forms which tends to peel away as the electrode is removed from the cell. Several compromise designs have been evolved with a large surface area but a small cross-section, usually involving fabrication in strip or tubular form. Stainless-steel tubes, sheathed in molyb-denum, have been used with some economy.[4]

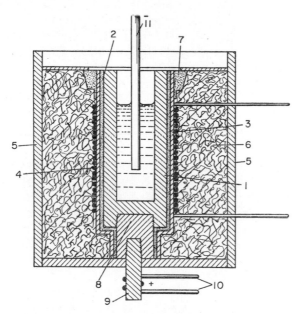

FIG. 7.2. Uranium electrolysis cell (Marden, J. W. *et al.* Ref. 19).

The standard salt bath mixture of 50 per cent calcium chloride, 50 per cent sodium chloride, with an addition of 5 per cent of KUF_5, is satisfactory for four runs at a temperature of 800°C, additional salts being added for make up after each run. After this it is necessary to recharge the cell with fresh salts owing to the accumulation of the higher melting calcium fluoride. About 10 lb of salt are then used per lb of metal product. This can be reduced to about 6 lb per lb of metal, if the temperature is increased to 900°C and the series continued to a total of eight runs. Cell maintenance cost is increased at the higher temperature to offset the gains in salt economy. The use of a bath based upon 8 per cent calcium chloride and 20 per cent sodium chloride at 800°C, allows 15 runs, or the series may be continued indefinitely if 10 per cent of the salts are discarded after each run. An equilibrium salt concentration is then established with about 60 per cent calcium chloride, 15 per cent sodium chloride, 15 per cent calcium fluoride and 10 per cent potassium chloride, excluding the uranium salt.

Operation of the electrolysis cells varies according to their individual design features. For example, the initial melting of the charge is by means of a resistance heater where this is installed, but in other cases the hot salt from a cell at the end of a run may be placed in the cold cell with an electrode, and heated by means of the d.c. electrolysis current supply. An a.c. supply can be used instead, in conjunction with a graphite electrode. More salts can then be added to the pool and allowed to melt. On other occasions, when molten salts are not available from a hot cell, they may be run in from a special gas-fired furnace. After the inert salts have been obtained in the cell in a molten condition, the potassium uranium fluoride is added with agitation. Some care is necessary since the addition of the first portion is accompanied by foaming. A fully charged cell contains 6 to 7 lb of uranium and the concentration is worked down almost to zero, to avoid loss of uranium salts in the product leaching operations.

During electrolysis, the current is adjusted to maintain the correct operating temperature (800–900°C), the design being such that the rate of electrolysis is also optimum. This may involve a current as high as 3000 A. Auxiliary heating elements are normally turned off for the whole electrolysis period. The colour of the fused salt mixture is a good guide to the progress of the electrolysis. The initial dark green colour becomes lighter green as the uranium content is decreased, until it is almost grey. The end is indicated by a brown colour, turning quickly to chocolate and finally fading to white. After this, sparkling particles of burning calcium may be seen on the surface, if electrolysis is unduly prolonged.

A pre-electrolysis technique has been found effective in removing impurities such as boron from the melt. Electrolysis takes place onto a separate cathode at 950°C, for only 5 min, with only 0·5–3 per cent of potassium uranium fluoride in the melt.[4]

The hot cathode, with its adhering uranium metal powder, is withdrawn from the melt, placed in a narrow vessel and "smothered" with fine dry sodium chloride. This excludes air and prevents the product from catching fire during cooling. It is sometimes possible to remove the electrode by twisting and withdrawing it from the plastic mixture of metal powder and salts. If this is not possible, chipping of the cold mixture of salt and powder away from the electrode by means of an air hammer is resorted to. The mixture contains about 2 lb of salt per lb of uranium.

The hard pieces of deposit from a number of electrodes are bulked into 100–200 lb batches, jaw crushed to about ¼ in. lumps and passed through rollers to crush to a powder. The powder is next leached in wooden tumbling barrels, i.e. vessels inclined at an angle of 45° and rotating at an appropriate speed. One pound of powder is added to every 4 lb of water and ice in the barrel, at a slow rate, so that the temperature does not rise above 30°C from the heat of solution of calcium chloride. After 10 min tumbling, the powder is allowed to settle and the water decanted by tipping. After three washes with distilled water, the powder is removed and passed through a wet disc-grinding operation to open up the metal aggregates and release particles of soluble chlorides and fluorides. Several additional washes in the tumbling barrels, with very short settling times, leave the metal powder in a pure condition.

Filtration is in small batches to minimize fire hazards, and is by means of simple vacuum filters. Vacuum drying is then carried out in ovens at 80°C.

About 10 to 15 per cent of the uranium metal is lost as fines in the washing operations, and this can be recovered free from insoluble oxides and fluorides by elutriation in a simple inverted cone type of elutriator, fed with water from the apex of the cone. The "sludge" of non-metallic insoluble matter follows the overflow, from which it is settled out and recovered chemically. The metal fines remain in the elutriator, to be removed at intervals, filtered, dried and added to the metal powder product.

The major losses of uranium in this process occur in the various grinding, washing, drying and handling stages after electrolysis itself. Additional losses and hazards can also be introduced as a result of fires, caused by the pyrophoric nature of uranium metal powder, unless great care is taken during the post-electrolysis operations.

The major impurities in uranium metal produced by this method (after vacuum melting) are iron 600 ppm, carbon 600 ppm, and silicon 150 ppm.[20] The specific gravity of the massive metal made from this powder is 18·9, suggesting a high quality product.

A refining cell has been used[21] for the production of high purity uranium by electrolysis, in which a normal grade of uranium metal is used as the feed material, in the form of a "soluble anode". A molybdenum cathode is employed. There is no large-scale requirement for uranium metal of greater purity than the normal nuclear reactor grade material, and consequently the cells are only operated on an experimental or development scale. The electrolytic technique, particularly with pre-electrolysis, can give high orders of refinement from other metals present in the melt, but materials of construction are the greatest source of contamination. A graphite cell is impracticable for this reason and borosilicate glass or fused silica are usually employed, The temperature is maintained as low as possible and for this reason it is preferable to use a lithium chloride (59 mol %)—potassium chloride (41 mol %) eutectic, which melts at 352°C. Uranium trichloride electrolyte, added to the other salts to the extent of 35 per cent, only raises this temperature to about 360°C, thus allowing an operating temperature of 400–25°C. After electrolysis, all the salts are readily removed by water leaching, being soluble chlorides. Uranium tetrafluoride is an alternative electrolyte in the same inert salts, and although it introduces another ion, it has the advantage that it is less hygroscopic than the chloride and can be produced in an oxygen-free and water-free condition.

Argon is used as an inert atmosphere, welding grade gas being first dried over magnesium perchlorate, and sometimes further purified by passing through a furnace containing uranium or vanadium metal at an elevated temperature.

In operation, a pre-electrolysis is carried out in a new cell, under normal operating conditions, for several days, to remove moisture and other impurities. A new molybdenum cathode is then inserted for the main electrolysis. The final cathode deposit is crushed and leached with water before washing in alcohol and ether, and vacuum drying. Any surface film of oxide may be removed during the leaching operations, if one of the water leaches is replaced by dilute acid.

ZIRCONIUM ELECTROLYSIS FROM A
CHLORIDE–FLUORIDE MELT

In recent years progress has been made in the manufacture of zirconium by electrolysis such that satisfactory nuclear grade metal can be produced. The economies of the process probably allow large scale production at a similar cost to the rival "Kroll" type reduction process.

The process operated by Messrs. Horizons Inc. on behalf of the U.S.A.E.C. involves electrolysis of potassium fluorozirconate (K_2ZrF_6) in a sodium chloride melt at 830°C to 850°C.[22, 23] This is carried out in a 5000 A cell and on a scale of 40 lb per batch. The cell design is shown in Fig. 7.3. The container consists of a graphite crucible, capable of holding a charge of about 300 lb of molten salts, which also acts as the anode. This is supported on, and surrounded by, refractory insulating bricks inside a mild steel shell which is nickel plated. The shell is water jacketed for cooling purposes. Heating is carried out by means of a sectioned graphite resistance heating element external to the molten salt container. The steel top of the shell, carrying the cathode, is attached to the main shell body by means of a bolted flange and gasket. The temperature of the cathode seal assembly is maintained at a low level by means of a water cooling jacket and insulating brick, and all joints are vacuum tight.

The cathode consists of a mild steel tapered rod immersed in the melt but threaded and screwed to a graphite rod, which passes out of the cell.

A high-grade argon atmosphere is provided, to exclude oxygen and nitrogen during operation. 99·98 per cent argon is further purified for use by passing through columns of phosphorus pentoxide and heated titanium sponge.

Before use, or after maintenance, the cell is evacuated to 35–125 μ at an elevated temperature. The initial evacuation is for 8 hr at 900°C, to remove moisture and organic materials from refractories, etc.

An electrolysis run is started by heating the cell to 830–50°C and adding a charge of 170 lb of pure, dry sodium chloride. When molten, 50 lb of vacuum-dried potassium fluorozirconate is added. Pre-electrolysis, to remove impurities onto a graphite cathode, as used in the smaller cells, is dispensed with in this cell. The steel cathode is fitted instead and the current density slowly raised to about 260–300 A/dm², and held at this figure in an atmosphere of added argon and evolved chlorine. Additional potassium fluorozirconate is added in the form of a 50 per cent mixture with sodium chloride, to increase the cathode deposit to its optimum size.

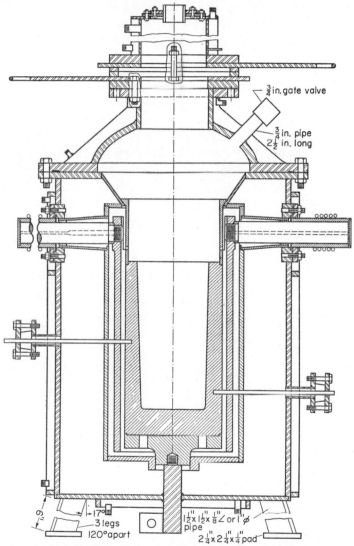

FIG. 7.3. Zirconium Electrolysis cell (Shelton, S. M., *Zirconium Production Methods*, Metallurgy of Zirconium, McGraw-Hill. U.S.A.E.C. Copyright).

At the end of electrolysis, the cathode is raised into the argon atmosphere above the electrolyte. The whole cell is cooled for removal of the cathode.

The appearance of the deposit is as shown in Fig. 7.4 and consists of a grey mass of loosely adhering dendritic zirconium metal powder, firmly bound to the steel rod by means of molten salts.

Recovery of the zirconium powder is essentially by the same means as the recovery of electrolytic uranium. The deposit is chipped away from the electrode, crushed, leached with water, filtered, and dried in air. The leaching operation in this case is carried out in a continuous cone washer resembling the elutriator used for separation of non-metallic particles in the case of uranium. As with uranium, no doubt the elutriating action assists in the removal of particles of graphite which have been entrapped with zirconium.

The rate of electrolysis is this "near-commercial scale" cell is 5–6 lb/hr of zirconium at a current efficiency of about 60 per cent, and the overall rate of production is 2·5 lb/hr. Oxygen contents range from 0·06 to 0·09 per cent, nitrogen is about 0·003 per cent and carbon contents are about 0·02 to 0·06 per cent. Other impurities in typical electrolytic powder are as follows:

Element	%
Silicon	0·003
Iron	0·01
Aluminium	0·01
Copper	<0·0005
Titanium	0·05
Calcium	<0·005
Magnesium	<0·001
Manganese	<0·001
Lead	<0·001
Molybdenum	<0·001
Nickel	0·004
Chromium	0·003
Tin	<0·001

Hafnium is usually present to the extent of 1 or 2 per cent in view of its close chemical similarity with zirconium, but separation procedures are available if "nuclear grade zirconium" is required free from this element.

The "as-cast" metal produced from electrolytic powder has a Rockwell B hardness of 80–83 (Brinell Hardness Number 150–65).

In a similar process used in the U.S.S.R. and described by Orgarev et al.,[24] advantages are claimed for a potassium chloride–potassium fluoro-zirconate melt, the principal improvement being the increased solubility of the salts at the leaching stage. This is presumably due to the absence of sodium fluoride.

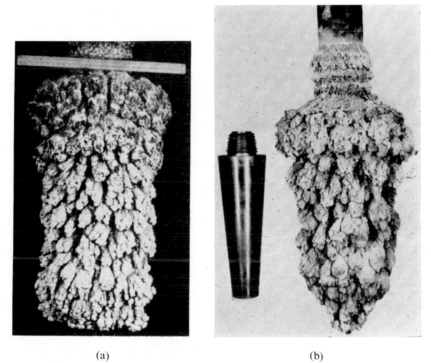

(a)   (b)

Fig. 7.4. Electrolytic zirconium powder on cathode: (a) typical zirconium cathode deposit produced in the large scale electrolytic cell; (b) zirconium cathode deposit compared with typical mild steel cathode (Raynes, B. C., *et al.* Ref. 23).

PRODUCTION OF THORIUM METAL BY ELECTROLYSIS

Thorium metal was manufactured in the 1930's by the Westinghouse Electric Corporation[25] using an electrolytic process based upon thorium fluoride in a sodium chloride/potassium chloride melt. The thorium fluoride was actually added to the melt as the double salt $KThF_5$.

A molybdenum cathode was employed with a graphite crucible as the anode and the electrolysis temperature was about 800°C. After a standard leaching operation with water, nitric acid, water again, and alcohol for drying, the finer particles often had too high a surface oxide content for compaction. The coarser particles only therefore were separated off for use.[26]

A similar process is operated on a large scale in the U.S.S.R.,[27] although chemical engineering details are not available. It is stated[28] to be important

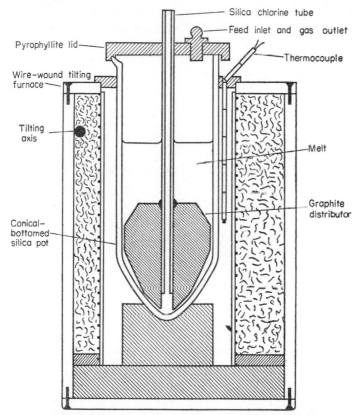

FIG. 7.5. Thorium tetrachloride production cell (U.K.A.E.A. copyright).

to exclude even traces of water, sulphur and phosphorus compounds. A major disadvantage of the process is the low thorium efficiency of 50 per cent. Part of this arises from the fact that sodium or potassium, or both, are liberated at the cathode, instead of thorium, when the thorium concentration in the melt falls below about 11 per cent. If electrolysis is stopped at this point, it results in the melt which adheres to the thorium metal on removal of the cathode, being heavily contaminated with thorium salts. The cathode deposit passes through a standard type of process involving crushing, leaching with water, gravity separation, washing with dilute nitric acid, and drying, for recovery of the pure metal power. The remaining soluble and insoluble thorium salts and slimes, etc., are recovered by chemical means and eventually recycled back to the electrolysis cell.

Each of the impurities, iron, sodium, potassium, chlorine, fluorine and oxygen are often present to the extent of hundreds, and sometimes thousands, of parts per million, in the product from this process.

Carbon, silicon and nitrogen contents can also be fairly high.

Thorium metal powder has recently been produced in the U.K.[4, 29] on a scale of at least 6 kg per batch by an all-chloride electrolytic route, and information is available upon which a large-scale process could be based. Thorium tetrachloride is first produced *in situ* in an inert melt composed of sodium chloride and potassium chloride in eutectic proportions. Thorium dioxide and carbon are reacted with gaseous chlorine under the surface of the melt at a temperature of about 800°C in the presence of a ferric chloride catalyst. The catalyst is added as iron powder or pyrite (FeS_2) in quantity equal to about 4 per cent of the weight of thoria. The ferric chloride, once formed, behaves as a "chlorine carrier" in the melt, by virtue of its ready reduction to ferrous chloride and subsequent rechlorination back to ferric chloride in contact with chlorine, i.e.

$$2Fe + 3Cl_2 \rightarrow 2FeCl_3$$

$$ThO_2 + C + 4FeCl_3 \rightarrow ThCl_4 + CO_2 + 4FeCl_2$$

and
$$2FeCl_2 + Cl_2 \rightarrow 2FeCl_3.$$

In this way, melts containing about 25 per cent of thorium are obtained.[4] Approximately 20 to 25 per cent loss of ferric chloride takes place by volatilization from the melt.

The carbon sometimes takes the form of a block of graphite which has a chlorine inlet tube down the middle and is shaped so as to act also as a chlorine distributor, as shown in the small scale chlorinator in Fig. 7.5. Alternatively, the carbon may be in more intimate admixture with the thoria, e.g. when produced by the calcination of a mixture of thoria and starch, followed by grinding. In this case, a reasonable chlorination rate is obtained in the absence of the ferric chloride catalyst, provided the temperature is raised to 900°C. This would probably be the preferred technique for large-scale operation since the removal of an iron catalyst before electrolysis presents difficulties. When iron is used, it can be removed by precipitation with small pieces of magnesium at a temperature of 600°C, and sintering of the resulting iron powder at 750°C. This is somewhat expensive, and removal of iron by pre-electrolysis on to an iron cathode is preferred. The cathode deposit from the pre-electrolysis is rechlorinated for the next batch. It is important to estimate precisely the point at which pre-electrolysis is allowed to stop. If it is continued until thorium metal or thoria begins to coat the iron powder, the latter is subsequently rechlorinated again only at a low rate.

Electrolyte preparation can be carried out in a silica vessel with a "Pyrophyllite" lid, resting inside an electric resistance furnace. Chlorine is added via a silica, alumina or "Mullite" tube dipping beneath the surface of the melt. The carbon dioxide and excess chlorine is allowed to escape via the joint between the vessel and lid, or is led away by means of a special outlet pipe.

The electrolysis cell is best constructed of a refractory of high alumina content, and containing as little silica as possible, owing to the ready attack of silica by thorium metal. The small-scale cell illustrated in Fig. 7.6, however, uses a silica pot and care is taken to prevent thorium metal contacting the silica wall or base. The small, 6 kg scale, model is heated externally, although a more conventional internal heating system is necessary for a production scale cell.

Production scale cells, both for chlorination and electrolysis, could not be made in a single piece, and construction from pure alumina bricks, bonded with alumina cement, is preferred. Although a single cell might be designed for both operations, it is preferable to use two separate cells, so that the two processes may be carried out simultaneously. The melt can be passed directly from the conversion vessel to the electrolysis cell via a tapping hole, which is sealed by cooling and released by melting. Alternatively, on the smaller (6 kg) scale, it may be convenient to solidify, break into lumps, and remelt in the electrolysis cell.

The electrode system can take several forms. In one of these a suspended graphite rod sheathed in "Mullite" is used as the cathode support, the electrode itself consisting of a small horizontal molybdenum disc fixed to the lower end, which in operation is located two or three inches above the cell base. The anode is a graphite annulus suspended from two graphite rods, a few inches above the molybdenum cathode. A molybdenum catch-plate rests on the base of the cell to collect thorium metal particles which fall from the cathode. This can be raised from the cell and drained in the same way as the cathode itself, by removal of the cell lid.

Dry argon is admitted to the cell by means of two Mullite inlet tubes, one above the surface of the melt and the other passing through the melt almost to the base. These are used both for purging, and during electrolysis.

In operation, the cell is first purged with argon at 650°C, electrolyte is added, and purging again carried out at 700°C for a number of hours. The electrodes are then adjusted in height and electrolysis carried out at 750–

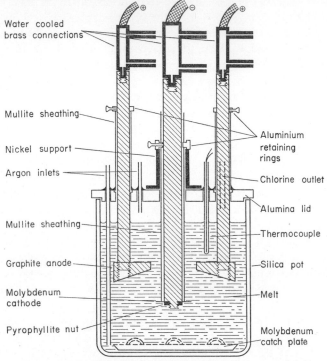

Water cooled brass connections

Mullite sheathing

Nickel support

Argon inlets

Mullite sheathing

Graphite anode

Molybdenum cathode

Pyrophyllite nut

Aluminium retaining rings

Chlorine outlet

Alumina lid

Thermocouple

Silica pot

Melt

Molybdenum catch plate

FIG. 7.6. Thorium electrolysis cell (U.K.A.E.A. copyright).

800°C, first at 350 A and then at a lower current, until little or no thorium remains in the electrolyte. Over-electrolysis results in low current efficiency, and the sodium liberated tends to attack the graphite and "Mullite" components of the electrodes. Over-electrolysis can be detected by the grey colour of the electrolyte which solidifies on the end of a silica rod dipped into the melt. After electrolysis, the lid and anode are removed. The cathode and catch plate, with the deposited thorium metal, are then lifted out carefully into an argon atmosphere to cool and drain. In the larger production scale cell, the cathode and catch plate would be lifted into an argon cooling chamber located above the cell, without the necessity of exposing to air before cooling.

The deposited thorium metal is freed from electrolyte in the usual manner, i.e. by crushing, successive washes with water at pH 6 to 7, a "polish" with dilute nitric acid, further water washes, and finally filtration and vacuum drying. Standard equipment is used for these operations, but it has sometimes been found advantageous to add a few pellets of massive thorium metal to the initial water washing operations, to break down aggregates of metal particles.

Elutriation is sometimes included before drying, in order to remove the low density impurity particles of carbon, alumina or silica, etc., Most of this impurity is confined to the smaller particle size ranges so it may not be necessary to elutriate the whole of the product.

The overall thorium efficiency of this process is about 90 per cent. Scrap metal, thoria or dissolved thorium salts (after precipitation and calcination) are recycled to the chlorination stage.

The chlorine efficiency is 50–60 per cent and in a well-designed cell the current efficiency can reach 80 per cent. The general level of impurities (in ppm) is as follows:

Iron	100– 600	Aluminium	100–400
Nitrogen	20– 80	Silicon	100
Oxygen	1000–5000	Chlorine	200–400
Carbon	100– 300	Sodium	100
Hydrogen	30– 90	Potassium	40– 80
Calcium	200		

A very pure grade of thorium metal can be produced in small quantities by fused salt electrolysis in a refining cell.[30] Thorium tetrachloride or tetra-fluoride is added to twice its weight of a lithium chloride, potassium choride eutectic (m.p. 352°C) and electrolysed between an anode of impure thorium metal and a molybdenum cathode, at a temperature of 400–50°C (forThF₄), or 600–50°C (For ThCl₄). A tubular-shaped container of fused silica is employed.

The electrolyte salts and impurities are leached out of the deposit by water, nitric acid and distilled water before rinsing in acetone and ethyl alcohol, for drying.

A comparison of the purity of this electrolytic product with the anode starting material is given below (Table 10).[29]

TABLE 10

Impurity	Anode, ppm	Electrolytic product, ppm
Aluminium .	50	<10
Boron .	0·5	0·2
Beryllium . .	1000	1
Calcium .	100	<20
Chromium .	20	<1
Copper .	5	1
Iron .	60	<5
Nickel .	40	<5
Lead .	5	<1
Silicon .	> 1000	<50
Potassium . .	—	100
Lithium .	—	100

PRODUCTION OF TITANIUM METAL BY ELECTROLYSIS

Titanium metal is generally manufactured by reduction of the tetrachloride with sodium or magnesium, but electrolytic methods have also been developed in an attempt to reduce costs.

Unfortunately, the most readily available pure intermediate, titanium tetrachloride, is a covalent compound which is insoluble in fused melt systems.

The stable double fluoride, K_2TiF_6, dissolved in fused sodium chloride, has been employed by Messrs. Horizons Inc.,[31] by analogy with their zirconium process. Chlorine is evolved on electrolysis, leaving an electrolyte rich in fluorides which have too high an electrical resistance[32] for satisfactory operation over a long period. Frequent replacement of the electrolyte is therefore necessary.

Electrolysis of an alkali fluoride melt containing titanium trichloride or dichloride is regarded as the most satisfactory process. A lithium chloride, potassium chloride eutectic, containing 60 mol % of the former, has a melting-point of only 350°C and allows electrolysis to be carried out satisfactorily at 550°C. The more conventional sodium chloride, potassium chloride eutectic is cheaper, but has a melting-point of 650°C.

The pure tetrachloride is first manufactured by standard chlorination techniques and is converted readily into the trichloride by reduction with hydrogen:

$$2TiCl_4 + H_2 \rightarrow 2TiCl_3 + 2HCl.$$

The dichloride is more difficult to produce in bulk but it can be tolerated as an impurity in the trichloride. Although the reaction equilibrium favours trichloride formation at low temperatures, a temperature of 1000°C is necessary for a reasonable reaction rate. A satisfactory technique[33] is to boil titanium tetrachloride and allow the vapour, mixed with hydrogen, to pass over a tungsten filament sheathed in silica and heated to 1000–1100°C. The trichloride product condenses on the walls of the reactor. The excess tetrachloride is condensed under reflux and the liquid dissolves the less volatile trichloride and carries it to the still. When the reaction has proceeded sufficiently, the excess tetrachloride is distilled away, leaving the trichloride in the form of a purple coloured crystalline deposit. This process is operated on a relatively small scale (about 0·5 tons per annum if run continuously), the reactor being of stainless-steel with a single glass condenser.

One modification of the above technique involves passing the tetrachloride with hydrogen through an electric arc struck between the electrolyte and a tungsten electrode; another is based upon cathodic reduction, the object being to produce the trichloride *in situ* in the electrolytic cell. If electrolysis is used as a purification process only, a "soluble anode" of impure titanium metal can be employed[5] and this allows titanium trichloride to be produced readily in the melt. A development of this process for a "winning cell" is to use an anode of titanium carbide, produced by high temperature reaction of rutile, or a purer oxide, with carbon, The carbide can even be added separately from the anode. In this way the direct production of the trichloride is avoided.

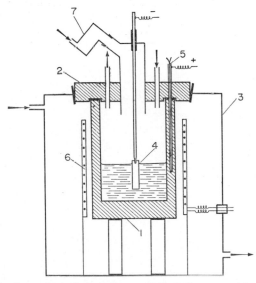

Fig. 7.7. Titanium electrolytic cell constructed from graphite: 1, graphite cell; 2, graphite cell top; 3, furnace; 4, cathode; 5, anode connection and thermocouple sheath; 6, heating element; 7, titanium trichloride reservoir (Bett, F. L. *et al.* Ref. 33).

The normal electrolytic process is carried out in a crucible of Acheson AGR Graphite which has been impregnated with coal tar and calcined to render it less porous. It has a lid of the same material. The crucible acts as the anode and the base is covered with alumina cement so that the chlorine gas is liberated at the walls, i.e. away from the vicinity of the cathode. A choice of cathode metals is available and silver, molybdenum, tungsten, nickel or massive titanium have been used. The cells used in the Australian process[33] (Fig. 7.7.) were sufficiently small to be heated externally by electric heating elements, thermally insulated by vermiculite powder. The cell includes a titanium trichloride reservoir for addition of successive batches and this can be purged through and into the cell with dry hydrogen during electrolysis.

In operation, a little hydrolysis takes place when making up the melt and the resulting oxide is reconverted back to chloride by means of a stream of hydrogen and hydrogen chloride through the electrolyte before electro-lysis. Pure hydrogen is then substituted during the electrolysis operation itself. Current densities up to 250 A/dm² have been used with titanium trichloride concentrations up to 15 per cent. Current efficiencies are usually 30–60 per cent, the higher figure being obtained when a porous silliminite diaphragm is used to separate into anolyte and catholyte compartments.

A promising modification to the electrolytic process[33] is to use a "hot spot cathode", i.e. a cathode only immersed in the electrolyte to a minimum extent. This allows a temperature to be reached in the region where titanium is deposited for it to be partially sintered to a sponge. Gradual withdrawal of the electrode allows a rigid cylinder of titanium sponge to be slowly produced.

Standard water leaching operations are employed as for other metal powders. Micro hardness determinations on the metal particles give figures of 70–100 VHN, which compare favourably with the figures obtained with metal produced by the iodide route. Unfortunately a more brittle metal is produced after argon arc melting, with a hardness of 300 VHN. The em-brittlement is probably caused by oxygen contamination of the surface of the powder, introduced during the leaching operations.

REFERENCES

1. DRIGGS, F. H. and LILLIENDAHL, W. C. Method of Preparing Rare Refractory Metals by Electrolysis. U.S. Patent 1,835, 025 (1931).
2. DRIGGS, F. H. Preparation of Rare Metals by Electrolytic Decomposition of their Fused Double Halogen Compounds. U.S. Patent 1,842,254 (1932).
3. DRIGGS, F. H. Electrode Material. U.S. Patent 1,835,026 (1931).
4. GIBSON, A. R. and BUDDERY, J. H. An Oxide–Chloride Conversion Process for the Extraction of Certain Metals. I.M.M. Symposium on the Extraction Metallurgy of Some of the Less Common Metals, London (1956).
5. GRAY, J. J. and CARTER, A. *Chemistry and Metallurgy of Titanium Production.* Royal Institute of Chemistry (1958).
6. Norton Grinding Wheel Company Ltd. Process for the Preparation of Substantially Pure Zirconium or Hafnium or Alloys thereof. British Patent 747,834 (1956).
7. KJELLGREN, B. R. F. and SAWYER, C. B. Method of Producing Metallic Beryllium. U.S. Patent 2,188,904 (1936).
8. KJELLGREN, B. R. F. and SAWYER, C. B. Metallic Beryllium. Canadian Patent 371, 194 (1938).
9. JAEGER, G. Process for the Preparation of Metallic Beryllium by Electrolysis. U.S. Patent 2,041,131 (1936).
10. WEST, H. W. *et al.* Investigation of Beryllium Production in Germany and Italy. B.I.O.S. Final Report No. 550, Item No. 21.
11. BRYANT, P. S. Beryllium Production at Milford Haven, I.M.M. Symposium on Ex-traction Metallurgy of the Less Common Metals, London (1957).
12. BEAVER, W. W. Technology of beryllium and beryllium oxide. *Progress in Nuclear Energy.* Ser. V, *Metallurgy and Fuels,* vol. 1. Pergamon Press (1956).
13. WILLIAMS, J. The powder metallurgy of beryllium. *Progress in Nuclear Energy,* Ser. V, *Metallurgy and Fuels,* vol. 1. Pergamon Press (1956).
14. POTVIN, R. Production of Beryllia and Beryllium at Degussa Plants. B.I.O.S. Final Report No. 158 Item No. 21 (Sept. 1945).

15. MOTOCK, G. T. Extraction and Uses of Beryllium in Germany. U.S. Bureau of Mines. Information Circular 7357 (June 1946).
16. SLOMAN, H. A. and SAWYER, C. B. The Beryllium Industries of Germany and Italy. F.I.A.T. Final Report No. 522.
17. WINDECKER, C. E. The production of beryllium by the electrolysis of beryllium chloride. The Metal Beryllium, p. 102. The American Society for Metals (1955).
18. LILLIENDAHL, W. C., WROUGHTON, D., NAGY, R. and MARDEN, J. W. Electrolytic Production of Uranium Powder. U.S. Patent 2,690,421.
19. MARDEN, J. W. et al. The Electrolytic Process for the Manufacture of Uranium. AECD–3687 (1946).
20. BUDDERY, J. H. and HEDGER, H. J. Production of uranium metal by electrolysis. Progress in Nuclear Energy, Ser. V, Metallurgy and Fuels, vol. 1. Pergamon Press (1956).
21. BLUMENTHAL, B. and NOLAND, R. A. High purity uranium. Progress in Nuclear Energy, Ser. V, Metallurgy and Fuels, vol. 1. Pergamon Press (1956).
22. STEINBERG, M. A., SIBERT, M. E. and WAINER, E. Extractive metallurgy of zirconium by the electrolysis of fused salts. II, Process development of the electrolytic production of zirconium from K_2ZrF_6. J. Electrochem. Soc. 101, No. 2, 63 (Feb. 1954).
23. RAYNES, V. C. et al. The extractive metallurgy of zirconium by the electrolysis of fused salts. III, Expanded scale process development of the electrolytic production of zirconium from K_2ZrF_6. J. Electrochem. Soc. 102, No. 3, 137–44 (Mar. 1955).
24. OGAREV, A. N. et al. Preparation of ductile zirconium by fused salt electrolysis. Proc. 2nd Int. Conf. on the Peaceful Uses of Atomic Energy, Geneva, 1958. Paper 2047.
25. WILHELM, H. A. Thorium. Progress in Nuclear Energy, Ser. V, Metallurgy and Fuels, vol. 1. Pergamon Press (1956).
26. CUTHBERT, F. L. Thorium Production Technology. Addison-Wesley, U.S.A. (1958).
27. KAPLAN, G. E. The production of thorium metal. Progress in Nuclear Energy, Ser. V, Metallurgy and Fuels, vol. 1. Pergamon Press (1956).
28. KAPLAN, G. E. Metallurgy of thorium. Proc. 1st Int. Conf. on the Peaceful Uses of Atomic Energy, Geneva, 1955. Paper 636.
29. BUDDERY, J. H., JAMRACK, W. D. and WELLS, R. A. The extraction of thorium. Chemistry and Industry, No. 8, p. 235 (21/2/59).
30. NOLAND, R. A. Electrolytic Refining of Thorium. U.S.A.E.C. and A.S.M. Conference on the Metal Thorium, Cleveland (1956).
31. Horizons Titanium Corporation, U.S.A. Fused Salt Bath for the Electrodeposition of the Polyvalent Metals Titanium, Tantalum and Vanadium. British Patent 791,151 (1958).
32. STEINBERG, M. A. et al. Preparation of titanium by fluoride electrolysis. J. Electrochem. Soc. 102, No. 6, 332 (June 1955).
33. BETT, F. L. et al. Some Investigations into the Extraction of Titanium by Fused Salt Electrolysis. I.M.M. Symposium on Extraction and Refining of the Rarer Metals, London (1957).
34. Horizons Titanium Corporation, U.S.A. Fused Salt Bath for the Electrodeposition of the Polyvalent Metals, Titanium, Tantalum and Vanadium. British Patent 791,153 (1958).
35. National Lead Company, U.S.A. Method of Producing Zirconium Metal. Australian Patent 29,464/57 (1957).
36. Horizons Titanium Corporation, U.S.A. Improvements in the Electrolytic Deposition of Refractory Metals. British Patent 790,870 (1958).
37. Ciba Ltd. Production of Metallic Niobium or Tantalum by the Electrolysis of Melts. Australian Patent 30,340/57 (1957).
38. MEISTER, G. Production of thorium, zirconium and uranium. Metal Progress 53, No. 4, 515 (Apr. 1948).

CHAPTER 8

IODIDE DECOMPOSITION PROCESSES

RARE metals have been produced in the highest state of purity by the thermal decomposition of their iodides, a process first applied to titanium by Van Arkel[1, 2] in 1925. Although the products of this process are in a compact form and are generally superior in purity to those from any other rare metal production process, it cannot unfortunately be operated on a large production scale.

Since the rare metal iodides are produced most easily by direct synthesis from the appropriate metal and iodine at relatively low temperature, the Van Arkel process has usually been employed as a purification process for the preparation of small quantities of exceptionally high-grade metal. A relatively low-grade metal, e.g. made by a calcium reduction route, is converted to iodide and then decomposed again to give the pure metal.

REACTION CONDITIONS

The metal must be capable of forming a volatile iodide at low temperatures, which decomposes again to solid metal at high temperatures.[3] In addition, the vapour pressure of the metal itself must be reasonably low at the temperature of the hot zone so that it does not tend to evaporate.

The essential part of the process, the thermal decomposition stage, is generally carried out on an incandescent filament heated by means of an electric current, the filament being made either of tungsten or molybdenum, or of the rare metal being produced. The initial diameter can be as little as one thousandth of an inch when tungsten or molybdenum are used, but it is normally thicker if the rare metal itself is employed. A deposit of metal gradually accumulates on the wire in the form of adherent crystals. The deposited product causes the wire to increase in diameter, and consequently it becomes necessary to increase the electric current to maintain the original temperature. The magnitude of this increase in current imposes a severe limitation on the maximum diameter of wire or rod which can be achieved and even in the largest production units this is only between 1 and 2 in. Efforts to expand the rate of production have therefore concentrated on increasing the length of filament rather than the diameter.[4]

The two metals for which this process has been primarily used are titanium and zirconium and the reactions are represented simply as:

$$TiI_4 \rightleftharpoons Ti + 2I_2$$

and
$$ZrI_4 \rightleftharpoons Zr + 2I_2.$$

It has also been applied to thorium, uranium and vanadium. Beryllium has been less successful owing to the reaction of beryllium iodide with the glass reaction vessel.[5]

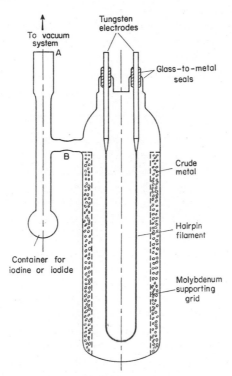

Fig. 8.1. Glass reactor for iodide decomposition (Shapiro, Z. M. Ref. 7. U.S.A.E.C. copyright).

Since the reacting iodide and the iodine produced are both vapours, it is clear that a volume increase takes place on production of the rare metal. Metal production is therefore favoured by low pressures. However, the pressure cannot be controlled at too low a value since the throughput of material would become unduly low for a given size of reactor. Also the reverse reaction, i.e. synthesis of the iodide from impure metal and iodine, is allowed to take place in the same vessel, and this would be impeded by very low pressures. In practice, pressures of a fews tens of millimetres of mercury are employed.

Since production of metals by this technique is carried out on a small scale, much of the equipment has been of a laboratory type. The reaction vessels are often made of glass or silica for example, as shown in Fig. 8.1. A reactor contains two electrodes passing through suitable seals and connected to the ends of a loop of wire forming the filament. A side-arm connects to a small container for the iodide and also to a vacuum system. Once evacuated, the system is isolated by sealing at point A. The interior of the reactor is lined with lumps of the impure form of the rare metal, often held in position away from the filament, by means of a molybdenum grid as shown.

The reaction is dependent upon the production of the metal iodide vapour, by heating the side-arm to several hundred degrees Centigrade in the first instance and then sealing of the bulb at point B. The vapour decomposes on the filament and the liberated iodine reacts with the crude rare metal, again at a few hundred degrees Centigrade, to re-form the iodide vapour. In effect, the iodine acts as an agent for mass transfer of the rare metal and leaves impurities behind which do not have sufficiently volatile iodides. In these circumstances, the bulb on the side-arm might be allowed to contain iodine instead of rare metal iodide.

The thermal dissociation itself usually takes place on the wire at a temperature of about 1100 to 1200°C and as the filament becomes thicker it is necessary to increase the current and lower the voltage drop across it to maintain the temperature. The net effect is a substantial increase in power consumption and therefore of heat radiated from the filament. The crude rare metal is heated to say 300–400°C during the early part of the run by means of an electrical resistance heater external to the reactor. The power supplied to this heater is gradually reduced to zero as the crude metal obtains a larger proportion of its heat by radiation from the filament. Finally, it may become necessary to replace the external heat source by a cooler to prevent the crude metal reaching too high a temperature, i.e. a temperature where the reactor wall might melt, or react with the crude metal. Even if this were avoided by suitable choice of reactor materials of construction, a wall temperature might eventually be reached in the absence of cooling where the equilibrium would tend not to favour the production of iodide.

At the start of a reaction it is advisable to have a supply of the iodide available inside the reactor rather than rely upon the synthesis reaction. This is because a surface skin of oxide inhibits reaction between the crude metal and iodine and gives rise to an induction period. Furthermore, the rate of production of iodide remains low if the iodine is led away from the reactor and contacted with crude metal in a separate vessel. This is believed to be due to the synthesis reaction being photochemical, i.e. catalysed by the radiation emitted from the glowing filament;[6] or alternatively some of the iodine is produced from the filament in an activated condition, possibly as atoms rather than molecules, and having only a small mean free path before conversion to the normal unactivated condition.

PLANT AND EQUIPMENT

The iodide decomposition process for any rare metal is always more expensive than other methods of production, because of the small scale of operation, with its relatively high capital cost and labour usage per unit.

Glass or silica equipment is fragile and impose a limit on the size of vessel which can be fabricated. In addition, the system is limited to relatively low power inputs because of the difficulties of sealing large electrodes into the vessel and removing heat through the walls. Also the vessel can only be opened up at the start or finish of a run, to change the feed or remove the product, by "glassblowing" operations which involve breaking and remaking the vessel.

Attempts have been made to design an all-metal plant and to increase the scale of operation, with some success. The selection of a suitable constructional metal has proved difficult however.[7] It is necessary to avoid corrosion by iodine vapour and the subsequent transfer of volatile metal iodides to the pure product. Thus only the most expensive metals, platinum, gold and tungsten, are entirely satisfactory. Molybdenum, Hastelloy B and Inconel, however, allow a reasonable compromise between cost and corrosion rate.

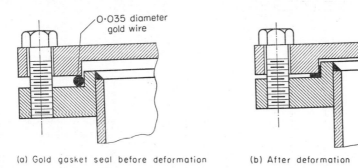

0·035 diameter gold wire

(a) Gold gasket seal before deformation   (b) After deformation

Fig. 8.2. Iodide decomposition reactor joint. (Shapiro, Z.M. Ref. 7. U.S.A.E.C. copyright).

In general, the whole of the reactor unit, including joints and valves, must operate in an iodine atmosphere at temperatures above 230°C. Gaskets have been made of Teflon, lead and aluminium wire but, in practice, none are as satisfactory as gold wire. The cost is reduced by recovery after use, whereas gaskets of other materials are completely expendable. The type of joint employed is shown in Fig. 8.2.

Valves of the conventional packed type are unsuitable for vacuum work. Bellows sealed valves are subject to corrosion and failure of the bellows, and diaphragm valves have also proved unsuccessful. A special valve designed for the purpose by the Westinghouse Electric Corporation, shown in Fig. 8.3, has proved reasonably satisfactory on zirconium production units.

A suitable temperature at the walls of the metal reactor can be maintained by means of a molten salt bath containing fused sodium and potassium nitrates and nitrites. The reactor is immersed in the bath and heat is applied to the salts by means of external electric heaters during the early part of the run. Later, when it is necessary to remove heat at a considerable rate, this is done by means of water sprays directed at the surface of the salt container. Alternatively, a cooling coil is immersed in the salts around the reactor. A suitable organic liquid is used inside the coil for cooling and the heat is finally transferred to water by means of an external heat exchanger, before feeding the primary heat transfer liquid back to the coil. The degree of cooling is dependent upon the flow rate of the organic fluid. It is convenient to establish automatic control of the heaters and coolant circulating pump, so as to maintain a constant temperature throughout a run.

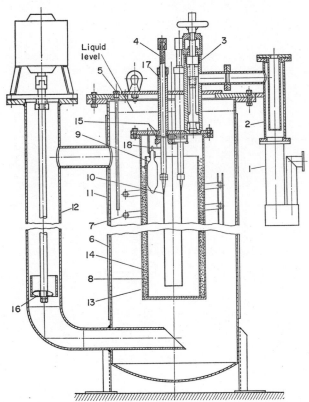

Fig. 8.3. Metal reactor for iodide decomposition: 1, high-vacuum pump; 2, cold trap; 3, nonrising stem valve; 4, copper electrode; 5, thermocouple; 6, immersion tank; 7, cooling coil; 8, molybdenum screen; 9, ZrI$_4$ bottle; 10, molybdenum electrode tip; 11, strip heaters; 12, circulator; 13, Hastelloy B vessel; 14, Zr sponge; 15, ceramic bushings; 16, agitator with shroud; 17, O-ring seal; 18, Zr wire holding bottle (9) in place (Shapiro, Z. M. Ref. 7. U.S.A.E.C. copyright).

For glass or silica reactors, the filament temperature is measured by means of an optical pyrometer and the current is increased as the rare metal deposit grows, while the voltage drop across the filament is decreased. The pyrometer measurement is lacking in precision owing to the presence of absorbing materials and becomes impracticable with a metal vessel, even when an observation window is used. An empirical adjustment of current is sometimes made instead, based upon an assumption that similar conditions are present from one run to another, leading to a similarity in the rate of increase in filament diameter. A relationship can be established however between current, voltage and temperature which is independent of diameter, i.e.

$$EI^{\frac{1}{3}} = L(4\rho\pi a^2 \sigma^2 T^8)^{\frac{1}{3}}$$

where E = current,
I = voltage,
L = length of wire,
ρ = resistivity,
a = emissivity,
$\sigma = 5 \cdot 735 \times 10^{-12}$ for a black body,
and T = temperature.

Thus for a constant temperature, material and length of wire,

$EI^{\frac{1}{3}} = K$, a constant.

The emissivity and resistivity may not be known precisely for a particular rare metal, but it is still possible to make use of the relationship between E and I if K is first evaluated empirically in experimental equipment where the temperature can be measured. Once the constant, K, has been determined, control equipment can be designed which will maintain the product of voltage and cube root of current at a constant value, and so ensure a stable temperature.[8]

The method of attachment of the two ends of the filament to the electrodes becomes of considerable importance as the scale of operation is increased. The design must provide a robust joint which will carry the large currents and must allow a deposit to build up at the joint, of the same diameter as that on the remainder of the filament. If undue cooling takes place near the electrode, less rare metal tends to deposit because of the lower temperature. The resulting thinner portion then tends to burn out as the current is increased. A number of designs used in the U.S.A. by the Battelle Memorial Institute, the Foote Mineral Company and the Westinghouse Electric Corporation[7] are shown in Figs. 8.4, 8.5, 8.6, 8.7 and 8.8. The electrode transition tip in Figs. 8.6 and 8.7 has been widely used[9] and with zirconium has allowed bars of 1·7 in. in diameter to be produced. That shown in Fig. 8.8 is regarded as equally satisfactory[10] but is cheaper to fabricate, being made principally from molybdenum wire. The various conconcentric rings of wires come into use successively as the bar of rare metal increases in diameter.

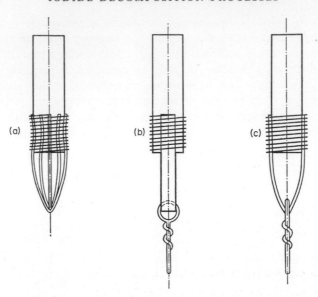

FIG. 8.4. BMI electrode transition tips: (a) Model 1; (b) Model 2, side view; (c) Model 2, front view (Shapiro, Z. M. Ref. 7. U.S.A.E.C. copyright).

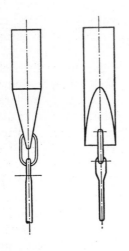

FIG. 8.5. Foote electrode transition tip (Shapiro, Z. M. Ref. 7. U.S.A.E.C. copyright).

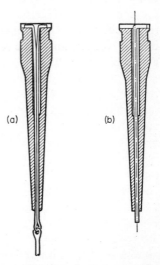

FIG. 8.6. Standard Westinghouse electrode transition tip, showing two methods of filament attachment (Shapiro, Z. M. Ref. 7. U.S.A.E.C. copyright).

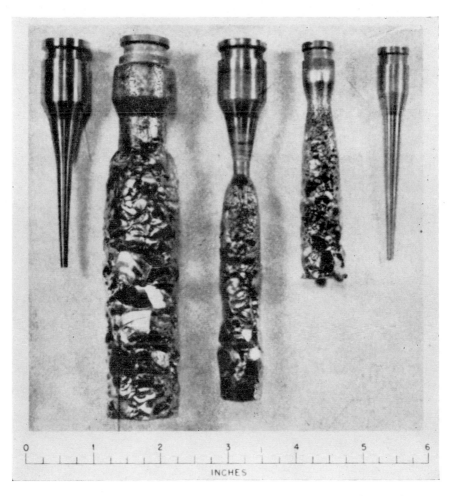

FIG. 8.7. Standard Westinghouse transition tip, showing deposit (Shapiro, Z. M. Ref. 7. U.S.A.E.C. Copyright).

Several methods of adding iodine or rare metal iodide at the beginning of a run have been employed. It is necessary to evacuate the heated plant and remove nitrogen and oxygen sorbed on the surface or on the crude rare metal. The iodine or iodide would be distilled out of the system under these conditions and therefore it must be added at a later stage or kept in a refrigerated side-tube during the evacuation. One method is to add it in a sealed glass bottle before evacuation and to break the glass wall afterwards when the deposition of rare metal is ready to begin. A less satisfactory technique is simply to make the addition through a tube against a positive pressure of inert gas, argon or helium, which is allowed to leave the reactor.

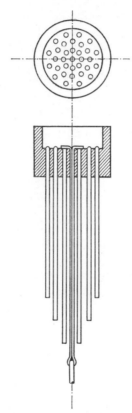

FIG. 8.8. Modified Westinghouse electrode transition tip (Shapiro, Z. M. Ref. 7. U.S.A.E.C. copyright).

The products obtained from the process are in the form of large crystals adhering to the filament in a tightly packed mass. The deposit is fairly regular since deviations from the normal thickness are self compensating to a certain extent, i.e. the thinner parts of the rod reach a higher temperature and therefore attract a greater proportion of the later deposit.

PRODUCT PURITY

Impurities in the rare metals produced by the iodide process can generally be reduced to a few tens of parts per million or less, for each element, provided care is taken in the selection of materials of construction. This initial advantage over other processes arises from the fact that the rare metals are produced without direct contact with a crucible or other container. Elements with volatile iodides should clearly be avoided in locations where the temperature is appropriate for attack by iodine vapour. Similarly, the crude feed should be as free from such elements as possible. For example, the whole of the zirconium impurity in a crude titanium feed would be carried over into the product, and vice versa, since the iodide process is equally suitable for the impurity as for the rare metal being purified. A large fraction of the iron and aluminium would be transferred, but decontamination factors from other elements such as nickel, chromium, carbon silicon and nitrogen are usually of the order of 10 to 100.

ALTERNATIVE FEED MATERIALS

One of the reasons for the high cost of rare metals made by the iodide process is the fact that in each case the feed material consists of the rare metal itself, often in only a slightly less pure form. Metallic sponge, made by the already expensive Kroll type magnesium reduction process, is in fact often used as a feed. Progress has been made in recent years in the use of cheaper feed materials; for example, a metal made by a simple calcium reduction or aluminium reduction[11] of an oxide, and, even more promising, the use of a carbide. The latter can often be produced by reaction of a fairly pure grade of oxide with carbon at a high temperature in a direct heated resistance furnace.[12] This then enables the iodide process to be regarded as a true extraction process rather than a metal purification process.

RECYCLING OF RESIDUES

Other economies can be made in the recycling of residue materials. Iodine, for example, is washed from the reactor, together with some iodide of the rare metal, and recovered by treatment with gaseous chlorine. Either free iodine, or the iodate of the rare metal, is precipitated according to the usage of chlorine. In the latter case, the iodate is dried and free iodine removed by calcination. The rare metal oxide residue is also recovered and recycled to an appropriate stage. A high proportion of the crude metal is in any case recycled untreated, except for perhaps a water wash and drying operation. Although this proportion may approach 90 per cent, the losses on recycling are comparatively small and the overall conversion efficiency may be as high as 95 per cent, indicating an irrecoverable loss of only 5 per cent.

CONTINUOUS OPERATION

Various attempts have been made to modify the Van Arkel process for continuous operation. These depend upon separation of the processes of production of the iodide and dissociation to the metal. The types of dissociation stage suggested have been based upon (a) passing the iodide vapour over a number of filaments in series, (b) passing the vapour through a hollow electrode feeding an electric arc struck between it and the pool of molten rare metal, (c) passing the vapour over a tube heated by induction to a high temperature, or (d) deposition upon a hot filament immersed in liquid iodide. None of these have yet led to a successful continuous process owing to a variety of practical difficulties.

PRODUCTION OF TITANIUM BY IODIDE DECOMPOSITION

Titanium was the first rare metal to be produced by the Van Arkel process.[1] It has been made for a number of years on a very small industrial scale using glass reactors, and more recently Inconel reactors have been employed on a somewhat larger scale.

Glass reactors described by Campbell[13] each contain a hairpin-shaped filament, 24 in. long, attached to tungsten electrodes which are sealed into the glass. The filament is of pure titanium, not more than about 0·003 in. diameter, suspended vertically, and a second one is sealed into the reactor in a similar manner in case of premature failure in use. A small tungsten weight is attached to the lowest point of the filament to maintain it in a vertical position.

Filament temperatures for titanium can be between about 1100 and 1600°C, but there is no gain in deposition rate by operating above 1450°C to 1500°C. A graph of deposition rate against filament temperature is shown in Fig. 8.9.

The crude titanium is held in position by a molybdenum grid around the wall of the reactor, and is maintained at a suitable temperature. 100 to 200°C is satisfactory in practice for the production of titanium tetra-iodide at the maximum rate. If higher wall temperatures are used, the rate of deposition on the filament decreases, approaching zero at 400°C, since the system then contains entirely titanium di-iodide instead of tetra-iodide, produced by the reaction:[14]

$$TiI_4 + Ti \rightleftharpoons 2TiI_2.$$

At higher wall temperatures, the di-iodide decomposes on the filament until at 550°C wall temperature, the deposition rate is faster than can be achieved with tetra-iodide. This high rate presumably results from the more rapid formation of the iodide or better conditions for diffusion to the wire, etc., since the thermal decomposition reaction itself is not the rate controlling step. Temperatures of this order are not recommended for operation in a glass reactor, however, except under special experimental conditions. The higher wall temperature has a distinct advantage in that iron and silicon iodides are unstable and thus unable to enter the vapour phase. Thus, they do not migrate to the filament and contaminate the product.

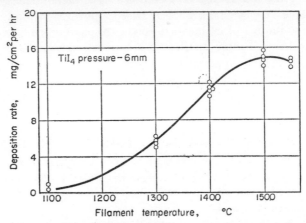

FIG. 8.9. Effect of filament temperature on the deposition rate of titanium (Runnalls, O. J. C. and Pidgeon, L. M. Ref. 16).

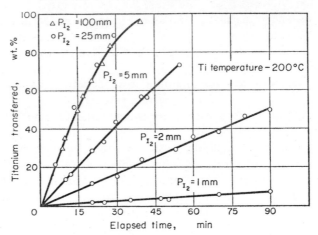

FIG. 8.10. Effect of iodine pressure on the transfer rate of titanium as TiI_4 (Runnalls, O. J. C. and Pidgeon, L. M. Ref. 16).

Various pressures have been used for operation of the process, usually between a few millimetres and a few tens of millimetres of mercury. The influence of iodine and titanium iodide pressures upon reaction rate[15, 16] is seen in Figs. 8.10 and 8.11 from Runnals and Pidgeon.[16]

Titanium metal filaments are used to replace tungsten when it is important to avoid contamination by the latter element. The lower strength of pure titanium at high temperatures makes it necessary to use a relatively thick filament and care is needed in the early stages to prevent breakage, by operating at as low a temperature as possible.

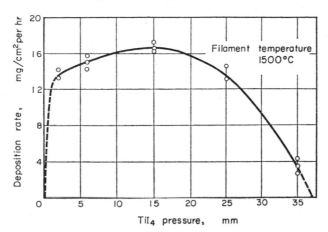

FIG. 8.11. Effect of TiI$_4$ pressure on the deposition rate of titanium (Runnals, O. J. C. and Pidgeon, L. M. Ref. 16).

The form of the titanium deposit is dependent upon the filament temperature and the crystalline form of the filament itself. In Fig. 8.12, the middle bar consists of a single crystal of titanium grown upon a filament, which itself consists of a single crystal of tungsten. The upper and lower bars demonstrate the effect of filament temperature, the larger crystals being deposited at 1300 to 1400°C and the smaller ones at only 1100°C.

An all metal plant made, for example, of inconel, is presumably as successful for the manufacture of pure titanium as for zirconium, but details have not been published. The commercial demand for the very highest grade titanium is, in any case, less than that for zirconium of comparable purity, and for most purposes titanium made by the Kroll magnesium reduction process is quite satisfactory.

PRODUCTION OF ZIRCONIUM BY IODIDE DECOMPOSITION

Because of its low neutron-capture cross-section and high resistance to corrosion, the manufacture of high-grade zirconium, free from hafnium, has been developed to a great extent in the U.S.A. for use in pressurized water reactors.

Attention was focused on the "crystal bar" zirconium made by the iodide route in addition to the Kroll magnesium reduction process. The iodide decomposition route gives a superior product, but at a higher cost.

Prior to the nuclear requirement, small-scale production was carried out by Messrs. Phillips of Holland. Manufacture by the American Foote Mineral Company followed after 1940, on a scale up to 6 lb per batch per unit, using 19 in. long filaments. The Westinghouse Electric Corporation's Atomic Power Division have manufactured zirconium in larger plant since about 1950. Their units are about 5 ft 6 in. long and 2 ft diameter, as seen in Fig. 8.13. 50 ft long filaments are used, bent into a multiple "hairpin" as shown in Fig. 8.14. About 100 lb can be deposited in each run and the Westinghouse Electric total production capacity is over 30 tons per annum.

Figure 8.15 shows a Westinghouse unit in cross-section. The filament, consisting of 0·095 in. diameter zirconium wire, is suspended in a number of vertical lengths, each supported between ceramic insulators. The whole filament forms a hollow wire cylinder, which is surrounded by a molybdenum grid and annular space backed with "crude zirconium" or zirconium sponge. The outer support of this annulus is the reactor wall itself, 2 ft in diameter, immersed in a salt bath. A large weight is attached to the base of the reactor to allow it to sink in the molten salts. The reactor top carries the electrodes and also has exhaust and iodine inlet connections. The salts are heated initially by means of immersion heaters and the molten salts are then circulated by means of a stirrer in an external draft tube. A cooling jacket is provided, external to the salt bath, which is fitted with water sprays.

Iodine addition is carried out by sublimation from a small hopper, which can be heated or cooled and opens to the reactor by means of a special valve. This, and the main evacuation valve, is fitted with an expendable gold ring seal, as is the removable head of the unit.

When zirconium sponge is used as the crude metal feed, it is loaded into the annular space in a wet condition, a charge weighing about 300 lb. About 7 lb of iodine is placed in the hopper and the unit assembled. The sponge is vacuum-dried in the unit at 200°C with solid carbon dioxide cooling of the iodine hopper. After drying down to a pressure of about 0·1 mm mercury, a high-vacuum pumping system is connected. Leak testing takes place as the pressure falls to about 10^{-5} mm. and the temperature is raised to 350°C. The evacuation valve is then closed and the iodine feed sublimed in to allow the deposition reaction to take place. These initial operations take up to 15 hr and thereafter deposition takes place at about 0·9 lb Zr/hr. The current is increased and the voltage decreased until the power supplied is about 75 kW. The voltage can be varied throughout a run from 245 V to 65 V and a current of 1600 A is available.

After completion of a run, the cooled unit is opened to a helium atmosphere and drenched with water as a fire precaution, before the bar of zirconium is removed. The considerable amount of surplus "crude" zirconium is washed and recycled, the overall yield then being about 95 per cent.

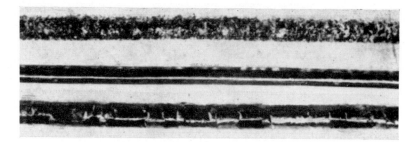

FIG. 8.12. Various types of titanium rods obtained by the iodide process. The middle bar was grown on a single-crystal tungsten filament while the others were formed on polycrystalline filaments. The upper rod was grown with the filament at 1100°C and the lower with the filament temperature between 1300 and 1400°C (McQuillan, A. D. and McQuillan, M. K. Ref. 15).

FIG. 8.13. View of Westinghouse zirconium plant (Shapiro, Z. M. Ref. 7. U.S.A.E.C. copyright).

FIG. 8.14. Zirconium crystal bar as removed from deposition vessel (Shapiro, Z. M. Ref. 7. U.S.A.E.C. copyright).

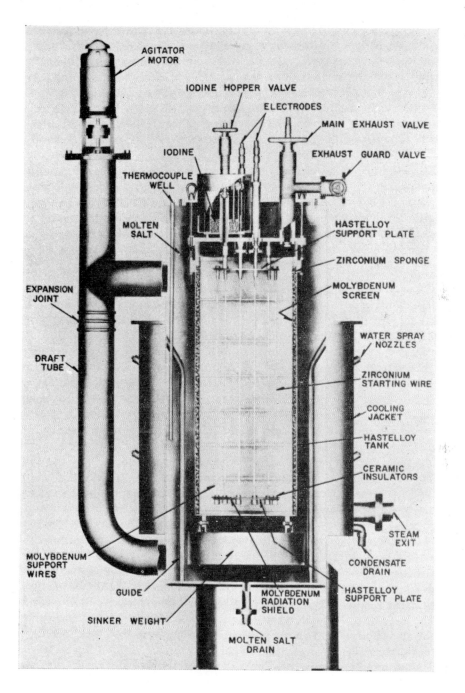

FIG. 8.15. Westinghouse zirconium production unit (Shapiro, Z. M. Ref. 7.
U.S.A.E.C. copyright).

Improvements to the process include the insertion of additional crude zirconium in the interior of the hairpin filament to increase the surface area available. Extra salt cooling must also be provided to the central zone by means of a re-entrant tube let into the base of the reactor.

An example of the high purity of the zirconium produced by the iodide decomposition route is as follows:[17]

Impurity	ppm	Impurity	ppm
Silicon	30	Magnesium	10
Iron	200	Lead	10
Aluminium	30	Nickel	30
Titanium	10	Chromium	30
Calcium	50	Nitrogen	10
Manganese	10	Oxygen	200
Copper	55		

A relatively cheap zirconium carbide feed material has been used in place of zirconium metal.[18] This is made by heating pure zirconium oxide with sufficient carbon to produce cabon monoxide, to temperatures of about 2000°C.

Pure hafnium, the chemical analogue of zirconium, was produced in small quantities, by the iodide decomposition route at 1300°C as early as 1930[19] and mentioned by Van Arkel even in 1925.

PRODUCTION OF THORIUM BY IODIDE DECOMPOSITION

Thorium metal has been purified by the iodide process but only on a scale of about 1 lb or less per run.[21] 48 mil tungsten or thorium filaments are suspended in standard type glass reactors and a feed is used of crude thorium metal chips cut from wrought plates.

$$ThI_4 \rightarrow Th + 2I_2.$$

A reactor is first out-gassed at 510°C and a pressure of 10^{-4} mm of mercury, for a number of hours, with the crushed iodine present in a refrigerated side-tube. Thorium iodide is then allowed to form at 260°C and volatilized at about 450°C for the decomposition reaction. The filament temperature is maintained between 900°C and 1700°C, 1000°C being found satisfactory.

Thorium tetra-iodide is more stable than the iodides of titanium or zirconium and temperatures as high as possible are required for its dissociation into thorium metal and iodine. At intermediate temperatures of say 500–600°C, the tetra-iodide reacts with thorium metal to produce the tri-iodide, ThI_3, particularly on long heating. The feed material tends to become coated with this lower iodide if maintained at temperatures below 600°C and, because of its lower volatility than the tetra-iodide, the rate of decomposition on the filament is considerably reduced.

At the end of a run, the top of the glass reactor is cracked to allow the product to be removed. The deposit of thorium tends to be less coherent than that of titanium or zirconium and this may be related to the low solubility of oxygen in thorium. This places a limit on the size of bars which can be produced, although there is at present no large-scale demand to justify the manufacture of bars longer than a few feet or of more than 0·5 in. in diameter.

The purity of thorium metal made by the iodide route is given as follows (Table 11).[22]

TABLE 11

Impurity	ppm in Thorium product	ppm in crude Thorium feed
Aluminium . .	Not detected spectrographically	20
Barium . . .	,,	Not detected spectrographically
Beryllium . .	0·2	200–2000
Boron . . .	Not detected spectrographically	0·5
Chromium . .	,,	20
Cobalt . . .	,,	10
Iron . . .	20	80
Magnesium . .	2	5
Nickel . . .	Not detected spectrographically	100
Phosphorus . .	,,	Not detected spectrographically
Potassium . .	,,	,,
Silicon . . .	,,	30
Tungsten . .	,,	Not detected spectrographically
Carbon . .	20	400
Hydrogen . .	10	170
Nitrogen . .	10	70
Oxygen . . .	180	2670

The hardness of the metal as deposited on the filament is typically 40 on the Vickers scale, although it varies from batch to batch according to the purity.

A small-scale process has been described by Scaife and Wylie[23] in which thorium carbide is used as the feed material. This is made by pelleting a mixture of finely divided thorium oxide with graphite and heating in a carbon resistance tube furnace above 2000°C, in an argon atmosphere. The rather pyrophoric carbide is then reacted with iodine at 500°C and 4 to 200 mm pressure, and sublimed under vacuum to give a yellow thorium tetra-iodide. This is then thermally decomposed on a tungsten filament at high temperature in the normal manner.

REFERENCES

1. VAN ARKEL, A. E. and DE BOER, J. H. Darstellung von reinen Titanium-, Zirkonium-, Hafnium-und Thoriummetall. Z. Anorg. Chem. 148, 345 (1925).
2. VAN ARKEL, A. E. and DE BOER, J. H. Process of Precipitating Metals on an Incandescent Body. U.S. Patent 1,671,213 (application 1925).
3. MAXWELL, C. R. Hot Wire Reduction of Metals. U.S.A.E.C. Report, MDDC-296 (1946).

4. The technology of zirconium. U.S. President's Materials Policy Commission Report. *Resources of Freedom*, vol IV, p. 83, Washington (1952).
5. SLOMAN, H. A. Researches on beryllium. *J. Inst. Metals* 49 (2), 377 (1932).
6. HOLDEN, R. B. and KOPELMAN, B. The hot-wire process for zirconium. *J. Electrochem Soc.* 100, No. 3, 120 (1953).
7. SHAPIRO, Z. M. *Iodide-Decomposition for Production of Zirconium. The Metallurgy of Zirconium.* McGraw-Hill, New York (1955).
8. DURNAL, R. G. An Indirect Method of Process Control. U.S.A.E.C. Report, AECD–2847 (1950).
9. SHAPIRO, Z. M. Apparatus for Attaching Filaments to Electrodes in Machines for Coating with Metal Vapours. U.S. Patent 2,637,297 (application 1951).
10. SHAPIRO, Z. M. Apparatus for Attaching Filaments to Electrodes in Machines for Coating with Metal Vapours. U.S. Patent 2,637,298 (application 1951).
11. BLUMENTHAL, W. B. and SMITH, H. *Industr. Engng. Chem. (Industr.)* 42, 249 (1950).
12. LOONAM, A. C. Production of Metallic Titanium. U.S. Patent 2,714,564 (application 1948, issued 1955).
13. CAMPBELL, I. E. *et al. Trans. Electrochem. Soc.* 93, 271 (1948).
14. FAST, J. D. Über die Darstellung der reinen Metalle der Titangruppe durch Thermische Zersetzung ihrer Iodide. V. Titan. *Z. Anorg. Chem.* 241, 42 (1939).
15. McQUILLAN, A. D. and McQUILLAN, M. K. *Titanium.* Butterworths Scientic Publications, London (1956).
16. RUNNALLS, O. J. C. and PIDGEON, L. M. Observations on the preparation of Iodide titanium. *A.I.M.E. J. Metals.* 4, No. 8, 843 (1952).
17. SHELTON, S. M., DILLING, E. D. and McCLAIN, J. H. The production of zirconium and hafnium. *Progress in Nuclear Energy*, vol. 1, *Metallurgy and Fuels*. Pergamon Press, London (1956).
18. HAGE, H. R. and SHAPIRO, Z. M. Preparation of Cheap Alternative Feed Material for the Manufacture of Zirconium Crystal Bar. U.S.A.E.C. Report, WAPD-TD–51 (1952).
19. DE BOER, J. H. and FAST, J. D. Über die Darstellung der reinen Metalle der Titangruppe durch thermische Zersetzung ihrer Iodide. II, Näheres über Zirkonium, and III, Hafnium. *Z-Anorg. Chem.* 187, 177 (1930).
20. RAYNOR, W. M. Some Aspects of the Iodide or Hot Wire Process for Manufacture of Zirconium. A.S.M. Symposium on Zirconium and Zirconium Alloys, Los Angeles (1953).
21. VEIGEL, N. D., SHERWOOD, E. M. and CAMPBELL, I. E. Preparation of high-purity thorium by the iodide process. *J. Electrochem. Soc.* 102, No. 12, 687 (1955).
22. VEIGEL, N. D. *et al.* Preparation of Iodide Thorium. The Metal Thorium. U.S.A.E.C. and American Society of Metals Conference on Thorium, Cleveland, Ohio (11/10/56).
23. SCAIFE, D. E. and WYLIE, A. W. A carbide-iodide process for high purity thorium. *Proc. 2nd Int. Conf. on the Peaceful Uses of Atomic Energy, Geneva*, 1958. Paper 1098.
24. VEIGEL, N. D. *et al.* The Preparation of High Purity Thorium by the Iodide Process. U.S.A.E.C. Report, BMI–77 (1953).
25. CUTHBERT, F. L. *Thorium Production Technology.* Addison-Wesley, Reading, Massachusetts (1958).

CHAPTER 9

FLOWSHEETS FROM ORE TO METAL

QUALITATIVE flowsheets are given for the extraction and purification of all the rare metals discussed in earlier chapters. As far as possible the examples chosen are typical of current practice or of recently proposed processes. Each flowsheet presented begins with a mineral ore and ends with a pure metal, whereas in practice the various component operations are sometimes divided between two or more plants; e.g. in the case of uranium, it is convenient to produce a concentrate containing about 70 per cent of the element near the minefield and to ship this to various refineries many thousands of miles away. Metal production may take place at the refinery, or in yet a third factory in association with subsequent metallurgical stages.

Where alternatives exist for each part of the flowsheet, the number of permutations involved in fitting these together to form complete flowsheets becomes quite large. In such cases, no attempt has been made to present all the alternative routes but merely to give two of these which differ substantially from one another. For some metals, e.g. thorium, it has thus been necessary to omit flowsheets showing extraction from the less common ores, or other sources.

Many of the possible complete flowsheets which have been omitted by the above basis of selection can easily be pieced together by the reader from the examples quoted in each chapter referring to specific unit operations. In other cases, the fairly extensive lists of references will be of assistance.

For simplicity, and because of the wide variations which exist in most cases, full quantitative details have been omitted from the flowsheets. In no case, therefore, do the flowsheets identify with any particular plant or plants. Some quantitative information is available in the examples given in the chapters describing specific processes and the quoted references at the end of each chapter. Many of the quantitative data, however, have not been published. In any case, changes tend to be made as processes develop and when new starting materials begin to be used.

URANIUM

Figure 9.1 shows what is perhaps the most common route to uranium metal. This is based upon a standard sulphuric acid leach of the ore and column type ion-exchange. The alternatives, of continuous ion-exchange, or resin-in-pulp methods, are only used in a relatively small proportion of plants at present. Whilst probably economic in some plants, they are not sufficiently proven to justify their installation in all cases, and especially their replacement of existing units. The concentrate refining stages based upon TBP extraction are fairly generally adopted at the present time, with minor variations. The fluidization stages are common to British and U.S. practice, but equal advantages may be claimed for other techniques such as the use of stirred beds or moving beds in the United States and in Europe. The final magnesium reduction to metal is supreme for all large-scale production plants.

Figure 9.2 presents a number of less commonly used stages, but all of them have commercial application in special cases. Pressure carbonate leaching of ores, which contain limestone can be cheaper than acid leaching and ion-exchange. This is followed by TBP extraction of the concentrate for final purification since any alternative would normally be based upon the same general chemical engineering principles and would only involve a different solvent. The older type of "dryway" process is then shown, with ammonia precipitation as the first step, since this still has applications for the production of special types of uranium dioxide. The final calcium reduction of oxide finds application on a relatively small scale, where the uranium metal product is required in powder form.

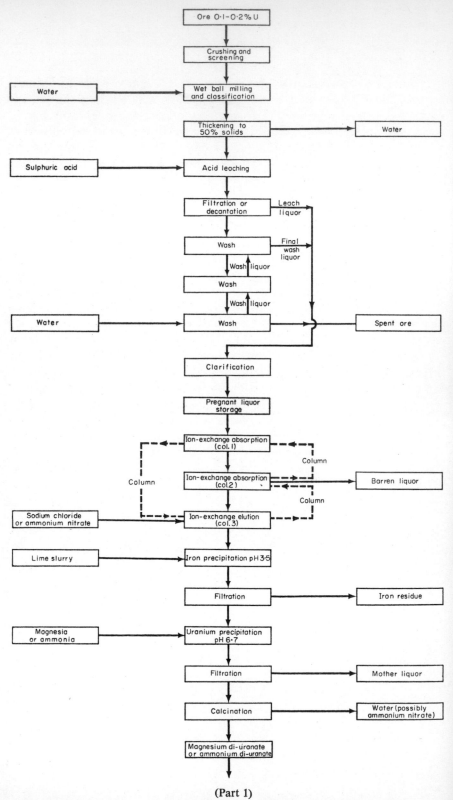

(Part 1)

FIG. 9.1. Extraction of uranium (acid leach, ion-exchange, fluidization and
magnesium reduction process).

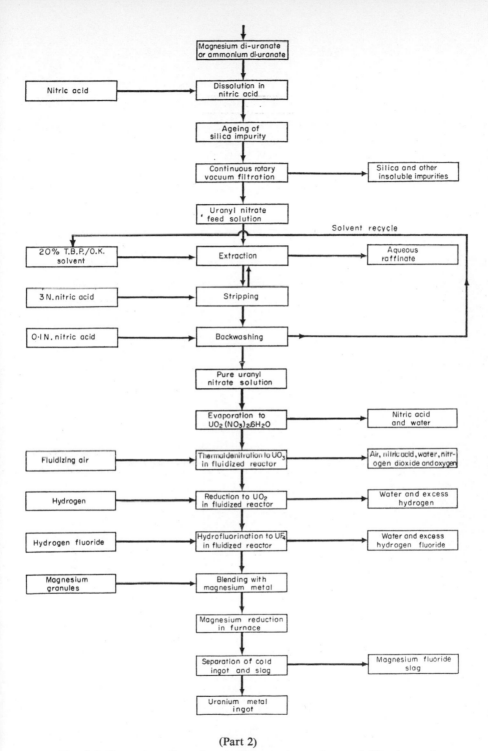

(Part 2)

Fig. 9.1. Extraction of uranium (acid leach, ion-exchange, fluidization and magnesium reduction process).

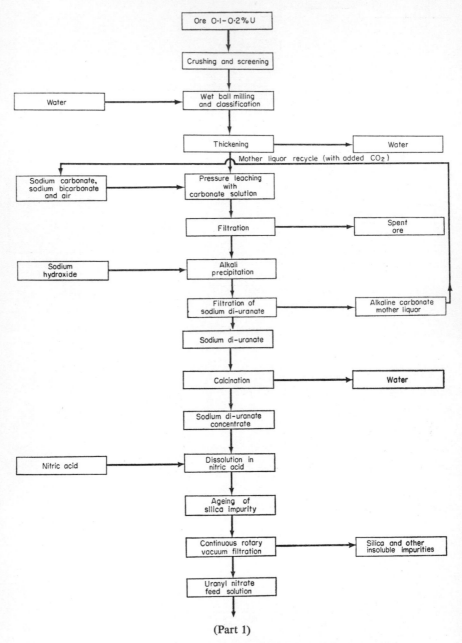

(Part 1)

FIG. 9.2. Extraction of uranium (carbonate leach, precipitation, calcium reduction of oxide process).

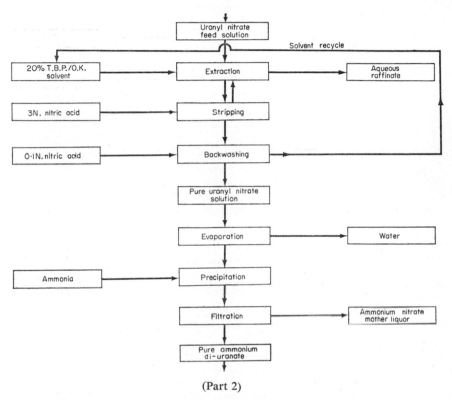

(Part 2)

FIG. 9.2. Extraction of uranium (carbonate leach, precipitation, calcium reduction of oxide process).

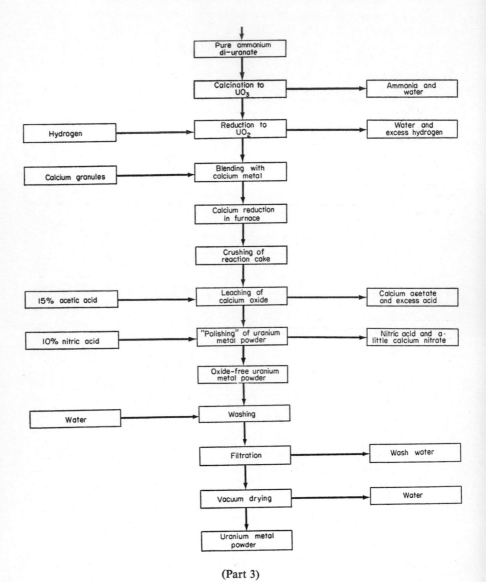

(Part 3)

Fig. 9.2. Extraction of uranium (carbonate leach, precipitation, calcium reduction of oxide process).

THORIUM

Thorium extraction usually involves either sulphuric acid or sodium hydroxide breakdown of monazite, and a flowsheet based upon each of these is presented in Figs. 9.3 and 9.4. Many alternative processes are available for the subsequent stages involving the elimination of gross quantities of rare earths and phosphate. The selection in practice is often traditional, but a logical appraisal would take into account the degree of final purity required and the available market for the rare earth and phosphate by-products. In some processes, the thorium itself is regarded as a by-product, when the process has been designed primarily for the extraction of rare earth elements. The relatively simple basicity separation step is actually shown in both Figs. 9.3 and 9.4. The deficiencies of this cheap technique can be remedied by the highly efficient solvent extraction stage which follows. TBP solvent extraction is now normally used in modern plants where high product purity is of paramount importance.

The cheapest type of nitrate-to-oxide conversion process, based upon thermal denitration, has been shown in Fig. 9.3. This can be carried out in a simple batch type of pot denitrator or in more elegant continuous plant for larger scale production. If a little iron impurity is introduced, the molten salt electrolysis stage which follows allows an opportunity for purification again before the metal powder is produced.

Figure 9.4 shows an alternative oxide production stage using the fairly expensive oxalic acid as a process reagent. A pure product is, however, obtained, as a fine, free flowing powder. Calcium reduction of the oxide to metal powder, as selected for Fig. 9.4., is used on a commercial scale and gives a very satisfactory product.

Ingot production processes are available for thorium as alternatives to powder production, but difficulties arise owing to the high melting-point of the metal.

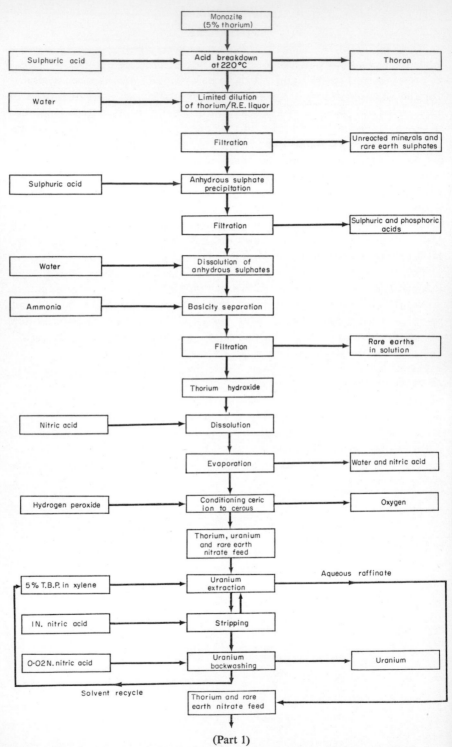

(Part 1)

FIG. 9.3. Extraction of thorium (acid breakdown, electrolysis process).

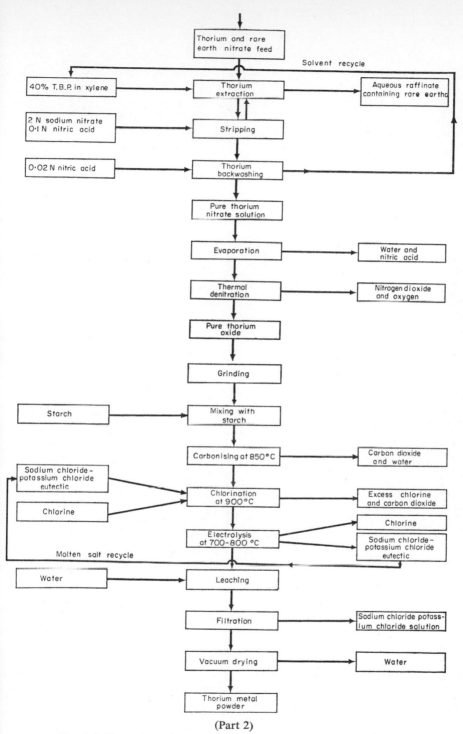

(Part 2)

Fig. 9.3. Extraction of thorium (acid breakdown, electrolysis process).

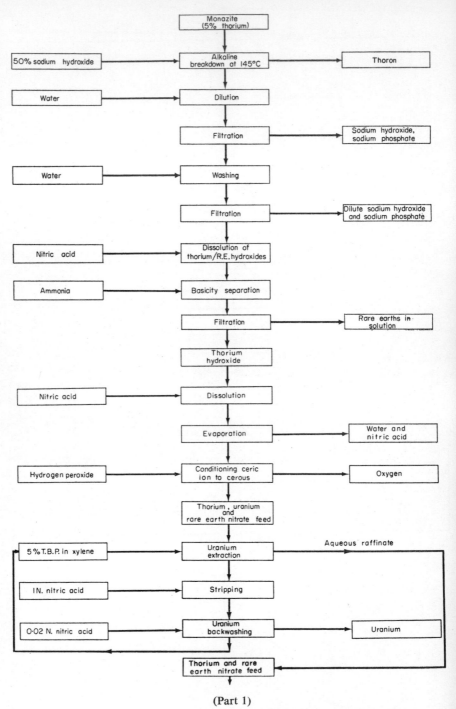

(Part 1)

FIG. 9.4. Extraction of thorium (alkaline breakdown, oxide reduction process).

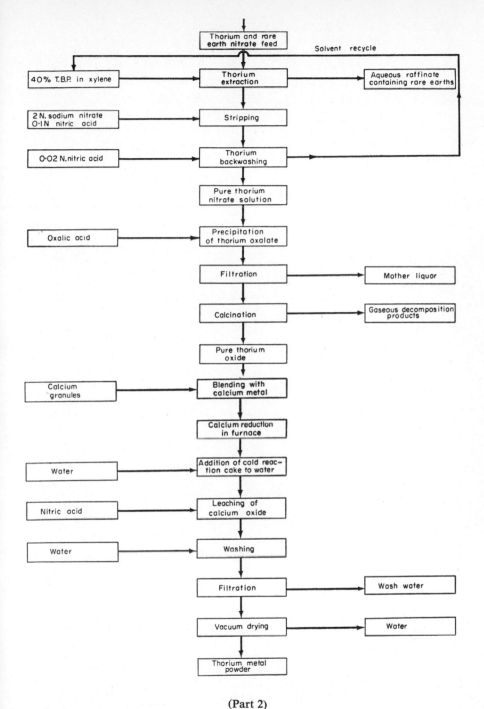

(Part 2)

FIG. 9.4. Extraction of thorium (alkaline breakdown, oxide reduction process).

ZIRCONIUM

Large quantities of zirconium have been, and still are being, produced by processes based upon the chlorination of zircon sand, as shown in Fig. 9.5, although the cheaper sodium hydroxide breakdown stage is available. Figure 9.5 also shows the older hexone–thiocyanate purification stage for removal of hafnium, although this is becoming obsolete. Precipitation of the fluorozirconate and recrystallization then leads naturally to molten salt electrolysis as the means of producing pure metal powder.

Figure 9.6 would generally be accepted as the more conventional route. The purification stages are based upon sodium hydroxide breakdown and TBP purification, now that satisfactory methods are available for the removal of residual silica from the former, which would otherwise cause

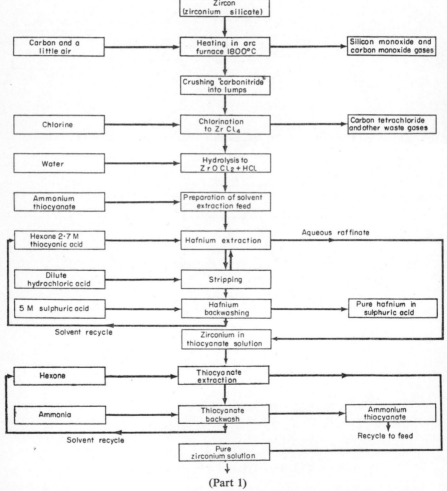

(Part 1)

FIG. 9.5. Extraction of zirconium (chlorination, hexone purification, electrolysis process).

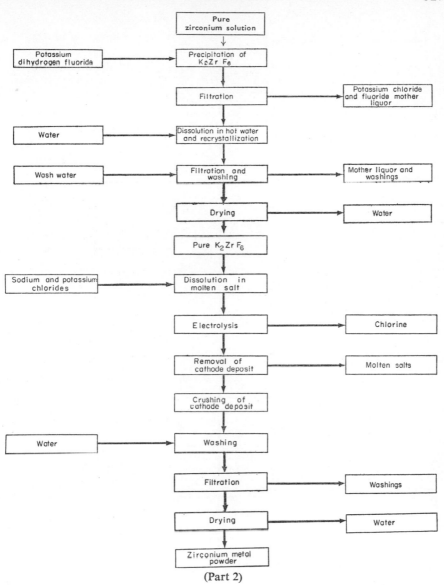

(Part 2)

FIG. 9.5. Extraction of zirconium (chlorination, hexone purification, electrolysis process).

emulsions to occur in the latter. Conversion to pure oxide is via the sulphite, although equally satisfactory alternatives are available. Chlorination of oxide, sublimation, and magnesium reduction occur next, and this is regarded as the standard technique for the production of high purity metal, in the form of sponge. The alternative iodide decomposition route has been developed considerably, and has the advantage of producing very high purity metal in massive form, but the cost of production is normally higher.

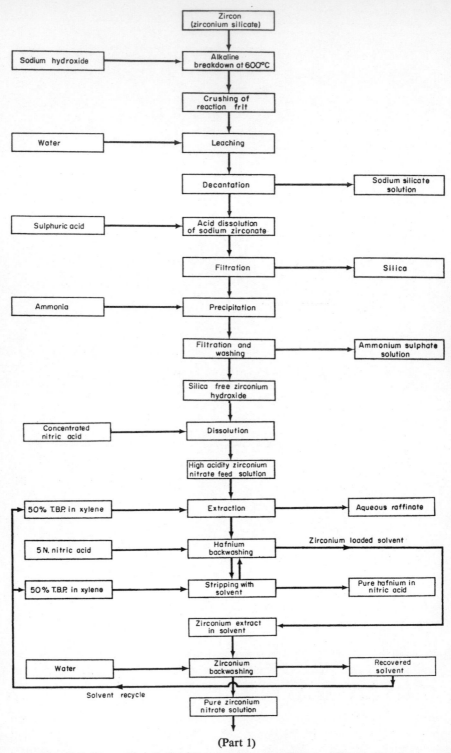

(Part 1)

FIG. 9.6. Extraction of zirconium (alkaline breakdown. TBP purification, Kroll reduction process).

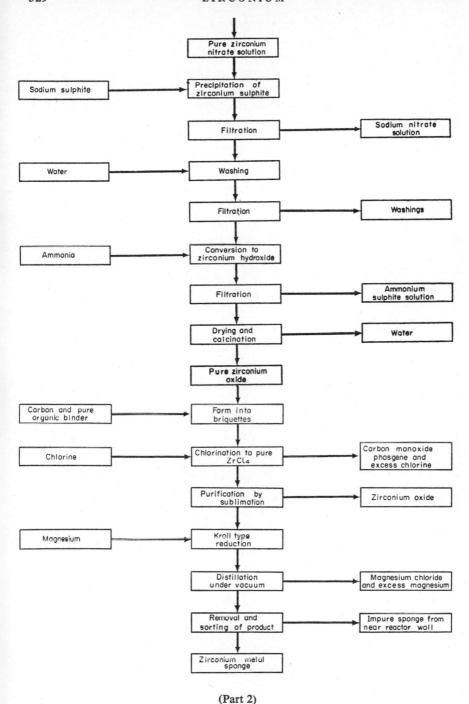

(Part 2)

FIG. 9.6. Extraction of zirconium (alkaline breakdown, TBP purification, Kroll reduction process).

HAFNIUM

The demand for hafnium metal is small. Figure 9.7 shows how it can be obtained in a high state of purity as a by-product from the manufacture of zirconium. The conversion of the pure by-product solution to oxide is via sulphite as in the case of zirconium, and similarly several alternative precipitants would each be satisfactory. The Van Arkel iodide decomposition process has been shown, in its cheapest form, i.e. based upon a carbide feed. Either of the two metal-producing stages shown for zirconium are equally applicable.

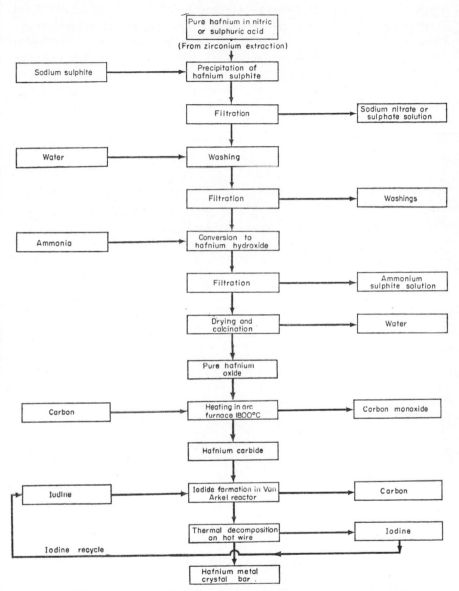

FIG. 9.7. Extraction of hafnium (zirconium by-product, oxide, carbide, iodide decomposition process).

TITANIUM

Pure titanium is usually made by chlorination of the purer but more expensive ore, rutile, followed by purification of the chloride and a Kroll type reduction to metal sponge. Figure 9.8 shows the most elegant chlorination technique based upon fluidization. Several alternatives can be used in place of hydrogen sulphide reduction for removal of oxychloride impurity, but fractional distillation is always necessary before a chloride of satisfactory purity is obtained. The flowsheet shows sodium as the final reducing agent, to metal sponge, but magnesium is equally applicable.

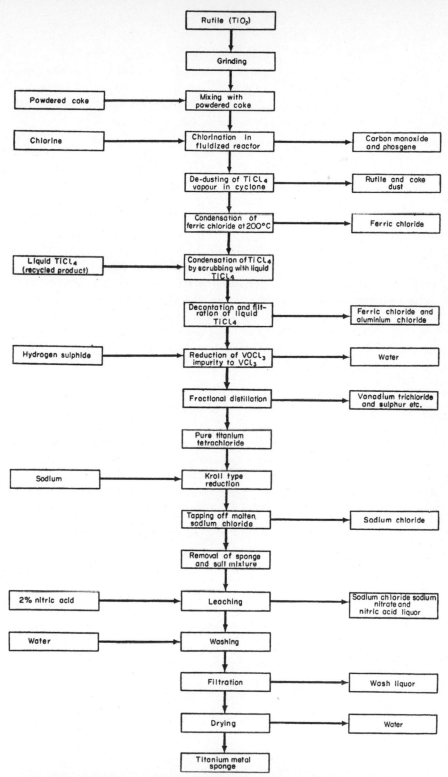

FIG. 9.8. Extraction of titanium (chlorination, distillation, sodium reduction process).

NIOBIUM

Niobium metal finds only limited application, since the more readily available tantalum has very similar chemical, physical and metallurgical properties. The two routes shown in Figs. 9.9. and 9.10 have, however, both been fully developed and operated on a limited production scale. Ferroniobium is used as the feed material in both cases since it is readily available, and processes based more directly on the columbite ore would show only small savings, if any, with an expensive final product.

In Fig. 9.9, the mixed chlorides are shown separated by a two-stage hydrogen reduction process. Both of these may be replaced by an alternative fractional distillation stage to remove iron and tantalum. A large number of theoretical plates are then required in the fractionating column, in view of the small differences of boiling-point between tantalum and niobium. The constructional materials must also be selected with care, to avoid reintroduction of iron impurity as a result of corrosion. A separate hydrogen reduction stage is then required, simply to convert niobium pentachloride into trichloride, and this is more easily accomplished in the absence of tantalum. Magnesium reduction of the trichloride is shown since direct magnesium reduction of the pentachloride is not so fully developed. Hydrogen reduction of trichloride is also possible but the product is less satisfactory.

The "wet" niobium route shown in Fig. 9.10 has more stages than the "dry" chloride route, but the overall process costs can be less. Dissolution of ferroniobium in aqueous potassium hydroxide is quite rapid and impurities other than tantalum are rejected in the insoluble residue. Solid sodium chloride crystals precipitate the sodium niobate and tantalate in pure condition. Conversion to oxides must be followed by ammonia treatment to reduce the chloride content to a sufficiently low level for operation of the very simple subsequent solvent extraction stage. Continuous or batch extraction can be used, depending upon the degree of removal of tantalum required. Conversion to the pure double fluoride is followed by the "closed bomb" technique of sodium reduction. The "open bomb" technique, as shown in Fig. 9.11 for tantalum production, is equally applicable to niobium and has been employed successfully. In either case, fairly elaborate leaching and drying stages are necessary for a highly pure product.

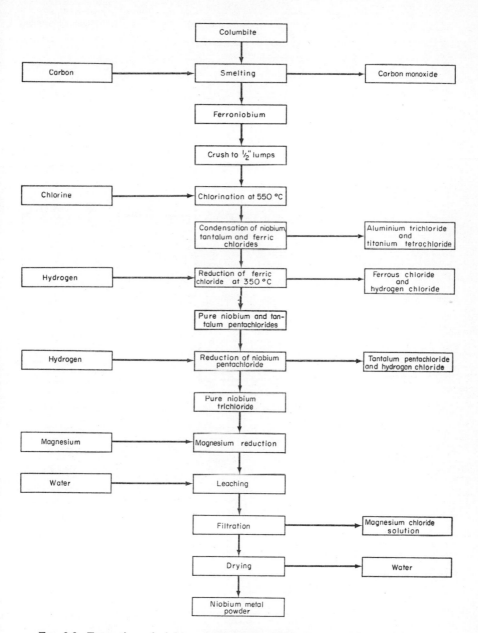

FIG. 9.9. Extraction of niobium (chlorination, hydrogen purification, magnesium reduction process).

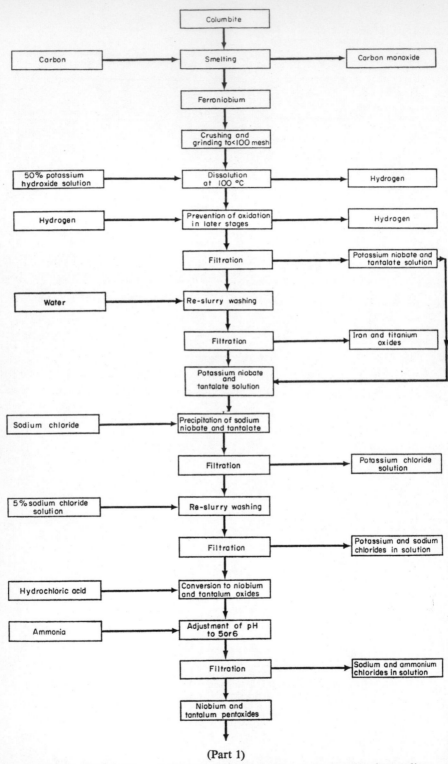

(Part 1)

FIG. 9.10. Extraction of niobium (alkali dissolution, solvent extraction, sodium reduction process).

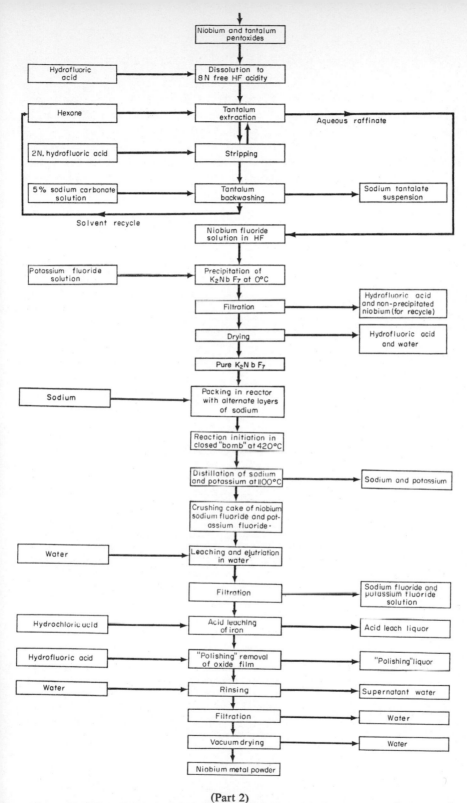

(Part 2)

FIG. 9.10. Extraction of niobium (alkali dissolution, solvent extraction, sodium reduction process).

TANTALUM

The fluoride route shown in Fig. 9.11 has been used commercially with considerable success, although purification by solvent extraction, as for niobium, might be preferred in future. The recrystallization of the double fluoride shown here can lead to high process losses if care is not taken to recycle mother liquors. The "open bomb" technique is shown for sodium reduction, with complex leaching and drying stages as for niobium. A methylated spirits rinse of the metal powder product, followed by air drying at 60°C, replaces the vacuum drying shown for niobium. These stages are, however, interchangeable for the two metals.

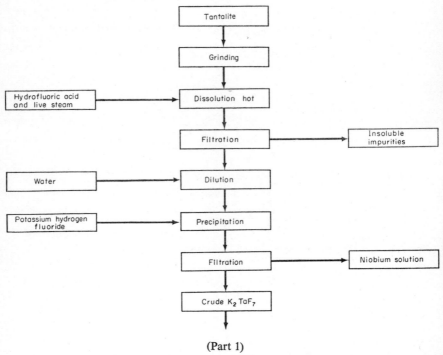

(Part 1)

FIG. 9.11. Extraction of tantalum (fluoride dissolution, re-crystallization of double fluoride, sodium reduction process).

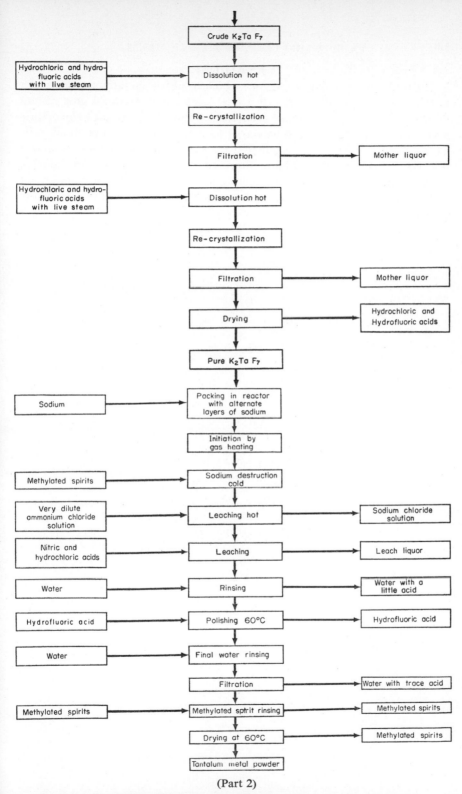

(Part 2)

FIG. 9.11. Extraction of tantalum (fluoride dissolution, re-crystallization of double fluoride, sodium reduction process).

VANADIUM

The route shown in Fig. 9.12 is one which has been operated commercially in the U.K. on a fairly small scale, quite successfully. As in the case of niobium, it is convenient to use the crude ferro alloy as feed to the chlorination stage. The chloride purification stages lead to pure vanadium trichloride, which is reduced with magnesium in a manner similar to that employed for titanium, zirconium or hafnium. Some of the complexities, applicable in the latter processes owing to the volatile nature of the chlorides, are absent with vanadium. The vanadium metal sponge has some properties in common with the other metal sponges.

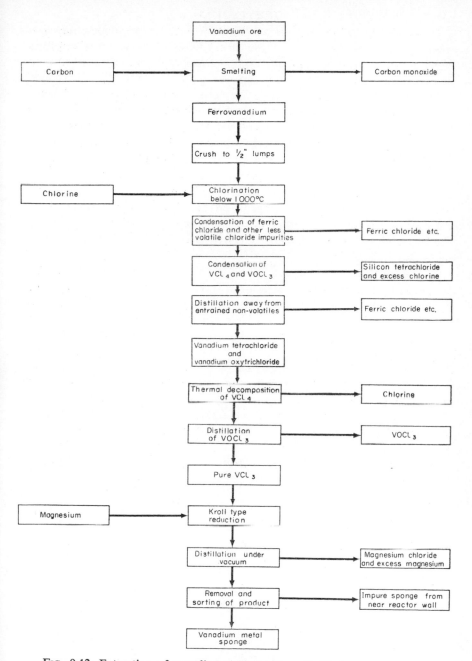

Fig. 9.12. Extraction of vanadium (chlorination, distillation, magnesium reduction process).

BERYLLIUM

In general, beryllium processes fall into two categories, depending upon whether they are based upon the breakdown of beryl with sulphuric acid or with a fluoride reagent. Typical processes, one of each type, are demonstrated in Figs. 9.13 and 9.14.

In Fig. 9.13, the heat treatments are necessary to improve the efficiency of the sulphation step. The latter can be engineered in several alternative types of plant. Alternatives are available for the subsequent steps to pure oxide, but usually based upon precipitation and crystallization, as is the one shown in Fig. 9.13. The precipitation of beryllium hydroxide by boiling an alkaline solution of sodium beryllate, is a particularly valuable purification step, and is also used in Fig. 9.14. Chlorination of oxide mixed with carbon is a standard type of operation as used for the preparation of chloride intermediates of other metals. Molten salt electrolysis is one of the two alternative commercial routes to pure beryllium metal, the other being shown in Fig. 9.14.

The use of sodium ferric fluoride as the breakdown reagent in Fig. 9.14 is probably the most advanced fluoride breakdown technique. Unlike the sodium silicofluoride alternative, this allows recovery and recycling of the valuable fluoride in a relatively simple manner. Conditions can be adjusted, with care, to give an insoluble residue from the leaching stage composed almost entirely of oxides, as shown, so avoiding waste of valuable fluorides. The production of pure oxide, by the sodium beryllate boiling technique, is then followed by the introduction of further fluorides at the pure intermediate stages, before final magnesium reduction of pure beryllium fluoride to metal. Consolidation of beryllium metal to a single ingot in a molten slag system is difficult, and the compromise is therefore accepted of forming it into "pebbles". The low specific gravity of beryllium metal is responsible for some of the complexity of the final stages of separation of the pebbles from slag.

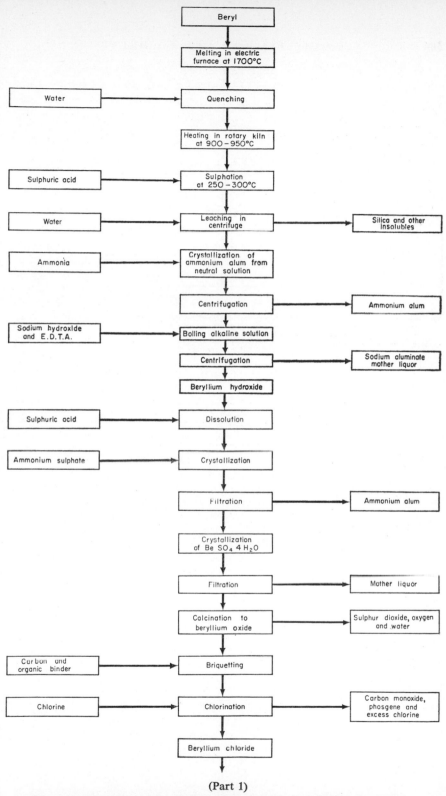

(Part 1)

FIG. 9.13. Extraction of beryllium (sulphuric acid breakdown, chlorination and electrolysis process).

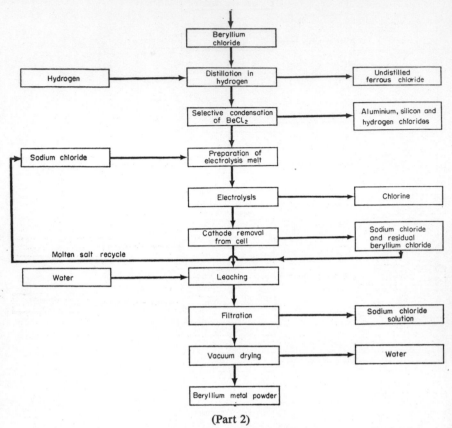

(Part 2)

FIG. 9.13. Extraction of beryllium (sulphuric acid breakdown, chlorination and electrolysis process).

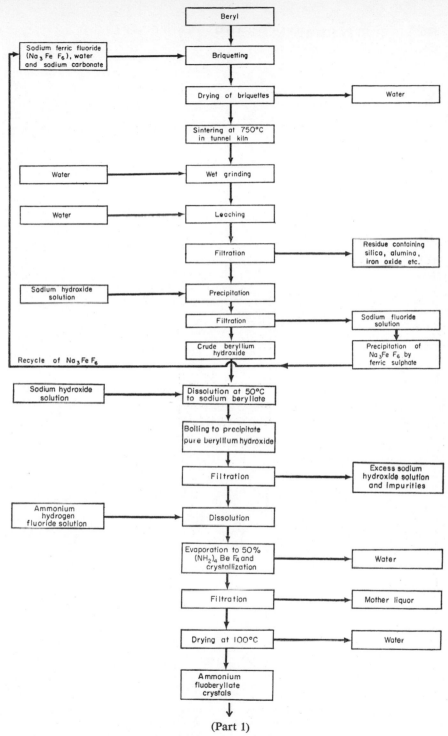

(Part 1)

FIG. 9.14. Extraction of Beryllium (fluoride breakdown, magnesium reduction of beryllium fluoride process).

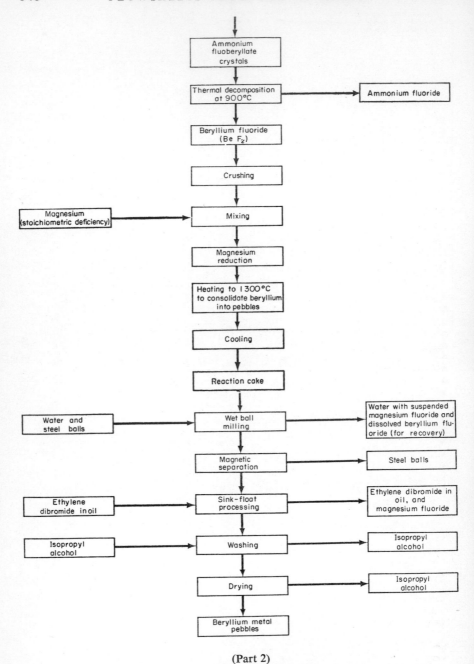

(Part 2)

FIG. 9.14. Extraction of Beryllium (fluoride breakdown, magnesium reduction of beryllium fluoride process).

INDEX